It's Time For a Change

Formerly Zhuāng Zhōu (莊周) dreamt (mèng 夢) he was a butterfly (húdié 胡蝶). He was very glad and pleased as a butterfly. As such, he flitted about satisfying his desires. He did not know Zhou. Suddenly he awoke. He was startled as he now appeared as Zhou. He did not know whether he was now Zhuang Zhou dreaming he was a butterfly or was a butterfly now dreaming he was Zhuang Zhou. Between Zhou and the butterfly, there certainly must be a commonality (yǒufèn 有分). This is called the transformation of things (wùhuà 物化).

The Zhuangzi
Chapter II

Translation from Santee, R. (2014). Zhuangzi's butterfly: It's time for a change. *The Empty Vessel: The Journal of Daoist Philosophy and Practice*, 5–7.

Zhuang Zhou (莊周) dreamt he was a butterfly
The butterfly was Zhuang Zhou
An organic, integral whole (yī tǐ 一體) undergoing
continual change and transformation
For everything, this is very much so across time.
Therefore, understand that the waters of Penglai
are recycled and become clear, shallow streams.
The melon farmer at Qingdao Gate
in ancient times was the Marquis of Dongling.
As wealth and fame are thus like this,
Why do you run hither and thither seeking them?

Li Bai
Ancient Winds, Number 9

Translation from Santee, R. (2014). Zhuangzi's butterfly: It's time for a change. *The Empty Vessel: The Journal of Daoist Philosophy and Practice*, 5–7.

It's Time For a Change

A Therapeutic Lifestyle Approach to Health and Well-Being

Robert G. Santee

Chaminade University of Honolulu

cognella®
SAN DIEGO

Bassim Hamadeh, CEO and Publisher

Gem Rabanera, Senior Project Editor

Abbey Hastings, Associate Production Editor

Jess Estrella, Senior Graphic Designer

Trey Soto, Licensing Coordinator

Natalie Piccotti, Director of Marketing

Kassie Graves, Vice President of Editorial

Jamie Giganti, Director of Academic Publishing

3970 Sorrento Valley Blvd., Ste. 500, San Diego, CA 92121

This is the one and only book in the world in which traditional Eastern philosophies and traditional Western sciences are naturally and excellently woven like a rainbow. It is a feat that only Bob Santee, who lives in the rainbow islands where Eastern and Western cultures miraculously harmonize, can accomplish. In this book, he reasonably unites Western knowledges like the theory of evolution, counseling, neuroscience, medicine, and physiology with Eastern Daoism, Confucianism, Buddhism, martial arts, and meditation. All of these knowledges aim to unravel human "life" as concentrated into one node: the "body." Hawaii is one of the few places where one can directly feel this intersection of "life" and the "body." I hope you will read this book and feel the glory of its embodied wisdoms, which will encourage you to live as you are, in the here and now.

Dr. Shintaro Yukawa (Ph.D. in Psychology)
Chairperson of Japan Society for Research on Emotions
Professor in Hakuoh University, Oyama city, Tochigi prefecture, Japan
Seventh Dan (Blackbelt) of Shito-ryu Karate

Brief Contents

Contents

Acknowledgments

To my wife, Charlene; our son, Ian; his wife, Joy; and our granddaughter, Keiriko; our son, Aaron; his wife, Karen; and our granddaughters, Emma and Lauren; and to our daughter, Jenai; our granddaughters, Liliana and Payson; and our grandsons Cameron and Kalani. Mahalo for being there. I am thankful for all of you.

To my longtime friend Marie Burghardt: As always, thank you for your insights and support.

To Dr. Xiu Zhang, my Baguazhang laoshi and friend, *xie xie* for teaching and guiding me in this art. I am grateful for your arranging and coordinating training with the various masters in Taijiquan, Baguazhang, and Qigong in Beijing, China. Your guidance and introduction to Chinese culture while we were in Beijing still resonates with me today. I am especially grateful for your commitment to following the fourth-generation master Shangzhi Wang of the traditional Yin Style of Baguazhang. Through this relationship you have provided workshops by him both in China and in Honolulu. This training linking back to its origins is priceless. Mahalo.

To Zhijian Cai, my Taijiquan and Qigong Sifu, for introducing me to and instructing me in the standardized Taijiquan forms and in the traditional qigong forms of the Yijinjing and Wu Qin Xi. Thank you.

Much appreciation and thanks to Pam Silva-Patrinos, the program manager for the Master of Science in Counseling Psychology (MSCP) program at Chaminade University, for all of your help, and especially for your positive presence.

I wish to thank Gem Rabanera, the project editor at Cognella, and Laura Pasquale, the acquisitions editor at Cognella, for all their guidance, suggestions, and support.

I wish to acknowledge and thank my colleague Dr. Shintaro Yukawa for his review of this book. Much appreciated.

I would like to thank Abbey Hastings and Berenice Quirino, Associate Production Editors at Cognella, Jess Estrella, Senior Graphic Designer at Cognella, and Tiffany Mok, Senior Content Marketing Specialist for their contributions toward the completion of this book

I would also like to thank the peer reviewers of this book for their comments, analyses, and suggestions.

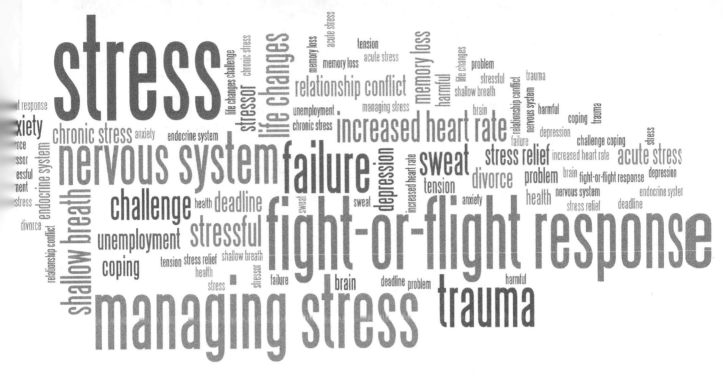

Introduction

After finishing this Introduction, you will be able to do the following:

- Indicate why a paradigm shift appears necessary to address chronic physical and psychological conditions
- Recognize how this text is a practical, purposeful and intentional shift from the standard paradigm/mainstream thinking regarding chronic physical and psychological conditions
- Describe how evolutionary theory can be utilized to thread Western science, Buddhism, Daoism, and Confucianism together to address chronic stress and the physical and psychological conditions associated with it
- Compare and contrast allostasis, the fight/freeze/flight or stress response, and allostatic load
- Explain how chronic stress may be related to chronic physical and psychological conditions
- Describe a holistic and integrative approach to chronic stress, health and well-being, self-care, and how it is related to therapeutic lifestyle changes, lifestyle medicine, and medical costs
- Indicate how meditation, yoga, and qigong are important for preventing and addressing chronic stress

- Describe how holistic, integrative, and therapeutic lifestyle change approaches are beneficial to both preventing and eliminating chronic stress

Health is a state of complete physical, mental, and social well-being and not merely the absence of disease or infirmity. The enjoyment of the highest attainable standard of health is one of the fundamental rights of every human being without distinction of race, religion, political belief, economic, or social condition (World Health Organization [WHO], 2006).

In his testimony before the United States Senate, the medical doctor and Harvard Medical School Professor Herbert Benson (1998) noted that (a) research indicates the symptoms reported in 60–90% of office visits to medical doctors are stress related; (b) the current medical model paradigm of drugs and surgical intervention are not adequate to address stress related disorders; (c) mind/body interventions such as meditation, yoga, prayer, repetitive exercises, and so on, which activate the **relaxation response**, the opposite of the **fight/freeze/flight or stress response**, are effective in addressing stress-related disorders; (d) the current medical approach to health and well-being needs to include self-care, essentially therapeutic lifestyle changes such as exercise, meditation, nutrition, and stress management techniques, for which the patient is accountable; (e) self-care reduces medical costs; and (f) the self-care approach should be integrative and holistic.

Research indicates that the symptoms reported in 60–90% of all office visits to primary care physicians have no identifiable organic cause (Avey, Matheny, Robbins, & Jacobson, 2003; Boone, & Anthony, 2003; Cummings, & VandenBos, 1981; Kroenke, & Manglesdorff, 1989; Nerurkar, Bitton, Davis, Phillips, & Yeh, 2013) and, most likely, are stress related. This being the case, it appears that the focus needs to turn to self-care and lifestyle changes to address underlying chronic stress.

It has been and is being argued in the research literature that the current focus in medicine—regarding chronic disorders, diseases, illness, and conditions, both physical and psychological—on risk factors is not adequate and that the focus should be on the underlying causes, which are lifestyle behaviors (American College of Lifestyle Medicine [ACLM], 2012/2015; **American College of Preventive Medicine** [ACPM], 2009,2018; Hyman, Ornish, & Roizen, 2009). The American College of Lifestyle Medicine notes, regarding the necessity of focusing on a lifestyle changes approach to health and well-being, that

80% or more of all healthcare spending in the U.S. is tied to the treatment of conditions rooted in poor lifestyle choices (ACLM, 2015).

The focus on **lifestyle changes** to address health care costs and overall health and well-being are fundamental to the **holistic and integrative approach** of both the American College of Lifestyle Medicine and the **American College of Preventive Medicine** (ACLM, 2012,2015; ACPM, 2009/2018). The goal of the **American College of Lifestyle Medicine** is to eventually have lifestyle changes the primary focus of intervention with pharmaceuticals and/or surgery, serving, when warranted, a supporting function (ACLM, 2012). The American College of Preventive Medicine in their "Lifestyle Medicine Initiative" provides the following holistic and integrative definition of lifestyle medicine:

> Lifestyle medicine is a scientific approach to decreasing disease risk and illness burden by utilizing lifestyle interventions such as nutrition, physical activity, stress reduction, rest, smoking cessation, and avoidance of alcohol abuse. Lifestyle medicine is the recommended foundational approach to preventing and treating many chronic diseases. (ACPM, 2018)

Chronic stress negatively impacts lifestyle behavior such that individuals may not exercise, may increase their sedentary behavior, may not get adequate restful sleep, may not eat nutritiously, may eat too much high caloric density food, may limit or not engage in social interpersonal relationships, may smoke, and/or drink alcohol, behavior which, in turn, is linked to chronic physical and psychological diseases, illnesses, disorders, and conditions (Charles, Piazza, Mogle, Sliwinski,

& Almeida, 2013; Cohen, Gianaros, & Manuck, 2016; Leger, Charles, & Almeida, 2018; McEwen 2006a, 2006b, 2008; McEwen & Lasley, 2002; McKenzie, & Harris, 2013; Mirowsky, 2011; Schneiderman, 2004; Schneiderman, Ironson, & Siegel, 2005; Smyth, Zawadzki, & Gerin 2013). These dysfunctional lifestyle behaviors are, themselves, another source of chronic stress and fold back on the initial source of chronic stress which, in most cases, is psychosocial in nature (perceived threats to one's sense of self and status such as arguments, interpersonal relationships, family, jobs, work, money, ideology, beliefs, concerns about the future, and so on), thus increasing the overall chronic stress and resulting in a vicious circle of chronic stress, which compromises one's overall physical and psychological health and well-being.

HOW STRESSED ARE WE?

The American Psychological Association's (APA) survey "Stress In America: Our Health at Risk" (APA, 2012a) noted that the average level of reported stress (5.2/10) exceeded the level of what the respondents consider healthy stress (3.6/10), 22% of the respondents indicated extreme levels of stress (8-10/10), and 39% of the respondents indicated their stress was higher than the previous year.

Commenting on the release of this survey, the then APA CEO and executive vice president Norman Anderson (APA, 2012b) noted,

America has a choice. We can continue down a well-worn path where stress significantly impacts our physical and mental health, causes undue suffering and drives up health care costs. Or we can get serious about this major public health issue and provide better access to behavioral health care services to help people more effectively manage their stress and prevent and manage chronic disease.

Various studies have shown that chronic stress is a major driver of chronic illness, which in turn is a major driver of escalating health care costs in this country. It is critical that the entire health community and policymakers recognize the role of stress and unhealthy behaviors in causing and exacerbating chronic health conditions, and support models of care that help people make positive changes.

The American Psychological Association's survey, released in February of 2017, "Stress In America: Coping with Change, Part 1" (APA, 2017a), noted that between August 2016 and January 2017 an increase in average stress levels rose from 4.8/10, the lowest in 10 years, to 5.1/10, the first statistically significant increase in 10 years; 20% of the respondents indicated extreme levels of stress (8–10/10), and 31% of the respondents indicated their stress was higher than the previous year. Using a total household income of $50,000 a year

before taxes as a dividing point (APA, 2017), the average stress level for those below this amount was 5.1 while it was 4.6 for those above this amount. Men (52%) and women (51%) were essentially the same regarding the most recent presidential election being a major stressor (APA, 2017). The American Psychological Association's survey, released in November of 2017, "Stress In America: The State of Our Nation" (APA, 2017b) noted that average stress levels for Black (5.0/10) and Hispanic adults (5.2/10) showed an increase from 2016, while for White (4.7/10) adults it did not change. According to the survey (APA, 2017b), women (5.1/10) reported a higher average stress level than men (4.4/10). Of particular note was that 45% of the respondents (Hispanic 56%, Black 43%, White 42%, Asian 42%) during the past month reported the stress symptom of lying awake in bed at night (APA, 2017b). Across generations, the survey indicated there was a clear difference between older adults (72-plus years old) with an average stress level of 3.3/10, baby boomers (53–71 years old) with an average stress level of 3.9/10, gen X'ers (39–52 years old) with an average stress level of 5.3/10, and millennials (18–38) with an average stress level of 5.7/10. The three most common sources of stress reported in the survey were future of our nation (63%), money (62%), and work (61%). Regarding specific issues causing stress, for the respondents in the survey the two most common answers were health care (43%) and the economy (35%).

The results of a Gallup poll (N = 1049) in December 2017 indicated approximately 80% of the respondents felt (frequently = 44%, sometimes = 35%) stressed on a daily basis (Saad, 2017). Chronic stress clearly appears to be, physically, psychologically, interpersonally and economically, a significant health and well-being problem. Based on the research noted, it appears quite clear that a **new paradigm**, one that is focused on lifestyle changes, is necessary to address chronic stress and the chronic physical and psychological conditions linked to it. It appears it is time for a change, and this book includes the necessary tools!

THE STRUCTURE OF THIS BOOK

The **adaptive problem** of chronic stress and the physical and psychological impairment that results are nothing new. Buddha, although not using the phrase "chronic stress," essentially diagnosed it as the human condition well over 2,000 years ago. He called it *dukkha*. He also offered an adaptive solution to its removal, which was holistic in nature. It integrated lifestyle changes across cognitive, affective, and behavioral domains with meditation as the key component. This **adaptive solution** is known as the eightfold path. For Buddha, the goal was to remove the self-generated and society-generated barriers to living life, to eliminate chronic unhappiness and dissatisfaction. In other words, eliminate *dukkha*.

In order to explore and address the long-standing issue of chronic stress, this text integrates both research from modern Western science and the ancient teachings of Buddhism, Daoism, and Confucianism with the common focus being lifestyle changes in both a preventive and therapeutic context. The holistic and integrated infrastructure of this text consists of evolutionary theory, neuroscience, the stress response, counseling or therapeutic intervention, and Buddhist, Daoist, and Confucian approaches/solutions to eliminating what we call chronic stress, all of which will be discussed in more detail in the following chapters. A brief explanation follows for each area.

Evolutionary Theory

The single thread that will allow the integration of both the research of Western science and the teachings of Buddhism, Daoism, and Confucianism is that of **evolutionary theory**. From the perspective of evolutionary theory, I realize that it is under/may be the umbrella of Western science; all of life is a continual process of change. Such is the case also for the teachings of **Buddhism, Daoism, and Confucianism**. While evolutionary theory indicates that survival is contingent on adapting to an ever-changing environment, the teachings of Buddhism, Daoism, and Confucianism are more likely to talk about survival being linked to being in harmony with the ever-changing environment.

From the perspective of evolutionary theory, no matter what cultural, ethnic, or diversity perspective guides you, we are all the same insofar as we all have evolved to generate adaptive solutions for adaptive problems relative to surviving in our various environmental contexts, no matter how different those solutions may be. In the United Nations Educational, Scientific, and Cultural Organization's (UNESCO) (1950) statement on race, it notes that scientific research, regarding the similarity of human beings, is in line with a quote from the *Lunyu* or *Analects* of Confucius (551–479 B.C.E.). This quote of Confucius from chapter 17 of the *Lunyu* states,

The nature (*xing* 性) of people is quite similar; through habit, custom, and practice they grow apart.[1]

---

1 Translations from the Chinese text of the *Lunyu* are mine. Chinese text can be found at http://www.chineseclassic.com/13jing/LeungYu/LeungYu01.htm. In addition, for all subsequent chapters in this text, all the translations of quotes from the Buddhist, Daoist, and Confucian texts are mine.

As part of our evolutionary tool kit we all have the ability to learn and to put into practice what we have learned to allow us to adapt/be in harmony with and to enjoy our ever-changing environment. In the first line in Book One of the *Analects* of Confucius (551–479 B.C.E.), Confucius states,

> Is it not pleasurable, to have the time/opportunity to put into practice what one has learned?

Another component of our evolutionary tool kit is our stress response. Our fight/freeze/flight or stress response evolved to assist us in addressing perceived real physical threats in our ever-changing environment. It evolved to be activated and immediately turned off once the threat was resolved. It did not evolve to be chronically activated or to be frequently activated, yoyoed, throughout the day. It is this chronic yoyoing of the stress response, which does not allow the body to recover, replenish the energy that was spent, repair itself, and return to **equilibrium/homeostasis**, throughout the day to perceived, self-generated/imagined psychosocial threats that appear to be the primary source of chronic stress. Chronic stress results in unhealthy, physical, and psychological lifestyle behavior such as being sedentary, not exercising, not getting adequate restful sleep, not eating nutritiously, excessive eating of calorie-dense food resulting in unnecessary weight gain, physical and psychological isolation from others, and smoking and drinking too much alcohol—all of which adds additional chronic stress to an already chronically stressed body and mind. Thus, resulting in a vicious circle of chronic stress.

Neuroscience

The neuroscience component of the infrastructure, which itself is embedded in our evolutionary toolkit, consists of **neuroplasticity**, the **negativity bias**, **mind wandering**, and the **default network**. All of these components are significantly

compromised by chronic stress as are areas of the brain such as the prefrontal cortex, hippocampus, and the amygdala.

As noted previously, learning is a fundamental aspect of our adapting to our ever-changing environment. Neuroplasticity is the physical representation of our learning by allowing new neural networks to be developed. The more we engage in certain behaviors the stronger and more readily accessible the neural networks that represent these behaviors become, thus reinforcing not only positive behaviors but also negative behaviors. In both cases, these are learned behaviors, hence the importance of consistent and regular practice when learning something!

The negativity bias is a tendency to look for threats, thus activating the stress response. While this was beneficial for our distant hunter-gatherer ancestors in an environment that was physically threatening, it is problematic insofar as for most of us our threats are primarily psychosocial and the activation of the stress response usually is not of any benefit for a perceived threat that is self-generated or imagined.

Mind wandering refers to disengaging from a task in the present in your environment, or focusing on past and/or future events with you as the main character, occurs on average approximately 50% of your waking life, and is associated with causing unhappiness (Killingsworth & Gilbert, 2010).

The default network is that aspect of the brain that you return to when you are not engaged in a task in the present, is the home of mind wandering, and is associated with your autobiographical sense of self.

Stress

It is important to note that the body naturally makes adjustments, such as heart rate increasing, blood pressure rising, breathing increasing, and energy expenditure relative to addressing the various demands of its environment (Selye, 1978), from simply getting out of bed and walking to the toilet in the morning to competing in a triathlon. This is normal stress, which is based on you choosing what to do, is under your control, and is referred to as **allostasis** or variable stability (McEwen 2006a, 2006b, 2008; McEwen & Lasley, 2002).

When the demands incorporate a perceived threat, such as a sudden loud noise that causes such changes as your heart rate increasing, your muscles tensing, your breathing increasing, and your energy being expended, the body changes are immediate, automatic, not a result of you choosing to do something and, not under your control and are referred to as your fight/freeze/flight or stress response. These immediate changes prepare you to address the perceived threat. When the threat is resolved, the stress response is deactivated, and the body reverts to the **default level** or homeostasis.

When life's daily perceived threat-based hassles, such as traffic, long lines, arguments, losing your car keys, your mobile phone being out of service range, the weather, no parking, a poor grade, inability to access Internet, computer crashes, forgetting to do your class assignment, and so on, occur frequently throughout your day, your fight/freeze/flight or stress response does not get an opportunity to completely turn off, thus not allowing your body and brain to recover, repair, replenish its energy, and rest. This is **chronic stress**! In addition, chronic rumination (past) and worrying (future) about your daily stressors appears to allow the stress response to be maintained and thus prevent the stress response from turning off as you engage in these two behaviors (Capobianco, Morris, & Wells, 2018; Charles et al., 2013; Gianferante et al., 2014; Leger, Charles, & Almeida, 2018; Zoccola, & Dickerson, 2012). This is **chronic stress!** This chronic rumination, worrying, and yoyoing of your fight/freeze/flight or stress response as a result of these daily stressors begins to cause significant wear and tear to your body, eventually resulting in significant physical and psychological damage. McEwen (2006a, 2006b, 2008; McEwen & Lasley, 2002) refers to this damage due to chronic stress as **allostatic load**. To make matters even worse, we can activate and maintain the fight/freeze/flight or stress response by merely thinking about or imagining, independent of a current perceived threat/hassle, a potential threat in the future or one from the past (Barrett, 2017; Kabat-Zinn, 2005; McEwen & Lasley, 2002; Sapolsky, 2004; Smyth, Zawadzki, & Gerin 2013; Stefano, Fricchione, Slingsby, & Benson, 2001). This process, if ongoing, is **chronic stress**! Chronic stress results in allostatic load.

Counseling

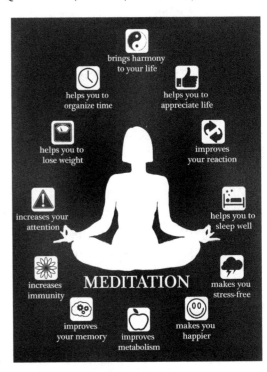

There has been an ongoing discussion/disagreement in the research literature relative to successful outcome in counseling/therapy being due to **common factors**, such as relationship, expectations, and specific ingredients, or to certain theoretical approaches, such as psychodynamic therapy, cognitive therapy, behavioral therapy, family therapy, and existential therapy, being more successful/effective than others relative to a specific complaint/problem such as depression or anxiety (Anderson, Lunnen, & Ogles, 2010; Duncan, 2002; Duncan, Miller, Wampold, &

Hubble, 2010; Freeman, & Freeman, 2014; Hunsley, & Di Guilo, 2002; Luborsky et al., 2002; Marcus, O'Connell, Norris, & Sawaqdeh, 2014; Rosenzweig, 1936; Wampold, 2001, 2015; Wampold, & Imel, 2015). In addition, there is also the **Diagnostic and Statistical Manual of Mental Disorders (DSM)** medical model, a disease-based, pharmaceutical-driven approach of the medical profession. Given the research presented so far, it would seem that reducing chronic stress might be a commonality between specific theoretical approaches, the common factors approach, and the medical model approach. It would also seem that incorporating therapeutic lifestyle changes might enhance the success of all three approaches. It appears a paradigm shift is warranted.

Chronic stress appears to be a shared underlying commonality/cause of both anxiety and depression (Ratey, & Hagerman, 2008; Schneiderman, Ironson, & Siegel, 2005; Steffen, Austin, & DeBarros, 2017). Given this apparent link, Steffen, Austin, and DeBarros (2017) recommend that the focus for addressing anxiety and depression should be on eliminating chronic stress, suggesting biofeedback and mindfulness as two possible solutions. Anderson and Shivakumar (2013) note that consistent exercise reduces the impact of the two major stress-related mechanisms, the sympathetic nervous system and endocrine system, and thus appears to have an impact on reducing anxiety.

There is considerable research indicating the benefits of exercise for reducing anxiety and depression (Asmundson et al., 2013; Broman-Fulks, Berman, Rabian, & Webster, 2004; Deboer, Powers, Utschig, Otto, & Smits, 2012; Powers, Asmundson, & Smits, 2015; Ratey, & Hagerman, 2008; Silveira, et al., 2013; Stathopoulou, Powers, Barry, Smits, & Otto, 2006). Blumenthal and colleagues have, over a series of studies, demonstrated that aerobic exercise is as effective as medication for addressing major depression (Babyak et al., 2000; Blumenthal et al., 1999, 2007; Hoffman et al., 2011). The psychologist Roger Walsh is a strong advocate for introducing various therapeutic lifestyle changes into the therapeutic environment to address chronic stress and psychopathology. He notes,

> Mental health professionals have significantly underestimated the importance of lifestyle factors (a) as contributors to and treatments for multiple psychopathologies, (b) for fostering individual and social well-being, and (c) for preserving and optimizing cognitive function. Consequently, therapeutic lifestyle changes (TLCs) are underutilized despite considerable evidence of their effectiveness in both clinical and normal populations. TLCs are sometimes as effective as either psychotherapy or pharmacotherapy and can offer significant therapeutic advantages. Important TLCs include

exercise, nutrition and diet, time in nature, relationships, recreation, relaxation and stress management, religious or spiritual involvement, and service to others. … In the 21st century, therapeutic lifestyles may need to be a central focus of mental, medical, and public health. (Walsh, 2011, p. 579)

The universality of stress, as well as the multiple benefits of both lifestyle changes and self-regulation skills for managing stress, suggests that these TLCs and self-regulation skills deserve to be central components of health professionals' training, personal and professional practice, and public outreach. (Walsh, 2011, p. 586)

We are continually engaged in a process of gathering, storing, expending, and replenishing energy to allow our body to function in the optimum manner it evolved in order to preserve physical, psychological, and interpersonal health and well-being, and to assist us in successfully adapting to our ever-changing environment. When this energy process is compromised, however, our body and brain are stressed. If this process is chronically interfered with, we

become chronically stressed. The psychologist and neuroscientist Lisa Barrett (2017) refers to this brain-monitored process of expending and replenishing energy, contingent on need, as "body budgeting" and emphasizes the importance of lifestyle behaviors for keeping it in balance. If body budgeting sounds familiar, it is also known as allostasis (Barrett, 2017). She notes,

> The science is crystal clear on healthful food, regular exercise, and sleep as prerequisites for a balanced body budget and a healthy emotional life. A chronically taxed body budget increases your chances of developing a host of different illnesses. (Barrett, 2017, p. 178)
>
> If your body budget is unbalanced for a long time you may experience chronic stress. Chronic misbudgeting is often diagnosed as stress, which is why people think stress causes illness. Chronic stress is dangerous to your health. (Barrett, 2017, pp. 203–204)

The neuroendrocrinologist Bruce McEwen notes that the best way to address chronic stress is engaging in positive lifestyle behavior. He states,

> Finally, and most importantly, as we come to understand allostasis and allostatic load, it becomes increasingly apparent that the best way to deal with stress is by maintaining our physical and emotional health. This means taking a long, hard look at lifestyle. (McEwen, & Lasley, 2002, p. 15)
>
> To keep allostasis functioning on the protective end of the spectrum, the most effective steps you can take are the simplest: exercise, a healthy diet, regular sleep, moderate to minimal alcohol intake, and no smoking. If this sounds suspiciously like what your grandmother always told you, all I can say is that according to the most sophisticated, up-to-the-minute, cutting edge science available, your grandmother was right. (McEwen, & Lasley, 2002, p. 136)

At this point, given the research discussed, there is considerably more throughout the remaining chapters; the approach to preventing, addressing, and managing chronic stress and the subsequent physical and psychological conditions associated with it appears to require a holistic, integrative approach that focuses on and incorporates therapeutic lifestyle changes such as exercise (aerobic, anaerobic, stretching, neuromotor), meditation, nutrition, reducing sedentary behavior, sleep, cognitive restructuring and reframing, time management, and interpersonal behavior. Given the preponderance of evidence, which will be explored in much more depth in the following chapters, a paradigm shift focusing on therapeutic lifestyle changes appears to be necessary to address chronic physical and psychological conditions linked to chronic stress.

Chinese and Buddhist Approaches to Managing Stress

As part of a holistic and integrative approach to preventing and managing chronic stress, it is important to incorporate behaviors/interventions that may differ/appear to differ along cultural dimensions. This is necessary as it will expand and enhance the framework for addressing chronic stress. As part of this process, it is fundamental to not let socially/academically defined, rigid categories or domains prevent us from considering the benefits offered by them. It is often the case that their boundaries are much more artificial than they are natural. Such may be the case for religion, philosophy, and psychology.

For some of you, you may be wondering how what appears to be Asian religious and/or philosophical traditions can even be considered to be integrated into a text on addressing chronic stress, much less counseling and therapy. The terminology, concepts, and practices may seem alien to you. They do not fit your world. Your vocabulary has no corresponding words for some of their concepts. You may even feel a little uncomfortable. After all, religion and philosophy are not psychology and psychology is not a religion or a philosophy. To make matters worse, it is from a tradition that is not even Western.

Historically, there has been a tendency to categorize existence and all that it entails into distinct and separate domains, whose boundaries are absolute and rigid. The philosopher and psychologist (two of those very distinct categories), William James (1842–1910) often considered the father of psychology (oops, another rigid category!), in the United States noted,

> Empiricist writers are very fond of emphasizing one great set of delusions which language inflicts upon the mind. Whenever we have made a word, they say, to denote a certain group of phenomena, we are prone to suppose a substantive entity existing beyond the

phenomena, of which the word shall be the name. But the *lack* of a word quite as often leads to the directly opposite error. We are then prone to suppose that no entity can be there; and so we come to overlook phenomena whose existence would be patent to us all, had we only grown up to hear it familiarly recognized in speech. It is hard to focus our attention on the nameless, and so there results a certain vacuousness in the descriptive parts of most psychologies. (James, 1890/1950, p. 195)

Let's look at psychology with its many supposed very distinct discipline boundaries such as social psychology, cross cultural/diversity psychology, lifespan development, abnormal psychology, personality, and cognitive psychology. Are they really that distinct? If they are all under the umbrella of psychology, shouldn't there be some commonality? The evolutionary psychologist David Buss (2004) looks at these boundaries and reframes them in the context of evolutionary psychology. He notes,

[C]urrent disciplinary boundaries within psychology may be somewhat artificial. Evolutionary psychology cuts across these boundaries and suggests the field of psychology would be better organized around the adaptive problems that humans have faced over a long expanse of evolutionary history. (Buss, 2004, p. 371)

The philosopher Alan Watts (1915–1973) reframed the apparent religious and philosophical traditions of Buddhism and Taoism, Vedanta and yoga within the context of psychotherapy. He especially saw the healing benefits of integrating these practices into psychotherapy (Santee, 2007). He notes,

If we look deeply into such ways of life as Buddhism and Taoism, Vedanta and Yoga, we do not find either philosophy or religion as these are understood in the West. We find something more nearly resembling psychotherapy. ... The main resemblance between Eastern ways of life and Western psychotherapy is in the concern of both with bringing about changes of consciousness, changes in our ways of feeling our own existence and our relation to human society and the natural world. (Watts, 1961, p. 11)

In the same sense, if you reframe the Buddhist, Daoist, and Confucian approaches, which you will be exploring in this text, as ways of generating adaptive solutions for adaptive problems in an ever-changing environment, of living life in a less stressful manner, and of informing, enhancing, and expanding the

Western counseling and therapy perspective, you may find them quite relevant to preventing and managing chronic stress. You will also find a more natural link. The psychiatrist Roger Walsh (2000) regards the relevance and benefit of integrating Asian therapies into Western counseling and therapy, and for addressing stress:

> There is growing evidence that Western psychotherapists may have significantly underestimated the psychologies and therapies of other cultures. This may be especially true for Asian therapies, which have often been dismissed as primitive superstitions despite the fact that some, but not all are highly sophisticated and effective systems. … Studying—or better yet, actually practicing—these techniques can provide both theoretical and practical benefits. Theoretical benefits include new perspectives on human nature, health, potential, and pathology. … On the practical side, Asian therapies are effective, simple, inexpensive, and often pleasurable. They can reduce stress, ameliorate multiple psychological and psychosomatic disorders, offer profound insights into the mind, accelerate mental and emotional development and foster latent capacities and potentials. Finally studying Asian systems has the healthy effect of unveiling and undermining ethnocentrism. (p. 407)

Meditation, Qigong, and Yoga

The American College of Sports Medicine (ACSM) has indicated that a comprehensive exercise program should include aerobic or endurance, muscular fitness, flexibility, and neuromotor or functional fitness exercises (ACSM, 2011; Bushman, 2017; Garber et al., 2011; Riebe, 2017). In addition to the focus on aerobic exercise, and incorporating muscular strength exercises and flexibility exercises, the ACSM has added **neuromotor or functional fitness** exercises to address concerns, especially for the elderly, such as balance, coordination, muscle strength,

flexibility, integration, agility, and proprioception (ACSM, 2011; Bushman, 2017; Garber et al., 2011; Riebe, 2017). The primary examples of neuromotor exercises are Taijiquan, qigong, and yoga.

The reason the forms of qigong and the asana of yoga are both being described in this text, in addition to what has been previously mentioned, is (a) they will provide you with a basic understanding of a multidimensional, non-Western mind/body approach to preventing and addressing chronic stress; (b) they incorporate breath control; (c) they can be utilized as moving meditation; and (d) the research clearly indicates the promising benefits of both qigong (Jahnke, Larkey, Rogers, Etnier, & Lin, 2010; Lee, Pittler, Guo, & Ernst, 2007; Liu, 2010; Ng, & Tsang, 2009, Wang et al., 2013, 2014; Yeung, Chan, Cheung, & Zou, 2018; Zou et al., 2018) and yoga (Bushman, 2017; Bussing et al., 2012; Cahn, Goodman, Peterson, Maturi, & Mills, 2017; Field, 2011; Gothe, & McAuley, 2015; Khalsa, & Elson, 2016; Li & Goldsmith, 2012; Maddux, Daukantaite, & Tellhed, 2017; Schmalzl, Powers, & Blom, 2015; Sharma, 2014; Streeter et al., 2010) for addressing chronic stress and related disorders.

Ideally, attending a class under the supervision of an instructor is the best way to learn. You will be able to receive personal instruction and feedback as your progress through the qigong postures and yoga asanas. In addition, in most cases you will be training with other students and this is beneficial for interpersonal relationships, motivation, adherence, and commitment. However, this may not always be possible.

This being the case, a basic, quite ancient and fundamental to qigong forms and Chinese martial arts in general, short version of a qigong form, often called standing like a stake or standing like a tree, called Zhanzhuang, will be described. The complete eight postures, standing qigong form known as the Baduanjin or Eight Pieces of Brocade, will also be described. In addition, a short series of yoga asanas will also be described. It is highly recommended you access videos for these practices and their various postures and asana via your search engine to observe the actual movements and transitions and for additional descriptions and explanations. For example, for the yoga asanas, simply put the name of the asana, provided in the text, into your search engine. You will get numerous videos, descriptions, and explanations for the particular asana.

In addition, given the research (Benson, 1998, 2000; Carter, & Carter, 2016; Chang, Dusek, & Benson, 2011; Davis, & Hayes, 2011; Fisher, 2017; Goyal et al., 2014; Hofmann, Grossmann, & Hinton, 2011; Hofmann, Sawyer, Witt, & Oh, 2010; Hoge et al., 2018; Kabat-Zinn, 2003, 2005; Tang, Hölzel, & Posner, 2015) regarding the physical and psychological benefits of meditation, various forms of sitting meditation such as mindfulness, counting your breaths, the relaxation response, safe space visualization, and loving-kindness meditation will be described. As with qigong and yoga, use your search engine to explore the various explanations and descriptions of these sitting meditations. There are also various free apps for your mobile devices that provide guided meditation and breathing practices. Apps and other mobile-friendly options make it possible for students to practice in the dorm, outdoors, or while traveling.

Managing Stress for Self and Others

Basically, this text is about (a) identifying and understanding chronic stress within the context of evolutionary theory and neuroscience; (b) understanding the importance of a holistic and integrative therapeutic lifestyle change approach, which addresses chronic stress by incorporating both Western and Asian perspectives and techniques across areas such as meditation, cognitive restructuring, exercise, sleep, sedentary behavior, nutrition, the immune system, time management, and interpersonal relationships; (c) applying this holistic and integrative therapeutic lifestyle change approach for preventing the occurrence of chronic stress for yourself; (d) applying this holistic and integrative therapeutic lifestyle change approach for addressing and eliminating chronic stress if it is already the case for you; (e) incorporating this holistic and integrative therapeutic lifestyle change approach into a counseling/therapy context to benefit others; (f) creating your own personal stress management program (PSMP) to prevent and eliminate, if it is the case, chronic stress; and (g) physical, psychological, interpersonal, and occupational self-care.

HOW TO USE THIS TEXT

The approach of this text is a practical, purposeful, and intentional shift from the standard paradigm/mainstream thinking as it combines Buddhism, Daoism, Confucianism, yoga, qigong, and meditation, both moving and stationary, with evolutionary science, neuroscience, counseling, and stress management into a holistic, integrative, therapeutic, self-care approach to overall health and well-being. It is time to recognize our Western ethnocentric bias and categorical rigidity, and the fact that we can also learn from these nontraditional, non-Western approaches such that they can inform and enhance our understanding of and offer adaptive solutions to addressing our overall physical and psychological health and well-being. As neuroscience has shown us, learning requires repetition and practice. Thus, there is a strong focus on establishing a solid foundation, especially in the first few chapters, in (a) the basic principles of evolutionary science, neuroscience, and the stress response and (b) the basic teachings of Buddhism, Daoism, and Confucianism. This foundation allows for a more fluid integration of the material in the later chapters.

The first three chapters set the foundation and context for exploring, understanding, and practicing a holistic and integrative therapeutic lifestyle change approach for preventing and eliminating chronic stress and the various physical and psychological conditions associated with it. These chapters cover evolutionary theory, neuroscience, the stress response, and Daoist, Confucian, and Buddhist approaches to preventing and eliminating chronic stress. They are the beginning points and infrastructure of the text. They are interwoven into the fabric of the remaining chapters.

Chapters 4 through 11 provide the content and focus of a holistic and integrative therapeutic lifestyle change approach for preventing and eliminating chronic stress. These chapters cover meditation, cognitive restructuring and reframing, exercise, nutrition, sleep, the immune system, time management, and interpersonal relationships. The content of all of these areas are intimately interrelated and interdependent.

Chapter 12 provides the blueprint for creating and applying a holistic and integrative therapeutic lifestyle change approach for preventing and eliminating chronic stress and the various physical and psychological conditions associated with it. Chapter 13 weaves in a holistic and integrative therapeutic lifestyle change approach for preventing and eliminating chronic stress and the various physical and psychological conditions associated with it into a counseling context.

Each chapter, all of which are interdependent, explores its specific content, presents research, and incorporates and describes practical applications, be it meditation, qigong, and/or yoga. Essentially the approach of this text is focused on self-care for preventing and eliminating chronic stress and the various physical and psychological conditions associated with it. Self-care is all about learning, putting what you have learned into practice regularly and consistently, and enjoying yourself on your journey. **It is time for a change!** Having read through this introduction, you have begun your journey. As Chapter 64 of the *Daodejing* states, "A thousand-mile journey begins with the first step" (Santee, 2007, p. 1).

TERMS

relaxation response
fight/freeze/flight response or stress response
lifestyle changes
holistic and integrative approach
American College of Preventive Medicine
American College of Lifestyle Medicine
chronic stress
evolutionary theory

new paradigm
adaptive problem
adaptive solution
dukkha
Buddhism
Daoism
Confucianism
equilibrium/homeostasis
neuroplasticity
Negativity bias
mind wandering
default network

allostasis
allostatic load
default level
common factors
Diagnostic and Statistical Manual of Mental Disorders (DSM)
neuromotor/functional fitness
meditation
qigong
yoga

EXERCISES

1. How do you prevent chronic stress?

2. How do you cope with chronic stress?

3. Why does a paradigm shift appear necessary to address chronic physical and psychological conditions?

4. Describe how evolutionary theory can be utilized to thread Western science, Buddhism, Daoism, and Confucianism together to address chronic stress and the physical and psychological conditions associated with it.

5. Describe a holistic and integrative approach to chronic stress, health and well-being, and self-care, and indicate how it is related to therapeutic lifestyle changes, lifestyle medicine, and medical costs.

6. Compare allostasis, the fight/freeze/flight or stress response, and allostatic load.

7. What is chronic stress?

VIDEOS FOR QIGONG

The following listed videos will allow you see how Baduanjin and Zhan Zhuang are performed. Simply copy the bold key words such as **Faye Yip Baduanjin Eight Pieces of Brocade,** access the Internet, and then Google it. It will take you to a site where you will see the video. The added information such as length of video/time will help you identify the specific video. The videos, which only have background music and the ones that describe the form are listed as well. The Baduanjin videos, listed under Baduanjin, take you through the entire sequence of the form as described in this text.

Both Zhan Zhuang videos have additional postures, but the three postures that are described in this text are all shown and described. As the sequence in this text only uses three basic postures, two of which are repeated, the sequence in the Zhan Zhuang videos are different. The Lam Kam Chuen Zhan Zhuang video is about 2 hours long and also describes a variation of the Baduanjin form.

Baduanjin
Faye Yip Baduanjin Eight Pieces of Brocade
Posted Aug 10, 2012. Time 12:12. Uploaded by eliteTaiChi. Just music.
Posted Feb 22, 2012. Time 12:12. Uploaded by Deyin Taijiquan Institute. Just music.
Perth Tai Chi Academy Eight Pieces of Brocade Baduajin
Posted October 29, 2016. Time 10:47. Talks you through/teaches the form.
Posted October 24, 2016. Time 12:12. Just music.

Zhan Zhuang
Zhan Zhuang Bill Smith
May 9, 2015. Time 3:18.
Teaches Zhan Zhuang.
Standing Meditation: Beginning Postures
Basic three stances from this text are shown and described in addition to others.
Zhan Zhuang Lam Kam Chuen
October 11, 2017. Time. 1:50:26.
Zhan Zhuang: Standing Like a Tree (by Master Lam Kam Chuen)
Describes and teaches Zhan Zhuang and a variation of the Baduanjin form. Provides background and context. Basic three stances from this text are shown and described in addition to others. Based on his book *The Way of Energy*.

REFERENCES

Anderson, T., Lunnen, K. M., & Ogles, B.M. (2010). Putting models and techniques in context. In B. L. Duncan, S. D. Miller, B. E. Wampold, & M. A. Hubble (Eds.), *The heart and soul of change: Delivering what works in therapy* (pp. 143–146). Washington, DC: American Psychological Association.

Anderson, E., & Shivakumar, G. (2013). Effects of exercise and physical activity on anxiety. *Frontiers in Psychiatry, 4*. Retrieved from https://www.ncbi.nlm.nih.gov/pmc/articles/PMC3632802/pdf/fpsyt-04-00027.pdf

American College of Lifestyle Medicine (ACLM) (2012). Lifestyle medicine standards. Retrieved from https://lifestylemedicine.org/ACLM/About/What_is_Lifestyle_Medicine/ACLM_Standards/ACLM/About/What_is_Lifestyle_Medicine_/ACLM_Standards.aspx?hkey=40358b66-687c-481d-8e34-2db52e6166e9

American College of Lifestyle Medicine (ACLM) (2015). *What is lifestyle medicine?* Retrieved from https://www.lifestylemedicine.org/What-is-Lifestyle-Medicine

American College of Preventive Medicine (ACPM) (2009). *Lifestyle medicine: Evidence review.* Retrieved https://cdn.ymaws.com/www.acpm.org/resource/resmgr/lmi-files/lifestylemedicine-literature.pdf

American College of Preventive Medicine (ACPM) (2018). *Lifestyle medicine initiative.* Retrieved from http://www.acpm.org/page/lifestylemedicine

American College of Sports Medicine (ACSM). (2011). *ACSM issues new recommendations on quantity and quality of exercise.* Retrieved from https://www.prweb.com/releases/2011/6/prweb8606343.htm

American Psychological Association (APA) (2012a). *Stress in America: Our health at risk.* Retrieved from http://www.apa.org/news/press/releases/stress/2011/ final-2011.pdf

American Psychological Association (APA) (2012b). *Latest APA survey reveals deepening concerns about connection between chronic disease and stress.* Retrieved from http://www.apa.org/news/press/releases/2012/01/chronic-disease.aspx

American Psychological Association (APA) (2017a). *Coping with change, part 1.* Retrieved from https://www.apa.org/news/press/releases/stress/2016/coping-with-change.pdf

American Psychological Association (APA) (2017b). *The state of our nation.* Retrieved from http://www.apa.org/news/press/releases/stress/2017/state-nation.pdf

Asmundson, G. J. G., Fetzner, M. G., DeBoer, L. B., Powers, M. B., Otto, M. W., & Smits, J. A. J. (2013). Let's get physical: A contemporary review of the anxiolytic effects of exercise for anxiety and its disorders. *Depression & Anxiety, 30*(4), 362–373.

Avey, H., Matheny, K. B., Robbins, A., & Jacobson, T. A. (2003). Health care providers' training, perceptions, and practices regarding stress and health outcomes. *Journal of the National Medical Association, 95*(9), 833–845.

Babyak, M., Blumenthal, J., Herman, S., Khatri, P., Doraiswamy, M., Moore, K., … & Ranga Krishnan, K. (2000). Exercise treatment for major depression: Maintenance of therapeutic benefit at 10 months. *Psychosomatic Medicine, 62*(5), 633–638.

Barrett, L. F. (2017). *How emotions are made: The secret life of the brain* [Kindle edition]. New York, NY: Houghton Mifflin.

Benson, H. (1998). Testimony of Herbert Benson regarding mind/body interventions, healthcare and mind/body medical centers before the United States Senate Appropriations Subcommittee on labor/HHS and education, Senator Arlen Specter, chairman, September 22, 1998.

Benson, H. (2000). *The relaxation response.* New York, NY: Harper.

Blumenthal, J. A., Babyak M. A., Doraiswamy, P. M., Watkins, L., Hoffman, B. M., Barbour, K. A., … & Sherwood, A. (2007). Exercise and pharmacotherapy in the treatment of major depressive disorder. *Psychosomatic Medicine, 69*(7), 587–596.

Blumenthal J. A., Babyak M. A., Moore K. A., Craighead, W. E., Herman, S., Khatri, P., … & Krishnan, K.R. (1999). Effects of exercise training on older patients with major depression. *Archives of Internal Medicine, 159*(19), 2349–2356.

Boone, J., & Anthony, J. (2003). Evaluating the impact of stress on systemic disease: The MOST protocol in primary care. *Journal of the American Osteopathic Association, 103*(5), 239–246.

Broman-Fulks, J. J., Berman, M. E., Rabian, B., & Webster, M. J. (2004). Effects of aerobic exercise on anxiety sensitivity. *Behaviour Research and Therapy, 42*(2), 125–136.

Bushman, B. (Ed.) (2017). *American college of sports medicine complete guide to fitness and health.* Champaign, IL: Human Kinetics.

Buss, D. M. (2004). *Evolutionary psychology.* Boston, MA: Allyn & Bacon.

Bussing, A., Michalsen, A., Khalsa, S. B. S., Telles, S., & Sherman, K. J. (2012). Effects of yoga on mental and physical health: A short summary of reviews. *Evidence-Based Complementary and Alternative Medicine.* Retrieved from https://www.hindawi.com/journals/ecam/2012/165410/

Cahn, B. R., Goodman, M. S., Peterson, C. T., Maturi, R., & Mills, P. J. (2017). Yoga, meditation and mind-body health: Increased BDNF, cortisol awakening response, and altered inflammatory marker expression after a 3-month yoga and meditation retreat. *Frontiers in Human Neuroscience, 11.* Retrieved from https://www.ncbi.nlm.nih.gov/pmc/articles/PMC5483482/pdf/fnhum-11-00315.pdf

Capobianco, L., Morris, J. A., & Wells, A. (2018). Worry and rumination: Do they prolong physiological and affective recovery from stress? *Anxiety, Stress & Coping, 31*(3), 291–303.

Carter, K. S., & Carter R., III. (2016). Breath-based meditation: A mechanism to restore the physiological and cognitive reserves for optimal human performance. *World Journal of Clinical Cases, 4*(4), 99–102. Retrieved from https://www.ncbi.nlm.nih.gov/pmc/articles/PMC4832119/pdf/WJCC-4-99.pdf

Chang, B., Dusek, J. A., & Benson, H. (2011). Psychobiological changes from relaxation response elicitation: Long-term practitioners vs. novices. *Psychosomatics, 52*(6), 550–559.

Charles, S. T., Piazza, J. R., Mogle, J., Sliwinski, M. J. & Almeida. D. M. (2013). The wear and tear of daily stressors on mental health. *Psychological Science, 24*(5), 733–741.

Cohen, S., Gianaros, P. J., & Manuck, S. B. (2016). A stage model of stress and disease. *Perspectives on Psychological Science, 11*(4), 456–463.

Cummings, N. A., & VandenBos, G. R. (1981). The twenty years Kaiser-Permanente experience with psychotherapy and medical utilization: Implications for national health policy and national health insurance. *Health Policy Quarterly, 1*(2), 159–175.

Davis, D. M., & Hayes, J. A. (2011). What are the benefits of mindfulness? A practice review of psychotherapy-related research. *Psychotherapy, 48*(2), 198–208.

DeBoer, L. B., Powers, M. B., Utschig, A. C., Otto, M. W., & Smits, J. A. (2012). Exploring exercise as an avenue for the treatment of anxiety disorders. *Expert Review of Neurotherapeutics, 12*(8), 1011–1022.

Duncan, B. L. (2002). The legacy of Saul Rosenzweig: The profundity of the dodo bird. *Journal of Psychotherapy Integration, 12*(1), 32–57.

Duncan, B. L., Miller, S. D., Wampold, B. E., & Hubble, M. A. (Eds.) (2010). *The heart and soul of change: Delivering what works in therapy.* Washington, DC: American Psychological Association.

Field, T. (2011). Yoga clinical research review. *Complementary Therapies in Clinical Practice, 17*(1), 1–8.

Fisher, K. (2017). *The benefits of meditation that are proven by science.* Retrieved from https://inspiyr.com/27125-2/

Freeman, D., & Freeman, J. (2014). Are all psychological therapies equally effective? Don't ask the dodo. *The Guardian.* Retrieved from https://www.theguardian.com/science/blog/2014/jan/23/psychological-therapies-mental-illness-dodo-bird-verdict?CMP=twt_fd

Garber, C. E., Blissmer, B., Deschenes, M. R., Franklin, B. A., Lamonte, M J., Lee, I. M., ... & Swain, D. P. (2011). Quantity and quality of exercise for developing and maintaining cardiorespiratory, musculoskeletal, and neuromotor fitness in apparently healthy adults: Guidance for prescribing exercise. *Medicine & Science in Sports & Exercise, 43*(7), 1334–1359.

Gianferante D., Thomas M. V., Hanlin, L., Chen, X., Breines, J. G., Zoccola, P. M., & Rohleder, N. (2014). Post-stress rumination predicts HPA axis responses to repeated acute stress. *Psychoneuroendocrinology, 49*(1), 244–252.

Gothe, N. P., & McAuley, E. (2015). Yoga and cognition: A meta-analysis of chronic and acute effects. *Psychosomatic Medicine, 77*(7), 784–797.

Goyal, M., Singh, S., Sibinga, E. M. S., Gould, N. F., Rowland-Seymour, A., Sharma, R., ... Haythornthwaite, J. A. (2014). Meditation programs for psychological stress and well-being: A systematic review and meta-analysis. *JAMA Internal Medicine, 174*(7), 357–368.

Hofmann, S. G., Grossman, P., & Hinton, D. E. (2011). Loving-kindness and compassion meditation: Potential for psychological interventions. *Clinical Psychology Review 31*(7), 1126–1132.

Hofmann, S. G., Sawyer, A. T., Witt, A. A., & Oh, D. (2010). The effect of mindfulness-based therapy on anxiety and depression: A meta-analytic review. *Journal of Consulting and Clinical Psychology, 78*(2), 169–183.

Hoffman, B. M., Babyak, M. A., Craighead, W. E., Sherwood, A., Doraiswamy, P. M., Coons, M. J., & Blumenthal, J. A. (2011). Exercise and pharmacotherapy in patients with major depression: One-year follow-up of the smile study. *Psychosomatic Medicine, 73*(2), 127–133.

Hoge, E. A., Bui, E., Palitz, S. A., Schwarz, N. R., Owens, M. E., Johnston, J. M., Pollack, M. H., & Simon, N. M. (2018). The effect of mindfulness meditation training on biological acute stress responses in generalized anxiety disorder. *Psychiatry Research, 262*, 328–332.

Hunsley, J., & Di Giulio, G. (2002). Dodo bird, phoenix, or urban legend? The question of psychotherapy equivalence. *Scientific Review of Mental Health Practice: Objective Investigations of Controversial and Unorthodox Claims in Clinical Psychology, Psychiatry, and Social Work, 1*(1), 11–22.

Hyman, M. A., Ornish, D., & Roizen, M. (2009). Lifestyle medicine: Treating the causes of disease. *Alternative Therapies, 15*(6), 12–14.

Jahnke, R., Larkey, L., Rogers, C., Etnier, J., & Lin, F. (2010). A comprehensive review of health benefits of qigong and tai chi. *American Journal of Health Promotion, 24*(6), e1–e25.

James, W. (1890/1950). *The principles of psychology*, Volume One. New York, NY: Dover Publications, Inc.

Kabat-Zinn, J. (2003). Mindfulness-based interventions in context: Past, present and future. *Clinical Psychological Science and Practice, 10*(2), 144–156.

Kabat-Zinn, J. (2005). *Full catastrophe living: Using the wisdom of your body and mind to face stress, pain, and illness*. New York, NY: Random House.

Khalsa, S. B. S., & Elson, L. E. (2016). *A Harvard Medical School special health report: An introduction to yoga*. Boston, MA: Harvard Medical School.

Killingsworth, M. A., & Gilbert, D. (2010). A wandering mind is an unhappy mind. *Science, 330*(6006), 932.

Kroenke, K., & Manglesdorff, A. D. (1989). Common symptoms in ambulatory care: Incidence, evaluation, therapy, and outcome. *American Journal of Medicine, 86*(3), 262–266.

Lee, M. S., Pittler, M. H., Guo, R., & Ernst, E. (2007). Qigong for hypertension: A systematic review of randomized clinical trials. *Journal of Hypertension, 25*(8), 1525–1532.

Leger, K. A., Charles, S. T., & Almeida, D. M. (2018). Let it go: Lingering negative affect in response to daily stressors is associated with physical health years later. *Psychological Science, 29*(8), 1–8. Retrieved from http://journals.sagepub.com/doi/pdf/10.1177/0956797618763097

Li, A. W., & Goldsmith, C. A. W. (2012). The effects of yoga on anxiety and stress. *Alternative Medicine Review, 17*(1), 21–35.

Liu, T. (Ed.) (2010). *Chinese medical qigong*. London, UK: Singing Dragon.

Luborsky L., Rosenthal R., Diguer L., Andrusyna T. P., Berman J. S., Levitt J. T., Seligman D. A. & Krause E. D. (2002). The dodo bird verdict is alive and well—mostly. *Clinical Psychology: Science and Practice, 9*(1), 2–12. Retrieved from http://www.wellness-factors.com/docs/press_room/Dodo-bird-meta-analys.pdf

Maddux, R. E., Daukantaité, D., & Tellhed, U. (2017). The effects of yoga on stress and psychological health among employees: An 8- and 16-week intervention study. *Anxiety, Stress & Coping, 31*(2), 121–134.

Marcus, D. K., O'Connell, D., Norris, A. L., & Sawaqdeh, A. (2014). Is the dodo bird endangered in the 21st century? A meta-analysis of treatment comparison studies. *Clinical Psychology Review, 34*(7), 519–530.

McEwen, B. S. (2006a). Protective and damaging effects of stress mediators: Central role of the brain. *Dialogues in Clinical Neuroscience, 8*(4), 367–381.

McEwen, B. S. (2006b). Stress, adaption, and disease: Allostasis and allostatic load. *Annals of the New York Academy of Sciences, 840*, 33–44.

McEwen, B. S. (2008). Central effects of stress hormones in health and disease: Understanding the protective and damaging effects of stress and stress mediators. *European Journal of Pharmacology, 583*(2–3), 174–185.

McEwen, B. S., & Lashley, E. N. (2002). *The end of stress as we know it.* Washington, DC: Joseph Henry Press.

McKenzie, S. H., & Harris, M. F. (2013). Understanding the relationship between stress, distress and healthy lifestyle behaviour: A qualitative study of patients and general practitioners. *BMC Family Practice, 14.* Retrieved from https://bmcfampract.biomedcentral.com/track/pdf/10.1186/1471-2296-14-166

Mirowsky, J. (2011). Cognitive decline and the default American lifestyle. *Journals of Gerontology, Series B: Psychological Sciences and Social Sciences, 66B*(S1), i50–i58. Retrieved from https://www.ncbi.nlm.nih.gov/pmc/articles/PMC3132766/pdf/gbq070.pdf

Nerurkar, A., Bitton, A., Davis, R. B., Phillips, R. S., & Yeh, G. (2013). When physicians counsel about stress: Results of a national study. *JAMA Internal Medicine, 173*(1), 76–77.

Ng, B. H. P., & Tsang, H. W. H. (2009). Psychophysiological outcome of health qigong for chronic conditions: A systematic review. *Psychophysiology, 46*(2), 257–269.

Powers, M. B., Asmundson, G. J. G., & Smits, J. A. J. (2015). Exercise for mood and anxiety disorders: The state-of-the science. *Cognitive Behaviour Therapy, 44*(4), 237–239.

Ratey, J. J., & Hagerman, E. (2008). *Spark: The revolutionary new science of exercise and the brain.* New York, NY: Little, Brown and Company.

Riebe, D. (Ed.) (2017). *ACSM's guidelines for exercise testing and prescription.* Philadelphia, PA: Lippincott, Williams & Wilkins.

Rosenzweig, S. (1936). Some implicit common factors in diverse methods of psychotherapy. *American Journal of Orthopsychiatry, 6*(3), 412–415.

Saad, L. (2017). Eight in 10 Americans afflicted by stress. *Gallup.* Retrieved from http://news.gallup.com/poll/224336/eight-americans-afflicted-stress.aspx

Santee, R. (2007). *An Integrative Approach to Counseling: Bridging Chinese Thought, Evolutionary Theory, and Stress Management.* Copyright © 2007 by SAGE Publications. Reprinted with permission.

Sapolsky, R. M. (2004). *Why zebras don't get ulcers.* New York, NY: Henry Holt and Company.

Schmalzl, L., Powers, C., & Blom, E.H. (2015) Neurophysiological and neurocognitive mechanisms underlying the effects of yoga-based practices: Towards a comprehensive theoretical framework. *Frontiers in Human Neuroscience, 9.* Retrieved from https://www.ncbi.nlm.nih.gov/pmc/articles/PMC4424840/pdf/fnhum-09-00235.pdf

Schneiderman, N. (2004). Psychosocial, behavioral, and biological aspects of chronic diseases. *Current Directions in Psychological Science, 13*(6), 247–251.

Schneiderman, N., Ironson, G., & Siegel, S. D. (2005). Stress and health: Psychological, behavioral, and biological determinants. *Annual Review of Clinical Psychology, 1*(1), 607–628.

Selye, H. (1978). *The stress of life.* New York, NY: McGraw-Hill.

Sharma, M. (2014). Yoga as an alternative and complementary approach for stress management: A systematic review. *Journal of Evidence-Based Complementary & Alternative Medicine, 19*(1), 59–67.

Silveira, H., Moraes, H., Oliveira, N., Coutinho, E. S. F., Laks, J., & Deslandes, A. (2013). Physical exercise and clinically depressed patients: A systematic review and meta-analysis. *Neuropsychobiology, 67*(2), 61–68.

Smyth, J., Zawadzki, M., & Gerin, W. (2013). Stress and disease: A structural and functional analysis. *Social & Personality Psychology Compass, 7*(4), 217–227.

Stathopoulou, G., Powers, M. B., Berry, A. C., Smits, J. A. J., & Otto, M. W. (2006). Exercise interventions for mental health: A quantitative and qualitative review. *Clinical Psychology Science and Practice, 13*(2), 179–193.

Stefano, G. B., Fricchione, G. L., Slingsby, B. T., & Benson, H. (2001). The placebo effect and relaxation response: Neural processes and their coupling to constitutive nitric oxide. *Brain Research Reviews, 35*(2), 1–19.

Steffen, P. R., Austin, T., & DeBarros, A. (2017). Treating chronic stress to address the growing problem of depression and anxiety: Biofeedback and mindfulness as simple, effective preventive measures. *Policy Insights from the Behavioral and Brain Sciences, 4*(1), 64–70.

Streeter, C. C., Whitfield, T. H., Owen, L., Rein, T., Karri, S. K., Yakhkind, A., ... & Jensen, J. E. (2010). Effects of yoga versus walking on mood, anxiety, and brain GABA levels: A randomized controlled MRS study. *Journal of Alternative and Complementary Medicine, 16*(11), 1145–1152.

Tang, Y. Y., Hölzel, B. K., & Posner, M. I. (2015). The neuroscience of mindfulness meditation. *Nature Reviews Neuroscience 16*(4), 213–225.

United Nations Educational, Scientific, and Cultural Organization (UNESCO). (1950). *The race question.* Retrieved from http://unesdoc.unesco.org/images/0012/001282/128291eo.pdf

Walsh, R. (2000). Asian psychotherapies. In R. J. Corsini & D. Wedding (Eds.), *Current psychotherapies* (pp. 407–444). Ithaca, NY: F.E. Peacock Publishers, Inc.

Walsh, R. (2011). Lifestyle and mental health. *American Psychologist, 66*(7), 579–592.

Wampold, B. E. (2001). *The great psychotherapy debate: Models, methods, and findings.* Mahwah, NJ: Lawrence Erlbaum Associates, Inc.

Wampold, B. E. (2015). How important are the common factors in psychotherapy? An update. *World Psychiatry, 14*(3), 270–277.

Wampold, B. E., & Imel, Z. E. (2015). *The great psychotherapy debate: The evidence for what makes psychotherapy work.* New York, NY: Routledge.

Wang, C. W., Chan, C. L. W., Ho, R. T. H., Tsang, H. W. H., Chan, C. H. Y., & Ng, S. M. (2013). The effect of qigong on depressive and anxiety symptoms: A systematic review and meta-analysis of randomized controlled trials. *Evidence-Based Complementary and Alternative Medicine: eCAM.* Retrieved from https://www.ncbi.nlm.nih.gov/pmc/articles/PMC3671670/pdf/ECAM2013-716094.pdf

Wang, C. W., Chan, C. H., Ho, R. T., Chan, J. S,, Ng, S. M., & Chan, C. L. (2014). Managing stress and anxiety through qigong exercise in healthy adults: A systematic review and meta-analysis of randomized controlled trials. *BMC Complementary and Alternative Medicine, 14*(8). Retrieved from https://www.ncbi.nlm.nih.gov/pmc/articles/PMC3893407/pdf/1472-6882-14-8.pdf

Watts, A. W. (1961). *Psychotherapy east and west.* New York, NY: Random House.

World Health Organization (WHO) (2006). *Constitution of the World Health Organization.* Retrieved from http://www.who.int/governance/eb/who_constitution_en.pdf

Yeung, A., Chan, J. S. M., Cheung, J. C., & Zou, L. (2018). Qigong and tai-chi for mood regulation. *Focus, 16,* 40–47. Retrieved from https://www.researchgate.net/publication/321299648_Qigong_and_Tai-Chi_for_Mood_Regulation

Zoccola, P. M., & Dickerson, S. S. (2012). Assessing the relationship between rumination and cortisol: A review. *Journal of Psychosomatic Research, 73*(1), 1–9.

Zou, L., Yeung, A., Quan, X., Hui, S. S. C., Hu, X., Chan, J. S. M., ... & Wang, H. (2018). Mindfulness-based Baduanjin exercise for depression and anxiety in people with physical or mental illnesses: A systematic review and meta-analysis. *International Journal of Environmental Research and Public Health, 15,* 321. Retrieved from https://www.ncbi.nlm.nih.gov/pmc/articles/PMC5858390/pdf/ijerph-15-00321.pdf

CREDITS

CHAPTER 1

Evolutionary Theory

After finishing this chapter, you will be able to do the following:

- Describe the relationship between the six components of the evolutionary process relative to adapting to various environmental contexts
- Demonstrate why it is important to understand the fight/freeze/flight or stress response and stress management within the context of evolutionary theory
- Demonstrate an understanding of the concept of continual change not only for evolutionary theory, but also for Confucianism, Daoism, and Buddhism
- Describe the relationship between our negativity bias, the default network, mind wandering/stimulus independent thought (SIT), and simulation
- Indicate why an understanding of neuroscience and our evolutionary tool kit is so important for understanding and managing chronic stress
- Describe the relationship between neuroplasticity, neurogenesis, learning, and stress management
- Describe the relationship between functional behavior, dysfunctional behavior, learning, and stress management
- Delineate the relationship between the stress response and the relaxation response within the context of yin and yang

Although some of the material in this chapter may appear to be different from the standard paradigm or traditional mainstream approach, the **adaptive problem**, chronic stress and overall health and well-being, is the same, while the **adaptive solution** offers a different approach or technique, which will inform and enhance our understanding of addressing the adaptive problem.

This chapter provides you with a framework and a set of basic concepts/processes to initially help guide you through the domain of stress, chronic stress, and stress management. In order to implement a successful stress management

program, it is necessary to understand human behavior within the context of evolutionary theory. We essentially have the same basic physical and psychological mechanisms that allowed our distant ancestors to engage in behavior that allowed them to survive, find a mate, reproduce, and maintain their gene pool in an ever-changing environment that contained significant physical threats. These evolution-based mechanisms, passed on to us via our DNA, are fundamental to our own survival. They have been passed on to us because the behavior they generate worked. These basic mechanisms are not different across cultures or ethnicities. At this level, we are the same. We are all human beings trying to navigate our way through the continually changing process we call life.

FUNDAMENTALS OF EVOLUTIONARY THEORY/PSYCHOLOGY

In this section, we are going to explore **six components of the evolutionary process** relative to navigating our way through life. These six components are an ever-changing environment, adaptive problems, cost-benefit analysis, adaptive solutions, functional behavior, and the mismatch. These components are all interrelated and must not be seen as distinct or separate.

An Ever-Changing Environment

Confucius overlooking a flowing river said, "Everything passes away like this! Not stopping day or night" (Santeee, 2007, p. 19).[1]

> **The very nature** of existence is a continual process of change.

Like the observation of Confucius, the observation that evolutionary theory rests on is that everything is a continual, interrelated process of change. The fundamental point of evolutionary theory is that those organisms that change their behaviors, via natural selection to adapt to the changes in the environment, are the ones who survive and pass on those adaptive mechanisms through their gene pool to their offspring. This of course takes a long time.

---

1 This quote from *Lunyu IX* and all other translations from the Chinese in this text are mine. The original Chinese text for the *Lunyu* can be found at http://ctext.org/analects

The very nature of existence is a continual process of change. It is natural. Just look around. Nothing is static. Everything changes. Your breath is a continual process of change. In and out. In and out. Try stopping it. What happens? You can only hold it so long before you are forced by your body, your evolutionary mechanism of breathing, to gasp for a breath. It does not want to remain unchanging; otherwise, it is dead!

At every level, from the microscopic to the cosmic, continual change/movement is happening. At the atomic level the electrons, neutrons, and protons are always moving and are hence changing. At the cosmic level, the planets spin and revolve around the sun—night and day, across the seasons. The sun rises and the sun sets, although, in reality, it is the continual revolving of the earth. Nonetheless, it is still change. Everything grows and is engaged in a process of continual change. How much control do you have over your thoughts? Sit for a moment and simply observe your thoughts as they gallop across the landscape of your mind. Notice how they automatically pop in and out of your mind, always changing.

The problem is that most people do not like a lot of change or major change. In fact, we have conditioned ourselves to pretty much be oblivious of the continual process of change. We try to make the world static so we have some sense of certainty. This is normal. It we do not have a relative sense of certainty we feel threatened as we do not know what is going to happen. This sets off the fight/freeze/flight response or stress response and we begin to feel anxious. Being anxious for the most part does not feel good, thus the need to make things static and routine. If the threats are realistic (for our distant ancestors they were primarily physical in nature) and can be resolved by the activation of the stress response, then it is an appropriate activation. In other words, **normal stress** allows us to recognize a problematic change, attend to and concentrate on it, and encode it in our brain so we can remember it for the future and motivates us to resolve it as well as gives us the energy to resolve it. We return to our static and routine world. We feel safe. To put this into context for you, just think about the not physical but certainly realistic midterm exam!

The problem is that most people do not like a lot of change or major change. In fact, we have conditioned ourselves to pretty much be oblivious of the continual process of change.

If the threat-based change is not realistic or imminent, is primarily psychosocial in nature, and is beyond your control, then the activation of the stress response will not help you resolve it. In fact, it may make things worse. Your stress response has been inappropriately activated! If this inappropriate activation is continuous, it leads to **chronic stress**, which is detrimental to our physical, psychological, and interpersonal health and well-being.

> **Chronic stress**

Underlying our anxiety about physical and psychological illness, loss, and feeling isolated and alone, our existential angst about the meaning and purpose of life, freedom, choice and responsibility, is the most salient change of which we have no control over and cannot avoid and is riddled with uncertainty, our destiny to die! For Yalom (1980, 2009), death anxiety is the foundation of our existential angst, the source of psychopathology, and the basis of the universal human condition of chronic stress. According to Yalom (1980, 2009), we develop defense mechanisms to keep the threat of this fundamental change out of our awareness and thus reduce the stress associated with it.

> **To resist change** compromises your physical and psychological health and well-being.

Daoism

On the other hand, the dynamic acceptance, based on observations that everything is a continual process of change, is easily seen in the writings of the Chinese Daoist philosopher Zhuangzi (4th–3rd century BCE). It was quite clear to him that change was not only ubiquitous, it was the destiny of everything. His specific focus on death as merely another change allowed to him to eliminate a source of chronic stress and move on to engaging and adapting to life.

Book of Changes

The concept of change and being in harmony with it is fundamental to understanding not only Chinese thought but also their sense of health, well-being, and being free from what we today call chronic stress. The concept of yin and yang (陰陽) provides the most basic explanation of the continual process of change. In the appendix of the over 2,000-year-old *Book of Changes* (*Yijing*) or *Changes of*

Zhou (Zhouyi), **Dao** or the Way/Path, the most fundamental concept of Chinese thought, is defined as

> [t]he dynamic, symbiotic, continually changing, cyclical process or *yin* and *yang* is called *Dao*. (for original translation see Chinese Text Project (CTP), n.d.a.)

Death and life are destiny. They are as ordinary as night and day. They are natural. They cannot be interfered with by people. They are the circumstances of all things (Guo, 1956, p. 16, lines 20–21).

Uncle Zhi Li and Uncle Hua Jie were observing Ming Bo Hills in the vastness of Kun Lun Mountains, the place where the Yellow Emperor rested. After a while, a willow tree grew out of the left elbow of Uncle Hua Jie. He was startled and expressed disgust. Uncle Zhi Li said, "Are you disgusted? Uncle Hua Jie said, "It is gone. How can I be disgusted? Life is to borrow. To borrow is to live, life is dust and dirt. Death and life are night and day. You and I were observing changes and now changes have caught up with me. Why should I be disgusted? (Guo, 1956, p. 46, lines 19–22).

The wife of Zhuangzi died. Zhuangzi was sitting on the floor, with his legs spread apart, beating on a basin and singing. Huizi said, "You have lived together, raised children, and grown old. That you do not weep is one thing. But beating a basin and singing; isn't that going too far?" Zhuangzi replied, "Not so! When she first died, how could I alone not be like others? Examining her beginnings, she originally was without life. Not moving, without life, originally without form. Not moving, without form, originally without *qi* (氣). Undifferentiated! Suddenly, within the obscurity a change and there is *qi*. *Qi* changes and there is form. Form changes and there is life. Now, another change and there is death. This is the movement of the four seasons. Spring, autumn, winter, and summer waiting on each other. She is presently lying down at rest in a gigantic room. Yet if I followed those who shouted and wept, I would consider myself as not understanding my destiny. Thus, I stopped! (Guo, 1956, p. 46, lines 15–19).

Huangdi Neijing

The importance of understanding the continual process of change, or **yin and yang**, and its relationship to illness is clearly indicated in the over 2,000-year-old medical text the *Huangdi Neijing* or the *Yellow Emperor's Discourse on Internal Medicine*. This text is believed to be the oldest medical text in China. In chapter 1

The Yellow Emperor said, "*Yin* and *Yang* is the way (*Dao*) of Heaven and Earth. They are the organizational patterns, regulators and guides for all things. They are the father and mother of all change and transformation. They are the root and beginning of life and death. They are the home of spiritual clarity. To treat illness, you must seek their root." (for original translation see CTP, n.d.b.)

Learn to adapt.
Be in harmony with change.

The *Huangdi Neijing* focuses on a holistic lifestyle that is in harmony with change and practices moderation. Those who follow this lifestyle, according to the *Huangdi Neijing*, are free from what we call chronic stress and have positive health and well-being, allowing them to living to be a robust 100 or more years old. If this lifestyle is not followed, then those individuals will be chronically stressed and die young.

Today, people act differently. They drink wine as if it were merely water. They are consistently rash and impulsive in their behavior. They are drunk when they enter the bedroom. Their desires exhaust their essence (*jīng* 精). They squander and dissipate what is truly real. They do not know how to maintain satisfaction. They are unable to control their spirit (*shen* 神). They devote themselves to instant happiness. Their daily life is without moderation. Thus, at the age of 50 they are feeble and weak. (CTP, n.d.b.)

Practice moderation.

It must be noted that fundamental to this lifestyle, advocated by the *Huangdi Neijing*, was the necessity to adapt one's behavior according to changes in the environment. In fact, in chapter 2, the text provides a description of the changes that occur across all four seasons. Regarding the spring it notes:

The three months of Spring are called issue forth and display. The sky and the earth produce life together. All things are thriving. At night lie down and go to sleep. Rise early in the morning, stretch out and take a brisk walk in the courtyard. By issuing energy the body recuperates. This is applying your will (*zhi* 志) to live and grow. Living and growing you will not weaken. Enjoying life and not punishing yourself. This is responding to the *qi* (氣) of spring. This is the Tao of nourishing life (*Yangsheng* 養生). (Santee & Zhiang, 2015; CTP, n.d.c.)

Buddhist teachings also emphasize the importance of understanding that everything is a continually changing process. In fact, not understanding that everything is impermanent, nonsubstantial and interdependent, in other words being ignorant of the nature of reality, leads to craving and the generation of **dukkha** or chronic stress (Santee, 2007). In the Buddhist text *The Sutra of Statements on Dharma (Dhammapada or Fa Ju Jing 法句經)* it notes

> Everything is always changing/impermanent.
> Everything is *dukkha* (chronic stress).
> Everything is interdependent/without self. (Santee, 2007; BFNN, n.d.)

Adaptive Problems

From the perspective of evolutionary theory/psychology, at the most basic level, **adaptive problems**, within the ever-changing environment, are related to, directly or indirectly, passing on one's gene pool. In other words, reproduction! Thus, issues concerning staying alive, shelter, safety, food, drink, interacting with others, finding a mate, mating, maintaining the gene pool, and growth are all adaptive problems. Each of these in turn generates a new set of adaptive problems, which in turn create another set of problems, and so on. In addition, the interactions between these various issues create another set of adaptive problems.

In one sense, we are daily faced with adaptive problems. They are primarily indirect in nature, but nonetheless they need to be addressed and resolved. They are essentially the same across all aspects of culture. We are all trying to survive! If a person is chronically stressed and seeks help, he or she has an unresolved adaptive problem in his or her environment (internal and/or external). If a person seeks counseling he or she has an unresolved adaptive problem in his or her environment (internal and/or external). In both cases, the unresolved adaptive problem is perceived as a threat. In most, cases the perceived threat is psychosocial in nature and generated by one's thinking. Thus, the adaptive problems we will be exploring throughout this text are primarily threat based and psychosocial in nature.

Cost-Benefit Analysis

When addressing these threat-based, psychosocial adaptive problems, the examination of the problem, from the perspective of evolutionary theory/psychology, often occurs within the format of a ***cost-benefit analysis***. If I make decision x, what will it cost me for the benefit that I seek? The decisions, of course, will vary across contexts and the degree of importance to the individual.

> **Adaptive problem**
> **Cost-benefit analysis**
> **Adaptive solution**

Think "midterm" once again. Is it a perceived threat? It is to varying degrees, depending on the person. Does the threat produce just enough anxiety that it motivates you to begin studying for the exam because the benefit you want is to do well? Is there much of a cost? Does the benefit of doing well on the exam outweigh the cost to begin studying? On the other hand, does the threat produce such an intense amount of anxiety such that you want to avoid, for as long as possible, studying for the exam? The cost is too great, at this point in time, to begin studying. The benefit you want is to eliminate the intense anxiety. Avoidance provides the benefit. The cost may be not doing well on the exam.

Adaptive Solutions

The evolutionary process provides us with a series of mechanisms that assist us in interacting with our continually changing environment, learning from our interactions with it, and solving adaptive problems over the course of our natural development. It is important to note that these mechanisms developed over time because of the interactions of our distant ancestors with their continually changing environment. *Adaptive solutions* allow us to functionally adapt to this ongoing process. We are engaged, on a daily basis, hopefully generating adaptive solutions for adaptive problems.

Functional Behavior

Our behavior serves a function. It solves adaptive problems in our continually changing environment. Consider the midterm exam one more time. Your studying behavior prepares you to do well on the midterm. Assuming your studying behavior is appropriate, and thus functional, you will do well on the exam.

On the other hand, you avoid studying because of your intense anxiety. This behavior will not resolve the adaptive problem of passing the midterm. Your behavior is dysfunctional as you most likely will not do well on the exam.

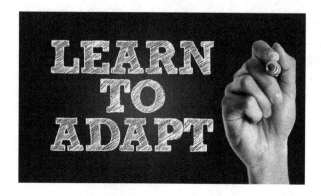

The Mismatch

The environment of our distant ancestors was considerably different from our environment today. They faced physical threats on a regular basis. The mechanisms provided to them via the evolutionary process assisted them in addressing and solving those physical threats.

We have the same mechanisms today. The problem is that, for the most part, our threats are not physical. They are primarily psychosocial. In many cases, these mechanisms do not help us solve our psychosocial threats. In fact, they often make things worse, thus, the mismatch!

OUR EVOLUTIONARY TOOL KIT

In this section, you will examine some of the fundamental survival mechanisms passed on down to us via the evolutionary process. Additional ones will be explored as you move through the text. What is of utmost importance is recognizing how the change in our environment from our distant ancestors can cause these mechanisms to be dysfunctional in many situations. These and other mechanisms will be utilized throughout the text to guide you through the domains of stress and stress management.

Be flexible.

Wired to Move

To survive we need to move. To find shelter, safety, food, and drink we need to move. To interact with others, find a mate, mate, maintain our gene pool, and to grow and protect ourselves we need to move. We are ***hard-wired to move*** (Ratey 2008). It is a fundamental aspect of our evolutionary took kit. Our higher-order functioning, our ability to learn, is rooted in the same aspects of the brain that direct and control our ability to move (Ratey 2008).

Physical threats of various sorts were a regular occurrence in the ever-changing environment of our distant ancestors. They needed to move to survive. They needed to move to adapt. A sedentary lifestyle was not an option.

In today's environment, a *sedentary lifestyle* is the norm. Approximately two thirds of the adult population is overweight. One third of this group is clinically obese (NIDDK 2012). Obesity and being overweight are associated with a wide variety of dis-orders such as type 2 diabetes, certain

types of cancer, cardiovascular disease, hypertension, stroke, kidney disease, liver disease, arthritis, anxiety, depression, and so on. Obesity has been assessed as a public health crisis (Levi et al., 2015). While it was long thought that diet was the primary cause of obesity, research is suggesting there is a positive cor-relation between lack of exercise and obesity (Bach 2014; Hannley 2014; Ladabaum, Mannalithara, Myer, & Singh, 2014), in other, words a sedentary lifestyle. Just think of the stress that excess weight puts on the body. For example, the heart has to work harder; there is excessive strain on bones, muscles, and joints; and the mechanical aspects of breathing are compromised.

The Negativity Bias

Ten people evaluate you. Nine say you are the greatest person on the earth. The 10th person says, "You stink, big time!" Who do you pay attention to? The nine people who were extremely positive toward you? The one person who was extremely negative toward you? If you are like most people, you pay immediate attention to the one person whose assessment of you was extremely negative. Why? Because you view it as a threat to your self-concept and your self-esteem. Why? Within the context of cognitive therapy, it is due to the fact that you have the distorted/irrational absolute belief that everybody must like you. Because you have this absolute belief and the expectation

that follows from it that whoever you interact with will like you, when someone expresses he or she does not like you, you feel threatened. This automatically sets off your **fight/freeze/flight response or stress response**, resulting in feeling anxious, among other uncomfortable sensations. In other words, you are stressed!

Within the context of cognitive therapy, this absolute belief is a cognitive distortion or bias known as **selective abstraction**. It is addressed, in one manner or the other, by disputing it. Where is it written that everybody must like you? Show me the evidence that everybody must like you. This absolute belief is then replaced with a preference such as, "It would be nice if everyone liked me, but that is not realistic." The preference is then linked to the change in feeling resulting from moving from an absolute belief to a preference. This process of cognitive restructuring does not, however, explain why we have this tendency to look for the negative over the positive or view it as a threat in the first place. It is certainly not a physical threat.

To make sense out of this we need to look at this situation within the context of evolutionary theory/psychology. Imagine your ancient, distant ancestor is walking on a field during the middle of the day. To the far left there are nine friends singing and dancing. They beckon your ancestor over to them. On the right, however, your ancestor notices a man, with blood all over his face, dragging a bloody animal leg bone and saying he is going to kill your ancestor. Does you ancestor ignore this one individual and slowly walk over to the nine friends who were clearly positive toward your ancestor? Not if your ancestor wanted to remain alive. The single threat clearly outweighs the nine positive individuals!

Thus, as part of our evolutionary tool kit we are wired with a **negativity bias**. This negativity bias kept our ancient, distant ancestors alert to physical threats, and the subsequent activation of their stress response, due to the perceived threat, prepared them to address and resolve the threat. You may, at this point, be noting to yourself that a negative judgment by another person toward you is not really a physical threat. So why would the stress response be activated? The answer is as our brain does not make a distinction between real physical threats and psychosocial, imagined or self-generated threats, generated by our thinking and beliefs, the fight/freeze/flee response will be triggered (Kabat-Zinn 2005; Seligman 2006; Stuart, Webster, & Wells-Federman 1993). Given the fact that our brain would rather mislabel something as a threat and be wrong than ignore a real threat and end up being lunch for some predator, the stress response will be activated. This worked fine for our ancient, distant ancestors who lived in an environment that was quite primitive, simple and straightforward but nonetheless a cauldron of aggression and violence (Hanson & Mendius 2009). For the most part, real physical threats were easily discernable.

Our current environment is quite different than our distant ancestors. For most of us, it is generally free from ongoing daily physical threats. Our formulation, however, into societies and the inherent competition amongst us in those societies has generated an endless series of potential psychosocial threats and the subsequent activation of the stress response. The problem is the stress response did not evolve to be continually activated or yo-yoed throughout the day. The continual activation and yo-yoing of the stress response results in chronic stress. Chronic stress is detrimental to our physical, psychological and social well-being.

Research has clearly established that our brain has an inherent negativity bias that has been passed down to us from our distant ancestors (Hanson & Mendius 2009). This negativity bias has been demonstrated in social-emotional development (Vaish, Grossman, & Woodward 2008). Fearful expressions are presented to awareness more quickly (Yang, Zald, & Blake 2008). Evaluations are more strongly influenced by negative data than positive data (Ito et al., 1998). A negativity bias is found across numerous categories and it appears to be more contagious than a positive bias (Rozin & Royzman 2001). The important point to note is that while the negativity bias, the looking for threats, is adaptive in many cases for us, it also can be quite detrimental to our physical, psychological, and interpersonal health.

Negativity bias
Default networking
Mind wandering

The Default Network

Advances in neuroimaging, such as functional MRIs, have opened a new window into how the brain functions (Raichle & Gusnard 2002). Of particular importance is the *default network*. The default network is a system of interconnected, highly correlated areas in the brain that is active when the brain is not focused on a goal-directed task in the environment (Buckner, Andrews-Hanna, & Schacter 2008; Raichle et al., 2001; Schilbach, Eickhoff, Rotarska-Jagiela, Fink, & Vogeley, 2008). In other words, when you are not focused on events in the external environment (evoked), the brain automatically returns to this system (intrinsic), hence the description as the default network (Buckner et al., 2008; Dastjerdi et al. 2011; Raichle & Snyder 2007). One of its many functions appears to be the monitoring of the external environment for potential threats (Hanson & Mendius 2009). It is also active when there is an internal focus on oneself, others, the past, the future, and the social environment (Buckner et al., 2008; Gusnard, Akbudak, Schulman, & Raichle 2001; Schilbach et al., 2008).

If a task is too difficult, too simple, repetitious, boring, routine, or not demanding, we lose our focus and attention. Our minds often return to the

default network and wander (Christoff, Irving, Fox, Spreng, & Andrews-Hanna, 2016; Mason et al., 2007; Mooneyham & Schooler 2013). It has been suggested that approximately half of our waking hours are spent *mind wandering* (Killingsworth & Gilbert 2010; Mooneyham & Schooler 2013). Does this wandering come with a cost? It often does. Performance in number of areas may be compromised. Mood may be compromised. Mooneyham and Schooler (2013) found significant costs across performance regarding reading, working memory, reaction time,

sustained attention, and intelligent tests and found that if often leads to a negative mood. Killingsworth and Gilbert (2010) demonstrated that the cause of unhappiness is a wandering mind, and that this wandering mind or **stim-**

ulus independent thought (SIT) is the primary operating mode of our default network (Mason et al., 2007).

Given the costs associated with mind wandering, why do we do it? Does it have any adaptive function? It is argued that there are significant adaptive benefits of mind wandering such as learning from the past, planning for the future, engaging in creative thinking, providing relief from boredom, stimulating thinking, allowing one to engage in self-reflection, and linking one's past, present, and future

(Killingsworth & Gilbert 2010; Mason et al., 2007; Mooneyham & Schooler 2013; Smallwood et al., 2011).

So, how often has your mind wandered during the reading of this chapter? How often does it wander while you sit in class? Walk to school? Drive or ride in a car? Eat a meal? Talk with a friend? What has been the result?

Simulations

One of the primary activities, as has been noted, that occurs while mind wandering is remembering the past and anticipating/imagining the future. In the process of doing this we create **simulations** of past events and future events (Barrett, 2017; Hanson & Mendius 2009; Niedenthal, 2007; Raichle, 2010; Schacter & Addis 2007; Smallwood et al., 2011). While this clearly has the adaptive functions

**Visit the present.
Be in the** here and now!

of enabling us to learn and reinforce successful behavior from the past, plan and prepare appropriate behavior for the future, allow us to imagine positive events in the future, and relive pleasant event from the past, it can also be quite detrimental (Hanson & Mendius 2009; **Schacter, 2012; Schacter et al., 2012**). Given our negativity bias, its association with threat-based thinking and the activation of the stress response, and the unhappiness associated with mind wandering, these simulations may turn into obsessions, anger, and depression about the past and excessive worry, anxiety, and fear about the future. In addition, as a result we find ourselves avoiding the present while lingering in the past and

the future. This leads to chronic stress as it compromises our ability to functionally adapt to our environment. *We can literally, by how we think, generate behavior by which we chronically stress ourselves to the point that we compromise our physical, psychological, and interpersonal health and well-being* (Benson & Casey 2013; Kabat-Zinn, 2005; Sapolsky, 2001; Seligman, 2006; Stuart, Webster & Wells-Federman, 1993).

Neuroplasticity

It was long thought that the adult brain did not change, that it was essentially fixed. This has turned out not to be the case as a significant amount of research has demonstrated that the brain's capacity to learn from experience, mental and physical, results in a rewiring or reorganization of its neural networks and thus changes the brain's configurations or structure (Boyd, 2015; Fuchs & Flugge, 2014; Kays, Hurley, & Taber 2012; Joja, 2013; Ratey, 2008). Boyd (2015) notes that there are three fundamental types of changes that occur in the brain. They are chemical, structural, and functional. The chemical is associated with short-term memory, the structural is associated with long-term memory and the re-wiring of neural networks, and the functional is associated with the parts of the brain that are most easily and readily available. This overall process is neuroplasticity.

Essentially, what this means is that we are engaged in a continual process of learning. The brain's primary function is to learn from our interaction/experience with the environment by generating adaptive solutions so that we can successfully and functionally adapt to various contexts. The more we practice, rehearse, or repeat patterns of behavior or thinking, the stronger the neural connections become and the more readily available and accessible those patterns of behavior become when we engage with various ever-changing environmental, internal, and external contexts. We have learned! Our capacity to adapt to our ever-changing environment, and thus survive, is contingent on our ability to learn (Green & Bavelier, 2008; Ratey, 2008). Learning is a fundamental component of our evolutionary tool kit.

While this process of practicing, rehearsing, or repeating patterns of behavior or thinking is clearly beneficial for learning and maintaining positive behaviors and thinking, the same process works in the creation and learning of dysfunctional behaviors and thinking. The more we engage in these problematic behaviors and thinking, the stronger these neural networks become and the more readily available and accessible these patterns of behavior become when we engage with various ever-changing environmental, internal, and external contexts.

In one sense, chronic stress is a process of continually strengthening maladaptive neural networks via primarily psychosocial threat-based thinking and behavior. This threat-based thinking and behavior becomes wired, if you will, in our brain. This in turn continues to generate further threat-based thinking

and behavior. Thus, our psychosocial threat-based thinking and behavior not only activates our stress response, it chronically maintains its activation as long as we continue to reinforce it with our psychosocial threat-based thinking and behavior. Given our negativity bias and our proclivity to mind wander, where we are essentially unhappy, this cycle of chronic stress is further reinforced. This vicious cycle of chronic stress literally causes psychological and physical damage to our body and brain (Benson, 1998; Joja, 2013; McEwen & Lasley, 2002; Ratey, 2008; Sapolsky, 2001).

This being the case, stress management is all about learning new behaviors and new ways to think. In order to understand stress and stress management we need to see them in the context of evolutionary theory/psychology. In order to wire in these new behaviors and thought process, thus causing the structure and function of the brain to change, they must be reinforced, practiced, repeated, or rehearsed on a regular and consistent basis (Boyd, 2015; Joja, 2013; Ratey, 2008). Thus, stress management, in one sense, is all about creating new neural patterns or configurations in our brain, which allow us to adapt to an ever-changing environment.

Chronic stress is not something new. Although not using the concept of chronic stress, the Buddha, well over 2,300 years ago, recognized its symptoms. He called it dukkha. For Buddha, dukkha was the human condition. It was universal in nature and applied to everyone. It was the adaptive problem. While dukkha is often translated as suffering, suffering does not adequately cover it. It is much more psychological in nature. A reading of a number of the sutras clearly indicate this to be the case, and chronic stress provides a much more enriched picture that covers both mind and body (Santee, 2007). This is especially appropriate when he indicates that the cause of dukkha is ignorance and craving. We are ignorant of the fact that existence, quite in line with evolutionary theory, is ever changing, impermanent, interdependent, and non-substantial (Nisker, 2000). Given this ignorance, individuals view the world as permanent, independent, and substantial. This being the case, they crave for the objects of their senses, they crave for existence, and they crave to engage in activities that allow them to avoid the unpleasantness, demands, and threats to their existence. This perspective, within the context of neuroscience, is wired in and continues to perpetuate itself as long as individuals repeat and replay the same thinking and behavioral patterns. From the perspective of Buddha, this perpetuation is known as **karma**.

Buddha's adaptive solution or treatment plan to be released from dukkha or chronic stress is called **the eightfold path**. It focuses on changing harmful, threat-based, negative seeing, thinking, and behaving and replacing it with correct seeing, thinking, and behaving. It uses meditation to stop the mind from wandering. It uses meditation to bring the mind out of the past and future to engage and gain insight into the nature of the present. This allows us to experience existence as impermanent, non-substantial, and interdependent.

Change:
Neuroplasticity
Neurogensis

Yin and yang
The relaxation response and the stress response.

Of special importance is correct effort. This requires commitment, motivation, enthusiasm, energy, and devotion to learning how to think, see, and behave in the correct manner. It allowed the practitioners to remove negative and harmful thinking and behavior, and prevent the arising of negative and harmful thinking and behavior in the future. In other words, it requires consistent and focused practice. This consistent and focused practice, from the perspective of neuroscience, is wired in the new way to see, think, and behave. It results in the removal of karma and the release from dukkha.

Neurogenesis

Neurogenesis refers to the fact that the adult brain is able to produce new neurons (Curtis, Kam, & Faull, 2011; Gage, 2002; Joja, 2013; Ratey, 2008). The two areas identified where this occurs are the hippocampus and the olfactory bulb (Gage, 2002; Eriksson et al., 1998). Of particular significance is the hippocampus as it is associated with memory and hence learning. Chronic stress is detrimental to both neurogenesis and neuroplasticity (Joja, 2013; Ratey, 2008). This in turn compromises our ability to learn how to change our thinking and behavior.

The Stress Response

Due to a perceived threat the sympathetic nervous system and endocrine systems are activated to prepare us, physically and psychologically, to fight/freeze/flee. The coining of the term *fight-or-flight* response is attributed to the physiologist Walter Cannon (1871–1945). Cannon focused primarily on the sympathetic nervous system. The endocrinologist Hans Selye (1907–1982) focused primarily on the endocrine system. He coined the term *general adaptation syndrome* to describe how the body responds to chronic stress and how it is detrimental to our physical, psychological, and interpersonal health and well-being. Although the stress response has been touched on earlier in this chapter and will be examined in depth in the

next chapter, it is important to re-emphasize that it is a vital component of our evolutionary tool kit and that normal stress brings, via temporary physical and psychological changes, adaptive problems to our attention, allows us to generate adaptive solutions, and motivates us to implement them. The problem is with chronic stress.

The Relaxation Response

The term **relaxation response** was coined by the cardiologist Herbert Benson (2001). It can refer to two processes. The first is the normal, automatic activation of the parasympathetic nervous system, which counters the stress response. The relaxation response is the yin to the yang of the stress response. During times of normal stress, once the perceived threat has been resolved the relaxation response automatically returns the body and mind to its normal state before the activation of the stress response. The second process is under our control. As a way to manage and prevent chronic stress, the relaxation response refers to the intentional activation of the parasympathetic nervous system by utilizing such practices as deep breathing, various meditative techniques, progressive muscle relaxation, yoga, taijiquan, and qigong. These practices relax both the mind and the body. It is important to note that for these practices to be optimally effective, they must be practiced and repeated on a regular and consistent basis in order for the new neural networks to be wired into the brain. These new neural networks will then supersede the previous maladaptive networks as they now become more easily and readily accessible.

EVOLUTIONARY THEORY AND STRESS MANAGEMENT

Evolutionary theory and our evolutionary tool kit figure prominently in all aspects of stress management. They provide us with understanding, tools, and context to assist us in functionally adapting and maintaining it in our ever-changing environment. The stress response, the relaxation response, exercise, nutrition, water consumption, the immune system, cognitive restructuring, meditation, sleep, time management, and interpersonal relations will all be explored within this domain.

At this point you are on your way to creating new neural networks in your brain regarding evolutionary theory and your evolutionary tool kit. For these basic concepts to wire in, be effective, and guide you through the text, they must be reviewed and reinforced on a regular basis. To truly understand stress and stress management and to implement a personal stress management program, they need to be placed in context. The context, as described, is evolutionary theory and your evolutionary tool kit.

PRACTICAL APPLICATION

In this section of the text, you will be taught various techniques that will activate your parasympathetic nervous system or relaxation response in order to help you reduce/eliminate your chronic stress, to prevent it arising in the future, and to enhance your health and well-being. They all work in reducing the time you spend in your default network, in mind wandering, and in replaying (simulating) events from the past and imagining (simulating) events from the future. Please note you are not eliminating spending any time in your default network, mind wandering, and simulating past and future events, as all of these processes have benefits. It is just that too much time spent is a source of chronic stress.

These techniques need to be practiced on a regular and consistent basis in order for their respective neural networks to wire into your brain such that you have easy and ready access to them and their benefits. This section will include basic sitting meditative/breathing exercises, qigong, or working with breath, and yoga. They all work on relaxing both your mind and body. These techniques can be used as part of your personal stress management program (PSMP) that you will be creating in chapter 13.

The first three techniques that will be described/shown are the most basic, foundational exercises/practices for meditation, zhanzhuang and yoga. They are the starting point for the additional techniques that will be shown throughout the remainder the text.

Meditation: Counting Your Breaths

This is a basic technique found in many disciplines and teachings. In order to successfully practice meditative techniques you need to meet the following requirements:

- Select a quiet place (no TV, smart phone, etc.) to practice where you will not be disturbed or distracted.
- Set a specific amount of time, repetition, or cycles that you will be practicing in this quiet place. You can, of course, add more time or cycles as you become comfortable with the process.
- Take a comfortable, relaxed sitting position where your head and body are properly aligned. In other words, no slouching, hunching, leaning sideways, or backwards, and so on.
- If possible, practice around the same time of the day and in the same place. Early morning is usually the best time.
- Be regular and consistent in your practice. The ideal is daily, but as a life tends to get in the way, try at least three times a week with a day off in between. Remember, consistent, regular practice is the way wire in the new neural networks and to learn.

Given these requirements are met, begin with your eyes open, slowly inhaling through your nose and slowly exhaling through your mouth. Repeat this for a total of five times. On the fifth exhalation close your eyes. With all further inhaling and exhaling only through the nose, begin the next inhalation by counting one to yourself. When you exhale count two. Repeat this process, counting up to 10. Count each inhalation with an odd number and each exhalation with an even number. If your mind wanders while you are doing this exercise, and it usually does, don't make any judgments about it. Just return to counting your breaths. If you lose your count, just start all over again. Again, no judgments! Do a total of five cycles. On the last exhalation open your eyes.

Upon finishing the meditation, note how you feel physically, mentally, and emotionally. Is there a difference between how you felt before you started the meditation and how you feel after the meditation? What did you notice? Did your mind wander? If so, how did you respond to its wandering? Did you lose count? If so, how did you respond to losing count? Were you able to stay focused throughout all five cycles?

Zhan Zhuang: Wuji

> Inhaling and exhaling essence (*jing* 精) and breath/vital energy (*qi*神), they stood in solitude observing and protecting their spirit (*shen*神) as they integrated and unified it with their body. (CTP, n.d.b.)

This quote from chapter 1 of the *Huangdi Neijing* is believed to be the earliest reference to a qigong practice that is known today as *Zhan Zhuang* (站椿) or standing like a stake/post (Chuen 1991, Liu 2010). The individuals who are standing in solitude are called the *zhenren* (真人) or authentic people. These were the role models who, being free from chronic stress, exemplified optimal health, well-being, and long life.

Zhan Zhuang is a fundamental exercise across most Chinese martial arts and qigong. It is believed to be the foundation of all of them. It is essentially about learning to root, center, still and empty the mind of agitation, circulate *qi* or vital energy/breath, and establish optimal health and well-being. For many it is an entry point for spiritual cultivation.

You will learn five *Zhan Zhuang* postures. You will initially do them individually. You can combine some of them or all of them into a *Zhan Zhuang* exercise routine. You will learn the first posture in this chapter, and you will learn a new posture in each of the next four chapters. It is suggested that you initially perform each posture for 1 to 2 minutes. You are of course free to be creative with the amount of time you spend. You can use a timer or your phone to track the time. Remember, consistent and regular practice is the way to wire in the new neural networks and to learn.

Essentially *Zhan Zhuang* is standing still in a relaxed manner with proper alignment, your eyes closed, and with your arms in various stationary positions. Breathe naturally through your nose and simply observe, without making any judgments, what you feel in your body. If your mind wanders, and it usually does, don't make any judgments; just refocus on your breath for a moment to reenter and then observe what you are feeling in your body.

This initial position is called *wuji* (無極). This concept comes from chapter 28 of the Daoist text the *Daodejing*. It essentially means without boundaries or limitless. There are no thoughts, worries, desires, or judging. You are simply in the present, observing what you are feeling in your body.

To perform this exercise, it is best to find a quiet place where you will not be disturbed or distracted. Relax. Begin by standing with your feet parallel, shoulder- or hip-width apart, whatever feels most comfortable. The weight is evenly distributed on both feet. Your feet are flat and there is no leaning or rolling of them to the sides, forward, or backward. Bend your knees slightly. Your arms hang naturally on your sides with your palms facing your thighs.

Relax. Your eyes are looking straight forward. To align your body, gently push both feet down and gently push your head up. Imagine you were a puppet being suspended by a string, centered on the top of your head, from above. Your shoulders will naturally sink. Your spine will align. Your jaw is parallel to the ground, and your tongue will gently touch the roof of your mouth behind your upper teeth. Gently shut your eyes. Breathe naturally through your nose. Relax. At this point, simply observe, nonjudgmentally, what you feel for the next couple of minutes throughout your body.

Open your eyes and take a deep breath and let it out. What did you notice? How are you feeling? Did you feel any discomfort? Did you notice certain parts of your body were tight or sore? Did you find yourself swaying side to side or backward or forward? Was your balance an issue? Do you notice a difference between how you felt before you started the *wuji* posture and how you feel after completing it? Did your mind wander? If so, were you able to easily refocus? Upon completing the exercise, is your mind still and empty? Did you find yourself making judgments about the exercise itself?

Yoga: Tadasana or Mountain Pose

Yoga literally means a union or joining together. As a philosophy or way of life yoga, as part of the Hindu tradition, was concerned with reuniting the individual soul *atman* with the universal soul *brahman*. It is about seeing and experiencing reality without any confusion or misunderstanding. It is about stilling the mind. As an oral tradition, it is well over 2,000 years old. It is believed that an individual named Patanjali systematized and organized this oral tradition into a set of four sutras known as the *yoga sutras of Patanjali* somewhere between 1,700 and 2,100 years ago. There is a strong emphasis in these sutras on committed, consistent, and regular practice.

There are many types of yoga. Hatha yoga is the yoga that most people think of when they hear the word yoga. It focuses on the *asanas* or body postures and is practiced primarily in the United States to calm the mind and enhance physical and psychological well-being. In other words, it is a path to reduce chronic stress. The five *asanas* that will be taught in this text are oriented toward reducing chronic stress and may be incorporated into your personal stress-management program. The mountain pose, or *Tadasana*, like the *wuji* position of the *Zhan Zhuang*, is performed by standing. However, they are also quite different, as you will soon discover.

There are numerous descriptions on how to perform the mountain pose. It is best to find a quiet place where you will not be disturbed or distracted. Begin by standing with your feet together and parallel, the sides of your big toes touching, and your heels very slightly apart. If this position causes problems with your balance, then place your feet parallel, pointing forward and hip-width apart. The weight is evenly distributed on both feet. Gently push your feet into the ground. No rolling of the feet to the sides, forward, or backward. Gently push your head upward. Pull up your kneecaps, activating your thighs. Your legs are straight but not locked. Your arms hang naturally on your sides with your palms facing your thighs, fingers together and gently pushing downwards. Your jaw is parallel to the ground. Your eyes are open and gaze straight forward. Slowly, deeply, and gently inhale and exhale through your nose. Hold this position for 30 seconds or somewhere between five to 10 breaths.

Upon finishing, slowly walk around for a minute or so. How do you feel? What did you notice while you were doing the posture? How does your body feel? How is your mind? Agitated? Still? Did your mind wander? If so, what did you do to address it?

Given the two standing exercises of *wuji* and the mountain posture, how do they compare? Do you notice a difference in feeling? Awareness? Do you have a preference?

Congratulations on completing all three stress-management techniques! Remember that for them to be effective, they must be practiced on a regular and consistent basis. As you become more comfortable with them, increase the time or number of breaths. In all cases, be flexible. Life does happen.

KEY TERMS

six components of the evolutionary process
adaptive problems
cost-benefit analysis
normal stress
chronic stress
Dao
yin and yang
dukkha

adaptive solutions
hard-wired to move
sedentary lifestyle
fight/freeze/flight response or stress response
selective abstraction
negativity bias
default network

mind wandering
stimulus independent thought (SIT)
simulations
karma
the eightfold path
relaxation response

EXERCISES

1. To really grasp the concept of continual change you need to experience it instead of just talking or reading about it. So, take 10 minutes or so, sit down, and just observe the world around you. Don't just look; smell, listen, touch, and taste. Move from sense to sense. What difference do you notice between reading about change and experiencing change? Any similarities?

2. From the perspective of evolutionary theory, all behavior is, essentially, functional. Monitor your behavior; this includes thinking, talking, and interacting with others during the day. What problems does your behavior solve? Do you notice any patterns?

3. Keep track of your mind wandering. How often during the day does your mind wander? Where does it go? Is there any pattern that sets it wandering? What is the function of your mind wandering? What problems does it solve?

4. How much time do you spend during the day wandering in the past and wandering in the future? What events are you reliving in the past? Imagining in the future? Why?

5. Given the negativity bias, how often and why during the day do you spend time complaining, whining, moaning, criticizing, awfulizing, catastrophizing, speaking in a negative manner, thinking in a negative manner, and behaving in a negative manner toward others and yourself. What problems does it solve? What does it allow you to avoid? To obtain? Remember, this is all threat-based thinking and, as such, it activates and maintains your stress response.

6. Take an inventory of yourself. Are you stressed? Do you have problems sleeping? Staying focused? Remembering? With attention? With energy? Are you tired a lot? Are you drinking enough water? Eating? Are you overweight? Underweight? Getting enough exercise? Studying? Is your mind agitated and bouncing all over? Interacting with others? How would you describe your physical state? Your psychological state?

7. What are you doing to address these areas? Remember you are not alone. Buddha referred to the human condition as dukkha or chronic stress.

8. How often during the day do you smile? When you are smiling how do you feel? When you are not smiling how do you feel? When you get up in the morning and look in the mirror, smile! See if you can spend a few moments each hour during the day simply smiling.

REFERENCES

Bach, B. (2014). Lack of exercise, not diet, linked to rise in obesity, Stanford research shows. *Stanford Medicine*. Retrieved from http://med.stanford.edu/news/all-news/2014/07/lack-of-exercise--not-diet--linked-to-rise-in-obesity--stanford-.html

Barrett, L. F. (2017). *How emotions are made: The secret life of the brain*. New York, NY: Houghton Mifflin.

Benson, H. (1998, September 22). Testimony of Herbert Benson regarding mind/body interventions, healthcare and mind/body medical centers before the United States Senate Appropriations Subcommittee on labor/HHS and education. Washington DC.

Benson, H., & Casey, A. (Eds.) (2013). *A Harvard Medical School special report: Stress management*. Boston, MA: Harvard Medical School.

BFNN. (n.d.). *Integrative approach*. Retrieved from http://book.bfnn.org/books2/1724.htm#a20

Boyd, L. (2015). After watching this your brain will not be the same [Video file]. Retrieved from https://www.bing.com/videos/search?q=lara+boyd+ted+talks&view=detail&mid=5908B6ECA70A1A86CCE95908B6ECA70A1A86CCE9&FORM=VIRE

Buckner, R. L., Andrews-Hanna, J. R., & Schacter, D. L. (2008). The brain's default network: Anatomy function and relevance to disease. *Annals of the New York Academy of Sciences, 1124*, 1–38.

Buss, D. M. (2015). *Evolutionary psychology: The new science of the mind*. Boston, MA: Pearson.

Chinese Text Project (CTP). (n.d.a.). *Book of changes*. Translated from https://ctext.org/book-of-changes/xi-ci-shang/zh

Chinese Text Project. (n.d.b.). *Yello Emperor's discourse on internal medicine*. Translated from https://ctext.org/huangdi-neijing/zh

Chinese Text Project. (n.d.c.). *Yangsheng*. Translated from https://ctext.org/huangdi-neijing/zh

Christoff, K., Irving, Z. C., Fox, K. C. R., Spreng, N., & Andrews-Hanna, J. R. (2016). Mind-wandering as spontaneous thought: A dynamic framework. *Nature Reviews: Neuroscience, 17*(11), 718–731.

Chuen, L. K. (1991). *The way of energy: Mastering the Chinese art of internal strength with chi kung exercise.* New York, NY: Simon & Schuster.

Curtis, M. A., Kam, M., & Faull, R. L. M. (2011). Neurogenesis in humans. *European Journal of Neuroscience, 33*(6), 1170–1174.

Dastjerdi, M., Foster, B. L., Nasrullah, S., Rauschecker, A. M., Dougherty, R. F., Townsend, J. D., … & Parvizi, J. (2011). Differential electrophysiological response during rest, self-referential, and non–self-referential tasks in human posteromedial cortex. *Proceedings of the National Academy of Sciences of the United States of America, 108*(7), 3023–3028. Retrieved from http://www.pnas.org/content/108/7/3023.full

Eriksson, P. S., Perfilievea, E., Bjork-Eriksson, T., Alborn, A., Nordborg, C., Peterson, D. A., & Gage, F. H. (1998). Neurogenesis in the adult human hippocampus. *Nature Medicine, 4,* 1313–1317.

Fuchs, E., & Flugge, G. (2014). Adult neuroplasticity: More than 40 years of research. *Neuroplasticity.* Retrieved from https://www.hindawi.com/journals/np/2014/541870/

Gage, F. H. (2002). Neurogenesis in the adult brain. *Journal of Neuroscience, 22*(3), 612–613.

Green, C. S., & Bavelier, D. (2008). Exercising your brain: A review of human brain plasticity and training-induced learning. *Psychology of Aging, 23,* 692–701.

Guo, XQ.F. (1956). *A Concordance to Chuang Tzu.* Cambridge, MA: Harvard University Press.

Gusnard, D. A., Akbudak, E., Schulman, G. L., & Raichle, M. E. (2001). Medial prefrontal cortex and self-referential mental activity: Relation to a default mode of brain function. *Proceedings of the National Academy of Sciences, 98*(7), 4259–4264. Retrieved from http://www.pnas.org/content/98/7/4259.full

Hannley, P. P. (2014). Move more, eat less: It's time for Americans to get serious about exercise. *American Journal of Medicine, 127,* 681–684.

Hanson, R. & Mendius, R. (2009). *Buddha's brain: The practical neuroscience of happiness, love and wisdom.* Oakland, CA: New Harbinger.

Ito, T. A., Larsen, J. T., Smith, N. K., & Cacioppo, J. T. (1998). Negative information weighs more heavily on the brain: The negativity bias in evaluative categorization. *Journal of Personality and Social Psychology, 75*(4), 887–900.

Joja, D. O. (2013). Learning experience and neuroplasticity: A shifting paradigm. *NOEMA, 12,* 159–170.

Kabat-Zinn, J. (2005). *Full catastrophe living: Using the wisdom of Your body and mind to face stress, pain, and illness.* New York, NY: Random House.

Kays, J. L., Hurley, R. A., & Taber, K. H. (2012). The dynamic brain. Neuroplasticity and mental health. *Journal of Neuropsychiatry and Clinical Neuroscience, 24*(2), 118–124. Retrieved from http://neuro.psychiatryonline.org/doi/full/10.1176/appi.neuropsych.12050109

Killingsworth, M. A., & Gilbert, D. (2010). A wandering mind is an unhappy mind. *Science, 330*(6006), 932.

Ladabaum, U., Mannalithara, A., Myer, P. A., & Singh, G. (2014). Obesity, abdominal obesity, physical activity, and caloric intake in U.S. adults: 1988–2010. *American Journal of Medicine, 127*(8), 717–727.

Levi, J., Segal, L. M., Rayburn, J., & Martín, A. (2015). State of obesity: Better policies for a healthier America 2015. *State of Obesity.* Retrieved from https://www.stateofobesity.org/

Liu, T. (Ed.) (2010). *Chinese Medical Qigong.* London, UK: Singing Dragon.

Mason, M., Norton, M. I., Vanhorn, J. D., Wegner, D. M., Grafton, S. T., & Macrae, C. N. (2007). Wandering minds: The default network and stimulus independent thought. *Science, 315*(5810), 393–395.

McEwen, B., & Lasley, E. N. (2002). *The end of stress as we know it.* Washington, DC: Joseph Henry Press.

Mooneyham, B. W., & Schooler, J. W. (2013). The costs and benefits of mind-wandering. *Canadian Journal of Experimental Psychology, 67*(1), 11–18.

National Institute of Diabetes and Digestive and Kidney Diseases. (2012). *Overweight and obesity statistics.* Retrieved from https://www.niddk.nih.gov/health-information/health-statistics/overweight-obesity

Niedenthal, P. M. (2007). Embodying emotion. *Science, 316*(5827), 1002–1005.

Nisker, W. (2000). *Buddha nature: A practical guide to discovering your place in the cosmos*. New York, NY: Bantam Books.

Raichle, M. E. (2010, March). The brian's dark energy. *Scientific American*, 44–49.

Raichle, M. E., & Gusnard, D. E. (2002). Appraising the brain's energy budget. *PNAS, 99*(16), 10237–10239. Retrieved from http://www.pnas.org/content/99/16/10237.full

Raichle, M. E., MacLeod, A. M., Snyder, A. Z., Powers, W. J., Gusnard, D. A., & Shulman, G. L. (2001). A default mode of brain function. *PNAS, 98*(2), 676–682. Retrieved from http://www.pnas.org/content/98/2/676.abstract

Raichle, M. E., & Snyder, A. Z. (2007). A default mode of brain functioning: A brief history of an evolving idea. *NeuroImage, 37*(4), 1083–1090.

Ratey, J. J. & Hagerman, E. (2008). *Spark: The revolutionary new science of exercise and the brain*. New York, NY: Little, Brown and Company.

Rozin, P., & Roysman, E. B. (2001). Negativity bias, negativity dominance, and contagion. *Personality and Social Psychology Review, 5*(4), 296–320.

Santee, R. (2004, July 22). *A Daoist and an existential psychotherapist: A comparative study.* Paper presented at the First World Hong Ming Philosophy Conference, Chaminade University of Honolulu. Honolulu, HI.

Santee, R. (2007). *An Integrative Approach to Counseling: Bridging Chinese Thought, Evolutionary Theory, and Stress Management*. Copyright © 2007 by SAGE Publications. Reprinted with permission.

Santee, R., & Zhang, X. (2015). Yangsheng (養生) and the yin style Baguazhang of wang fu and wang shangzhi. *Empty Vessel: The Journal of Taoist Philosophy and Practice, 22*, 24–30.

Sapolsky, R. M. (2001). *Why zebras don't get ulcers: An updated guide to stress, stress-related diseases, and coping*. New York, NY: W. H. Freeman.

Schacter, D. L. (2012). Adaptive constructive processes and the future of memory. *American Psychologist, 67*(8), 603–613.

Schacter, D. L., & Addis, D. R. (2007). The cognitive neuroscience of constructive memory: Remembering the past and imagining the future. *Philosophical Transactions of the Royal Society, 362*(1481), 773–786.

Schacter, D. L., Addis, D. R., Hassabis, D., Martin, V. C., Spreng, R. N., & Szpunar, K. K. (2012). The future of memory: Remembering, imagining, and the brain. *Neuron, 76*(4), 677–694.

Schilbach, L., Eickhoff, S. B., Rotarska-Jagiela, A., Fink, G. R., & Vogeley, K. (2008). Minds at rest? Social cognition as the default mode of cognizing and its putative relationship to the "default system" of the brain. *Consciousness & Cognition, 17*(2), 457–467.

Seligman, M. (2006). *Learned optimism: How to change your mind and your life*. New York, NY: Random House.

Smallwood, J., Schooler, J. W., Turk, D. J., Cunningham, S. J., Burns, P., & Macrae, C. N. (2011). Self-reflection and the temporal focus of the wandering mind. *Consciousness and Cognition, 20*(4), 1120–1126.

Stuart, E. M., Webster, A., & Wells-Federman, C. L. (1993). Managing stress. In H. Benson & E. Stuart (Eds.), *The wellness book: The comprehensive guide to maintaining health and treating stress-related illness* (pp. 177–188). New York, NY: Simon & Schuster.

Vaish, A., Grossman, T., & Woodward, A. (2008). Not all emotions are created equal: The negativity bias in social-emotional development. *Psychological Bulletin, 134*(3), 383–403.

Yang, E., Zald, D. H., & Blake, R. (2007). Fearful expressions gain preferential access to awareness during continuous flash suppression. *Emotion, 7*(4), 882–886.

Yalom, I.D. (1980). *Existential psychotherapy*. New York, NY: Basic Books.

Yalom, I.D. (2009). *Staring at the sun*. San Francisco, CA: Jossey-Bass.

CREDITS

- Fig. 1.1: Copyright © Depositphotos/fffranzzz.

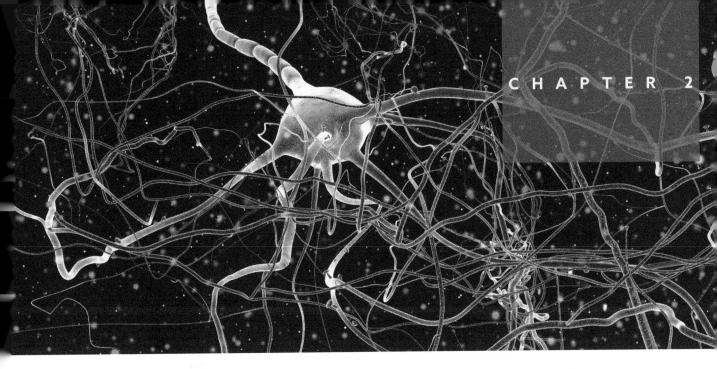

The Stress Response, the Relaxation Response, and Neuroscience

This chapter introduces a broader understanding of the fundamentals of the stress response (fight/flight/freeze) and the relaxation response (feed/breed/digest/rest). A specific focus will be on allostasis (normal stress), threat-based thinking or acute stress (fight/flight/freeze response), and allostatic load (chronic stress). The relationship between neuroscience and stress will be explored. Various variables associated with stress will be examined. After reading it, you will be able to do the following:

- Compare normal stress, the threat-based thinking fight/freeze/flee response, and chronic stress
- Explain the difference between the appropriate activation of the stress response and the inappropriate activation of it
- Indicate the difference between allostasis and allostatic load
- Describe the short pathway and long pathway to the activation of the stress response and explain the difference between them
- Explain the difference between a neurotransmitter and a hormone

- Indicate how chronic stress physically damages the brain and the body
- Indicate and describe the function of the body systems involved in the activation of the stress response
- Describe how chronic stress is intimately intertwined with age, gender, developmental stages, LGBT, ethnicity/race, socioeconomic status, discrimination, substance and alcohol abuse, physical and mental health
- Explain Buddha's concept of *dukkha*, including how it is related to chronic stress.
- Indicate how the primary source of chronic stress for both the *Zhuangzi* and for us today is psychosocial in nature

CATEGORIES OF STRESS

*There are three basic types of stress. They are **normal stress**, **threat-based thinking/ fight, freeze or flight response**, and **chronic stress**. The first two categories are generally beneficial for one's well-being, while chronic stress is detrimental to one's health and overall well-being. One common misunderstanding is that when people hear the word "stress" they immediately think of something negative and detrimental. They do not see any benefits of stress, in any manner, at all. Let's first look at normal stress.*

Normal Stress/Allostasis

*Normal stress is essentially the body's reaction to the regular demands placed on it throughout the day by various, internal and external, environmental contexts. Normal stress includes the changes the body and brain go through in order to assist you in addressing and resolving various **adaptive problems**.*

You are sitting in a chair in the library and decide to walk up two flights of stairs to look for a specific book. Getting the book is your adaptive problem. What you do to get the book is your adaptive solution. To implement your adaptive solution your body must make some changes, from sitting in a chair with minimal demands on your body and brain to standing up, which makes new demands on your body and brain. In order to stand up your heart rate, breathing, and blood pressure will increase somewhat. Your muscles will be activated. These automatic changes in your body represent the stress placed on your body by the demands required for standing up from a sitting position.

Another set of demands cause additional stress on your heart, breathing, blood pressure, and muscles as you walk to the stairs, moving from being standing and stationary to walking. When you begin walking up the stairs, depending on your level of fitness, there will be a new set of demands on your body as your heart rate, blood pressure, breathing, and muscle tension automatically increase accordingly.

In other words, your body will be stressed as it adapts to walking up the stairs. Once you reach the third floor, your body will automatically readjust as it is now walking on a different terrain. As the demands on your body are not as great as you are now walking on a flat surface, your heart rate, breathing, blood pressure, and muscle tension will gradually decrease to a level that is appropriate for walking on this flat surface. As you walk along looking for the book, changes in your brain occur: You become more attentive and focused, relative to the demands from the environment regarding the location of the book. This is normal stress. This stress is beneficial as it allows you to solve the adaptive problem of finding a specific book.

Going for a brisk walk or a run clearly puts demands or stress on your body as your heart must work harder, your blood pressure increases, your breathing becomes more rapid thus increasing your use of oxygen, and your large muscles, especially your legs, also work harder. If done on a consistent and regular basis, with adequate rest and not overtraining, this type of stress increases your overall cardiovascular fitness and general physical and psychological well-being.

As you continue to practice on a regular basis, the stronger the neural networks become, both for the specific aerobic exercise and the additional physical and psychological benefits you will receive, the more readily accessible they become and the more efficient your brain and body become in brisk walking or running and engaging life in general. Your body and mind/brain are adapting to the demands, stress, or changes put on them. Essentially, you are learning across a number of domains via the rewiring and strengthening of your neural networks as a result of consistent practice. This is **neuroplasticity** (Boyd, 2015; Fuchs & Flugge, 2014; Hanson & Mendius, 2009; Kays, Hurley, & Taber, 2012; LeDoux, 2002; Joja, 2013; Ratey, 2008).

Whether it is getting out of bed in the morning, getting into to bed at night, exercising, participating in a sport or martial art, meditating, driving a car, eating, drinking, sleeping, listening to a lecture, playing with your friends or kids, reading a book, watching TV, playing a video game, and so on, all of these activities, which are a result of your deliberate, considered choice where you are essentially in control, require the body and brain to make changes relative to the particular demands or stress being placed on it. All of these changes are potentially beneficial to you for solving or addressing some type of adaptive problem or demand in your environment. This is normal stress or **allostasis** (Goldstein & Kopin, 2007; Logan & Barksdale, 2008; McEwen, 2002; Schulkin, 2010; Sterling & Eyer, 1988). At this point you should have a fairly good idea that normal stress is part of everyday living and is beneficial for you. Let's now turn to what is commonly referred to the stress or fight/freeze/flight response.

The Fight/Freeze/Flight or Stress Response

*The **fight/freeze/flight** or **stress response** evolved to assist our distant ancestors in addressing perceived acute, real physical threats in their ever-changing environments, be that other humans, animals, the weather, the terrain, the environment, and so on, the stress response would kick in. It was reactive (think perceived threat) in nature. Unlike our choice of activities, which is under our control, activation of the stress response is not really under our direct control. The stress response activated various physiological and psychological mechanisms, which prepared our distant ancestors to address the perceive threat. Once the **adaptive problem**, the perceived threat, was resolved via an implemented **adaptive solution**, the body and mind would return to its normal state as the result of the activation of the **relaxation response**.*

The activation of the stress response assisted our distant ancestors in surviving. The physical and psychological changes that occurred within the individual as a result of the activation of the stress response allowed them to adapt to their ever-changing environment. Our distant ancestors were continually on the lookout for potential physical threats to their well-being and survival, as the environment they lived in was quite dangerous, in not only the threats just mentioned, but also decisions about what food and liquid was safe to ingest and what shelter would truly protect them created pressure, hence, our **negativity bias** to avoid such threats!

As part of our evolutionary tool kit, we are pre-wired to react to such potential threats as loud sudden sounds, certain smells, the dark, fast and sudden movements, and so on. They set off the stress response, which warns us of potential threats, prepares us to react, encodes this information in our brain for the future, motivates us to react, and leads to our subsequent reaction. For example, do you find yourself somewhat anxious and hyperalert when you are navigating your way through the dark with little or no light, especially if you are outside? Why do you think scary movies work so well in the dark? Would they be just as scary if the room was brightly lit? Along this line, why are sudden and/or fast movements and loud and/or sudden strange sounds part and parcel of scary movies? Reacting to these potential threats kept our distant ancestors alive. For example, as the dark limited our ancestors' vision, potential predators roamed about looking for prey, and not being able to see the landscape adequately increased the probability of being injured. Therefore, our ancestors tended to not be active during the night, thus increasing their chances for survival.

At this point you should clearly understand that the first two types of stress are clearly beneficial to our physical and psychological health and well-being. It is now time to turn to what most people think of when they hear the word stress: **chronic stress**. It is chronic stress that is physically and psychologically detrimental to our overall physical and psychological health and well-being.

Chronic Stress/Allostatic Load

*Chronic stress is the ongoing continual activation (on/off, on/off, on/off) and/or the yoyoing throughout the day of the stress response. As a result, it is linked with various assaults on our physical, psychological, and interpersonal health and well-being. The research is quite clear regarding the global damage that chronic stress inflicts on us. It is associated with many known impacts, including cardiovascular disease, cancer, diabetes, biological aging, gastrointestinal disorders, obesity, weight gain, the common cold, shrinkage in parts of the brain, memory problems, cognitive problems, learning problems, anxiety, depression, premature death, problems with sleep, pain intensity and duration, suppression of the immune system, susceptibility to infections, hypertension, and eating disorders (Logan & Barksdale, 2008; McGrady, 2007; Sapolsky, 2004; Selye, 1978). The cumulative damage done to our body and brain by relentless ongoing chronic stress is called **allostatic load** (Ganzel, Morris, & Wethington, 2010; Goldstein & Kopin, 2007; Juster, McEwen, & Lupien 2010; McEwen, 2000, 2002, 2004, 2015; McEwen & Stellar, 1993; McEwen, Nasveld, Palmer, & Anderson 2012).*

The problem is that the stress response is being inappropriately and unrealistically activated in situations, essentially those that are psychosocial, where it is unable to provide any assistance regarding the situation. In fact, it often makes things worse. Such events as long lines; traffic; people not listening to you; arguments with others; things not going the way you expect them to; people looking at you funny, rolling their eyes when you are talking, and/or commenting negatively about how you look; significant others, classmates, coworkers, friends, bosses, teachers, family, and people in general not behaving the way you expect them to; the weather; and the environment are all, depending how you perceive and think about them, potentially unrealistic psychosocial threats that can set off and maintain your stress response.

Complaining about a long line in a bank is not going to make the line move any quicker. Nonetheless, it is this threat-based negativity regarding the long line that sets off your stress response and maintains it as long as you continue to complain to yourself about it. It is the yoyoing of the normal hassles of life, such as the long line, throughout the day that serve as a major source of potentially and inappropriately activating our stress response. The stress response did not evolve to be continually turned on and off throughout the day, and so this continuous yoyoing of the stress response leads to the problems associated with chronic stress.

The major problem is that you do not even have to be involved with the daily psychosocial hassles of life to activate and maintain the stress response. You can be sitting at home replaying your day or even situations from months ago and simply recall the hassles and/or negative events that occurred. This is enough to set off the stress response and maintain it as long as you continue to think about them. To make matters worse you can simply imagine, anticipate, or expect that something awful is going to happen in the future, be it the next day or a year from now, and your stress response will activate and be continually maintained as long as you think about it. (This anticipatory stress can become a major problem in dysfunctional relationships, for example.) The cumulative effect of the continual inappropriate activation of the stress response is detrimental to your physical and psychological health and well-being.

The fight/freeze/flight or stress response evolved to address real, acute, physical threats. Its activation is to be short term: perceived threat, address, and turn off. It did not evolve to be continually or chronically activated. It did not evolve to be activated by our mere imagination that an unrealistic psychosocial threat is happening or just happened. It did not evolve to be activated by our unrealistic expectation or anticipation that something threatening may happen in the future. Yet, in modern life, the stress response is maintained as we continually think about these various unrealistic potential threats. Our brain does not make a distinction between a real physical threat, a real psychosocial threat, or an unrealistic/imagined psychosocial threat; it would rather be wrong labeling something as a threat than ignoring a real threat and suffering the consequences.

The primary source of chronic stress and the maintaining of it is our psychosocial, threat-based perceptions, beliefs, and thinking (Benson & Casey, 2013; Kabat-Zinn, 2005; Sapolsky, 2004; Seligman, 2006; Stefano, Fricchione, Slingsby, & Benson, 2001; Stuart, Webster, & Wells-Federman, 1993). *It is our mind wandering, guided by our negativity bias, in our default network, simulating the past and the future by replaying our negative experiences and/or anticipating, expecting or imagining future ones.*

Although we may think that chronic stress is something relatively recent, it is quite clear from the following quote, over 2,200 years ago, from chapter 18 of the *Zhuangzi*, that chronic stress (although this terminology was not used at that time) was a significant problem both physically and psychologically. It is also clear that the primary source was psychosocial in nature and directly related to related one's perceptions, beliefs, and thinking:

> How should one act and what should one depend on? What should one avoid and what should one deal with? What should one move towards and what should one move away from? What should be liked and disliked? That which is respected in the world is wealth, honor, longevity and approval. That which is enjoyed is a comfortable life, tasty food, beautiful clothes, pleasant sites and sweet sounds. That which is not respected is poverty, dishonor, dying young and

disapproval. That which is not enjoyed is a life that is not comfortable, a mouth that does not have tasty food, a body that does not have beautiful clothes, eyes that do not have pleasant sights and ears that do not have sweet sounds. If these are not attained, there is tremendous stress (dà yōu, 大憂) as well as dread (jù, 懼). Those who treat the body (xíng, 形) in this way have an agitated and obsessive mind. Now for those who are rich, they suffer and are made ill as they accumulate more wealth th[a]n they can possibly use. Those who treat the body (xíng, 形) in this manner are fragmented. Now those of high status, day and night[,] contemplate good and what is not good. Those who treat their body (xíng, 形) in this manner are quite distant from the world around them. People are born and all of life is a participation in stress (yōu, 憂). Those who seek a long life are ignorant. They stress (yōu, 憂) endlessly about dying. Why bother? To treat the body (xíng, 形) in this manner is to be distant from their destiny. (The character you 憂 which is translated as stress in this quotation has the meanings of worry, grieve, sorrow, anxiety, sad, depressed, melancholy, etc. The four components that make up this character give a sense of both the mind and body being compromised and restricted.) (Santee, 2005; Guo, 1956, p. 46)

APPROPRIATE AND INAPPROPRIATE ACTIVATION OF THE STRESS RESPONSE

The stress response or fight/freeze/flight response can be activated with beneficial consequences or detrimental consequences. The appropriate activation of the stress response helps the individual in addressing and resolving a perceived threat. The inappropriate activation of the stress response usually occurs as the result of an unrealistic imagined or anticipated psychosocial threat. It not only does not help, it often makes things worse.

The Appropriate Activation of the Stress Response: Physical Threats

Consider the following scenarios.

You are on a street corner and step out onto the crosswalk, you have a green light, to walk across the street. Out of the corner of your eye you see a fast-moving object increasing in size heading right at you. You immediately jump back. The car roars past you. This entire process took a second or so. You did not process or analyze the object. You just jumped! You now notice that your heart is beating fast, your breathing is rapid, your body is shaking and feels jacked up, you have butterflies in your stomach and notice you are sweating. Your stress response just saved your life. Its activation is clearly appropriate.

If you took time to process what the fast-moving object was, determine that it was a car, and then decided to jump, you would have been roadkill. The acute stress response is designed to immediately alert you to a real physical threat, provide you with the appropriate physical and psychological changes to respond, and to get you to react as quickly as possible. Once the acute threat has been clearly avoided or resolved, your body will slowly return to its previous state.

If you are in an airplane and suddenly the plane runs into turbulence and starts bouncing around, your stress response, at least for most people, immediately kicks in. This is clearly a perceived threat to your physical well-being! You become anxious and hyper-alert. Your heart rate and breathing increases. The butterflies are fluttering about in your stomach. You are no thinking about anything else. Once the turbulence dissipates, the plane levels off and you are no longer perceiving a physical threat, the relaxation response is activated, and you return to your previous state.

You are walking along on the side-walk outside of your university texting on your phone. Suddenly, a loud, increasing barking sound and the sound of something hitting a fence pervades your awareness. Your body tenses, your heart feels like it is going to pop out of your chest, your breathing seems to be out of control, and you can feel the sweat dripping down your sides. You automatically jump back and turn toward the sound. A huge dog, appearing to trying to knock the fence down, is growling and barking at you. For what appears to be eternity, you are frozen in place. Finally, you catch your breath and briskly walk away. The sound of the dog fades. As you get further way, you let out a big sigh. Your body and mind begin to return to your "texting state" of a few moments ago. Once again, this is the automatic activation and deactivation of the stress response.

As discussed, the major sources of our stress are not real physical threats. They are more psychosocial in nature. However, in the face of some clear threat the activation of the stress response is appropriate and assists us in addressing and resolving the perceived threat. Others, however, are more unrealistic or imagined and the activation of the stress response in these situations is inappropriate as it does not assist us in addressing the perceived threats and often makes things worse.

The Appropriate Activation of the Stress Response: Psychosocial Threats

As with the physical threat scenarios, let's consider a couple of scenarios that include a real psychosocial threat.

You are driving your car on the freeway talking with your friends and listening to music. As you come around a large bend you notice a police officer, sitting on a motorcycle pointing her radar gun right at you. The adaptive problem! What happens next: If you are like most people you instantly perceive her as a threat and your fight/freeze/ flight response or stress response is automatically activated. You do not hear the music or your friends. You have tunnel vision directed to the police officer. Your attention is only directed at her. Everything else has just disappeared. Your grip on the steering wheel tightens. Your body stiffens. You may not have even been speeding, but your foot immediately goes to the break and you slow down. Your breathing becomes rapid and shallow while your heart rate increases. You begin to sweat. Your stomach is full of butterflies.

As you drive by the police officer you are checking in your rearview mirror to see if the police officer has put down her radar gun, mounted her motorcycle, and is heading your way. When you notice she has not moved and is pointing her radar gun at traffic coming toward her, your world starts returning to you. The music has returned and your friends have reappeared. Your grip on the steering wheel lessens. Your body begins to relax. Your heart rate returns to normal. The butterflies are gone. You let out a big sigh. This entire process may have only lasted less than a minute!

What just happened and why? Although not a physical threat to you, the police officer on the motorcycle presented as a realistic psychosocial threat to you. This psychosocial threat was the potential of getting a ticket, having to pay for it, possibly going to traffic court, losing time in your normal day, and the possibility of your insurance premiums costing more money. As noted in chapter 1, your brain does not make a distinction between a real physical threat, a real psychosocial threat, an imagined physical threat, or an imagined psychosocial threat. The stress response will be activated in all cases and remain activated until it is resolved. In the case of a real physical threat or a real psychosocial threat, the activation of the stress response will, in most cases, help you in addressing the threat. In the case of an imagined physical or psychosocial threat, its activation will provide no assistance at all and often makes things worse.

In this case, the activation of the stress response focused you on the real psychosocial threat, which resulted in your foot going to the brake. The anxiety that was felt alerted you to the problem, removed all other distractors, allowed you just to focus on the threat, and motivated you to generate an adaptive solution. The muscle tension prepared your leg to move toward the brake. The adaptive solution was stepping on the brake. Because your body temperature rises as an effect of your heart rate becoming rapid, your blood pressure rising, your blood flow increasing, and your breathing becoming rapid and shallow, the body sweats to cool down. The butterflies in your stomach are a direct result of the rerouting of your blood to the major muscles so you can respond appropriately, thus, the lifting your leg so your foot can quickly and easily step on the brake. As digesting food in your stomach is not relevant to addressing the threat, the blood to your stomach is reduced, hence the butterflies!

The appropriate activation of your stress response in this case, and in the previously mentioned cases where there were real, perceived physical threats, has been orchestrated by your **hypothalamus,** a component of the brain, which stimulated, in addition to the **sympathetic nervous system**, the **adrenal medulla,** the inner aspect of the **adrenal gland,** which sits on top of your kidneys, to release the hormone **adrenaline** or **epinephrine**, thus initiating and extending the changes and reactions that have been described.

Once the adaptive solution has been generated and acted on and the adaptive problem has been resolved, the hypothalamus stimulates the relaxation response, the **parasympathetic nervous system**, which releases the **neurotransmitter acetylcholine,** resulting in the body changes that occurred, because of the activation of the stress response, returning to normal. The appropriate activation of the stress response has clearly assisted you in resolving a real adaptive problem. So, stop! Take a few deep breaths; this activates your parasympathetic nervous system and lets your mind and body relax. This entire process will be discussed in more detail later in this chapter. (Oh, by the way, what about your friends in the car with you? What do you think happened to them during the entire process?)

Let's review another scenario where energy was directed in a healthy way:

> Your phone rings at 4:00 p.m. Your application for the job you applied for 3 weeks ago and really want has been accepted. The head of personnel would like for you to come in for an interview tomorrow at 9:00 a.m. You can feel the anxiety and mobilization of energy associated with the activation of the stress response (you want to do well and get the job) creeping up as you express your gratitude. You use the anxiety and energy to focus and motivate yourself to fully prepare for the interview. You go online and review what you had previously read about the company, its history and its mission statement. The relaxation response has kicked in. Feeling comfortable with your knowledge about the organization, you go out for a brisk walk. Upon returning you have a well-balanced dinner, watch some comedies on TV, the negativity bias is nowhere to be found, and then, relaxed, head to bed at 10:00 p.m. You do a few focused breathing exercises, no mind wandering here, and gently fall asleep. At 6:00 a.m. you awake rested, take care of basic needs, and go out for a 2-mile run.

Upon returning you shower, clean up, and have a healthy breakfast. You dress, smile at yourself in the mirror, give yourself a thumbs up, and head out for the interview confident, prepared, and relaxed.

The automatic activation of the stress response and thus the anxiety (not doing well in the interview is clearly a threat) motivated and focused you on positively preparing both physically and psychologically. Eating dinner and breakfast and getting a restful sleep eliminates three potential stressors to the body and the mind. The brisk walk in the evening and especially the run in the morning before the interview enhance learning, memory, and cognitive flexibility (Ratey, 2008).

The Inappropriate Activation of the Stress Response

You are back on the freeway again driving your car. As you come around the bend the cars in front of you are at a stop. As far as you can see the cars are not moving. Your grip tightens on the steering wheel. You let loose an expletive! You jam your foot onto the brake. Your car is at a complete rest. You mutter to yourself, "Now what? How long is this going to take?" You look at your watch. You look out at the sea of cars. Nothing is moving! Your body is getting tenser. The anger is building. You feel like you are about to explode. Sweat is dripping down your back. You shake the steering wheel. You pause and then slam your palm onto the horn.

As the traffic presents as a threat to your (false) expectation that you should always have clear sailing when you are driving, your stress response is automatically activated. Remember, your brain does not make a distinction between a real physical threat, a real psychosocial threat, or a completely unrealistic or imagined psychosocial threat. Your body tightening and sweating, your anger, and your behavior of yelling and beating up your steering wheel and horn, are all expressions of and fueled by the inappropriate activation of your stress response. Its activation did not help nor could it help you resolve your unrealistic psychosocial threat. Your behavior and anger were not going to make the traffic move. In fact, it made things worse as your body and mind were significantly stressed.

Ask yourself about the last time you sat in traffic. Did you have the slightest sense of the traffic interfering with your goal of getting home, going to a movie, getting dinner, meeting a friend, and so on? Was there even just an inkling of frustration, irritation, impatience, annoyance, or anger? If so, your stress response was inappropriately activated. As long as you continued to dwell on or comment negatively (remember the negativity bias) on the traffic, your stress response stayed inappropriately activated. It certainly was not going to make the traffic clear up.

When you enter a bank and see long lines with only a few tellers open, are you anxious, impatient, bothered, and/or upset? If so, it is because your stress response has been activated because your unrealistic psychosocial expectations are being threatened. Its activation is inappropriate as it is not going to make the lines move any faster. In fact, not only did it not make the lines move any faster, it made you feel worse.

Remember the last time you got into an argument? Did you notice voices getting louder? Was your body tense? Did you feel your heart racing? Did you feel anxious? Did you notice you were sweating? Did your hands ball up into fists? Did you feel angry? Did you find yourself thinking and saying negative (remember your negativity bias) things to and about your adversary? If so, your stress response was inappropriately active. All the physical and psychological changes that occurred because of its inappropriate activation did not help you resolve the argument. Again, it made you feel worse. (By the way, by remembering the argument and replaying it, do you notice any changes in how you feel, right now, as a result of your simulation of the argument?)

Next scenario:

> Earlier in the day you got into an argument with a friend and it did not end on a pleasant note. You were furious with what was said about you—a psychosocial threat! To say that you were stressed would be an understatement. Later in the day, sitting on a chair at home, staring into space, your mind wanders into the default network and replays the unpleasant encounter, negativity bias, with your friend. Within a few moments, you are just as stressed out as you were when the argument actually happened by just thinking about the negative event.
>
> Later that evening, lying in bed trying to go to sleep, you imagine your friend making up terrible and untrue (the negativity bias once again) stories about you and the argument and then tomorrow telling your other friends, a clear, although imagined, psychosocial threat to you. Your stress comes roaring back, in this case by just imagining what you think your friend is going to do. As you continue to worry about what may or may not happen, you notice you have been lying in bed for 2 hours. You have an extremely important meeting with your boss in 7 hours to discuss a major project. You need to get some sleep. You now start to imagine everything going wrong (negativity bias) at the meeting: "What if the boss gets so mad that he fires me? What am I going to do then?" On top of that you now start to worry about the fact that you cannot get to sleep. This stresses you out even more.

The more that you engage in this type of thinking the stronger the neural networks associated with it become and, thus, they are more readily accessible, and consequently, the more quickly you can think yourself into being stressed. Remember, evolution supplies us with a negativity bias; it served our distant ancestors well, but we do not have the same environment nor the same threats. While the threats of our distant ancestors were physical, ours are primarily psychosocial and it is often the case that the activation of the stress response does not help address these threats. It often makes things worse.

In addition to our thinking, our lifestyle and behavior contribute significantly to the damage done or allostatic load to our body by chronic stress. Getting too much sleep or not enough sleep puts continual, inappropriate stress on our body. Not getting a sound, restful sleep also puts continual, inappropriate stress on our body. Eating too much or not enough puts continual, inappropriate stress on our body. Not eating in a nutritional manner puts continual, inappropriate stress on our body. Not staying hydrated puts continual, inappropriate stress on our body. Getting too much or not enough exercise puts continual, inappropriate stress on our body. Essentially any lifestyle behavior that is excessive or deficient puts continual, inappropriate stress on our body.

Let's now turn to why and what exactly is going on when the stress response, both acute and chronic, is activated.

What Happens When the Stress Response is Activated and Why?

When the fight, freeze, or flight response or stress response is initially activated during an acute threat, a series of physiological changes occur, alerting the individual to and preparing the individual for responding to a perceived threat. These changes happen automatically and, in most cases, are beneficial. On the other hand, these changes, which are, generally, beneficial during acute activation of the stress response, are often quite detrimental when the stress response is chronically activated. Let's look at what is going on during the acute activation of the stress response.

Acute Activation

Psychologically, the individual in this state is aroused, hyperalert, and anxious. These changes alert the individual to a potential threat, which results in scanning the environment, looking for and focusing on the threat, and motivates the individual to address it.

The pupils of the eyes dilate. This allows more light into the eyes and increases the ability to perceive and focus on the threat, thus, potentially increasing the possibility of surviving. Hearing is enhanced, allowing you to be more aware of auditory associated threats.

The **cardiovascular system** goes through a series of changes for the purpose of pushing oxygen and nutrients quicker to the areas that need it to respond. Heart rate and blood pressure increase. Vessels on the surface engage in vaso-constriction, thus increasing blood pressure and rerouting more blood to larger muscles and other relevant areas. Blood vessels in large muscles engage in vasodilation, which allows more and quicker blood flow to them. Blood-clotting factors are increased. This reduces chances of bleeding to death as a result of an injury or wound.

Pulmonary system changes such as lung bronchi dilation and rapid breathing increase the amount of oxygen in the blood. These changes increase energy metabolism, which is vital for addressing and responding to the perceived threat.

Muscular system tenses prepare the individual to physically respond, such as fight, freeze, or flee from the perceived threat.

Within your digestive system, the gastrointestinal component is suppressed. Saliva production is decreased. As energy is needed to address the perceived threat, there is no need to expend energy digesting food. As more energy is potentially needed, the liver increases the breaking down of **glycogen**, how sugar is stored, into **glucose**, how sugar is used, and releases it into the blood stream to be metabolized into energy. Insulin production and its release by the pancreas is suppressed. As sugar needs to be in the blood stream for energy metabolism, you do not want it to be taken out by insulin.

The **humoral branch** of the immune system is enhanced. This protects against injury, wounds, or infections as a consequence of addressing the perceived threat. Inflammation is suppressed. This allows the joints and movement not to be compromised regarding the perceived threat.

In the urinary system, the kidneys decrease urine production. This results in increasing blood volume, allowing more fluid to carry nutrients and oxygen.

TABLE 2.1 **Acute activation of the stress response**

CHANGE	BENEFIT
EYES	Pupils dilate. Lets in more light to enhance vision and focus. Tunnel vision to stay focused on perceived threat.
PSYCHOLOGICAL	Anxiety occurs. Alerts us and keeps us aroused and hypersensitive to potential threats.
HEART	Rate increases. Pushes nutrients and oxygen faster to parts of the body that need energy to address threat.

CHANGE	BENEFIT
BLOOD PRESSURE	Increases. Pushes nutrients and oxygen faster to parts of the body that need energy to address threat.
LUNGS	Breathing increases. Bronchi of lungs dilate. Increases oxygen in blood for energy metabolism in cells.
BLOOD VESSELS OF SKIN	Vasoconstriction. Increases blood pressure, reroutes more blood to large muscles that need it for fighting, fleeing, or freezing. Lowers possibility of excessive superficial bleeding from skin.
BLOOD VESSELS OF LARGER MUSCLES	Vasodilation. Increases blood flow to larger muscles for fighting, fleeing, or freezing.
GASTROINTESTI-NAL SYSTEM	Activity, including saliva production, decreased. Energy is needed for reacting to threat not for digesting food.
PANCREAS	Insulin production and its release is decreased. Need higher levels of sugar in blood stream for energy pro-duction.
LIVER	Releases more glucose by breaking down glycogen. Higher levels of blood sugar are needed for energy.
MUSCLES	Tense. Preparation for immediate action of fighting, freezing, or fleeing.
KIDNEYS	Decreased urine production. Increases blood volume.
SKIN	Sweating occurs. Cools body because of heat produc-tion due to energy expenditure.
IMMUNE SYSTEM	Humoral immune system enhanced. Protection against injury, wounds, or infections relative to acute threat. Inflammation suppressed. Allows joint move-ment not to be compromised.
BLOOD	Clotting factors increased. Reduces chances of bleed-ing to death because of an injury.
HEARING	More aware of auditory stimuli associated with threats.

Given your understanding of the acute activation of the stress response, let's now look at what happens when it is chronically activated.

Chronic Activation

The chronic activation of the stress response is destructive (allostatic load) across all systems of the body. It is linked to compromising and impairing the functioning of the brain, including the **amygdala, hippocampus,** *and* **prefrontal cortex** *(Arnsten, 2009; McEwen, 2004; McEwen, Nasveld, Palmer, & Anderson, 2012; McGrady, 2007; Ratey 2008; Sapolsky, 2004). The amygdala is associated with detecting, processing, and responding to threats, emotional processing, and emotional memory. The hippocampus is associated with contextual memory and learning. The prefrontal cortex is associated with such areas as decision making, problem solving, planning, one's personality, regulation of complex behavior, and so on. Essentially, it appears that the prefrontal cortex is responsible for the executive functions of the brain.*

Research links the chronic activation of the stress response to cardiovascular disorders, problems with the digestive system, suppression of the immune system, impairment of the respiratory system, obesity, fatigue, chronic pain, aging, problems with the musculoskeletal system, and mental health issues (Goldstein & Kopin, 2007; Marin et al., 2011; McEwen & Lasley, 2002; McEwen, Nasveld, Palmer, & Anderson, 2012; McGrady, 2007; Sapolsky, 2004).

TABLE 2.2 **Chronic activation of the stress response**

CHANGE	POSSIBLE PROBLEMS BECAUSE OF CHRONIC ACTIVATION
EYES	Pain, discomfort, blurred vision, sensitivity to light. Increase of interocular pressure. Chronic tunnel vision contributes to rumination, closed mindedness, obsessive/compulsive behavior, chronic worrying, and compromised ability to look for alternative solutions. Peripheral vision, psychological and physical, compromised.
PSYCHOLOGICAL	Anxiety disorders. Mood disorders. Learning, memory, attention, concentration, and thinking compromised.
HEART	Heart is overworked. Heart disease.
BLOOD PRESSURE	Hypertension.
LUNGS	Lungs overworked. Pulmonary disorders.
BLOOD VESSELS OF SKIN	Hypertension. Circulatory system compromised.

CHANGE	POSSIBLE PROBLEMS BECAUSE OF CHRONIC ACTIVATION
BLOOD VESSELS TO LARGER MUSCLES	Circulatory system compromised.
GASTROINTESTI-NAL SYSTEM	Digestive disorders (such as nausea and even ulcers or colitis).
PANCREAS	Diabetes or other imbalances of blood sugar.
LIVER	Diabetes.
MUSCLES	Headaches, muscle pain, fatigue.
KIDNEYS	Problems with blood circulation and blood vessels. Functioning and filtering compromised by high blood pressure and high levels of sugar in blood.
SKIN	Excessive sweating.
IMMUNE SYSTEM	Both the humoral and cellular branches of immune system suppressed. More susceptible to infections, disease, and cancer. Chronic inflammation. Joint mobility compromised. Joint pain. Body loses its ability to regulate inflammatory process.
BLOOD	Excessive clotting leads to stroke and heart attack.
HEARING	Tinnitus.

A Buddhist Perspective on Chronic Stress

*In the Sutra of Distinguishing the Four Noble Truths (di fenbie jing 諦分別經), Sariputra, one of Buddha's two chief disciples and second only to Buddha in regards to the ability to teach, explains to the monks the meaning of the noble truth of **dukkha** in the sermon that was just given by the Buddha. He states,*

> Friends. What is the noble truth of dukkha (ku 苦) or stress? Birth is stressful, growing old is stressful, death is stressful, anxiety is stressful, depression is stressful, the body is stressful, the mind is stressful, worrying and grieving are stressful, and not getting what one seeks/desires is stressful. All of these are stressful. In essence, the human condition is stressful. (Santee, 2007, pp. 94–95; Tripitaka, n.d.)

Given the range described regarding the concept of *dukkha*, it should be quite clear that it is used to describe what we today call chronic stress. In addition, for Buddha and Sariputra, *dukkha* is the universal condition of the human being. In other words, being chronically stressed is not something that just happens; it is the very nature of being human. There is a release, however, from *dukkha*, which will be explored in later chapters of this text.

So, what is exactly is occurring in the brain when the stress response is activated? Let's look.

The Pathways Leading to the Activation of the Stress Response

Essentially, there are two pathways or roads that lead to the activation of the stress response (Ledoux, 2002, 2015). There has been, however, some controversy regarding the role of the amygdala in processing emotions and regarding how many pathways, links, or roads are involved (de Gelder, van Honk, & Tamietto, 2011; Pessoa & Adolphs, 2010).

The first road or pathway is the low road, which is the short pathway. Information comes through the senses to the **thalamus**, which is essentially a relay station that sends sensory information to many parts of the brain, and then is sent to the **amygdala**. The amygdala determines if the information is a threat and, if so, sends it on to the **hypothalamus,** which activates the stress response.

At essentially the same time the thalamus is sending information to the amygdala, it is also sending information to the **sensory cortex**. The sensory cortex interprets the sensory information sent by the thalamus. If the information is ambiguous or too vague, it is then sent to the **hippocampus,** which puts the information into a context. If the context suggests a threat, the hippocampus relays information to the amygdala, telling it to let the hypothalamus know that it is a threat and to continue to maintain the stress response. If the hippocampus determines that the sensory information is not a threat, it relays information to the amygdala, telling it to let the hypothalamus know it is not a threat. If it is not a threat the hypothalamus turns off the stress response by activating the relaxation response. This is the long pathway or high road.

So, let's put this into a context. Mom and Dad are walking down the hallway of their house looking for Junior who has been a handful of late. They suspect he is upstairs in the TV room. As they pass by the bathroom, Junior, who is hiding inside, just out of sight of his parents, activates his air horn, letting loose an extremely loud and sudden noise. From an evolutionary perspective, this is a potential threat. Mom and Dad both jump. They are both quite startled. The stress response has been appropriately activated. This is the low road or short pathway. They both turn toward the sound and see Junior laughing and rolling on the floor. Information has been processed and put into a context—not a threat. This is the high road or long pathway. They begin to get somewhat composed and relax a little. The relaxation response has been activated.

TABLE 2.3   Limbic system and pituitary gland

COMPONENT	FUNCTION
THALAMUS	Relay station that sends sensory information to many parts of the brain.
AMYGDALA	Detects threats, emotional memory.
HYPOTHALAMUS	Control center for fight/freeze/flight response. Activates sympathetic nervous system, endocrine system, and HPA axis. Homeostasis, allostasis, hunger, thirst, circadian rhythms, sexual behavior.
HIPPOCAMPUS	Contextual memory, learning.
PITUITARY GLAND	Major endocrine gland that secretes numerous hormones such as growth hormone, antidiuretic hormone, adrenocorticotropic hormone, thyrotopic hormone, and gonadotrophins that are used for various bodily functions. HPA axis.
CORPUS CALLO-SUM	Connects right and left hemispheres of the brain, allowing both sides to talk to each other.
CEREBRAL CORTEX	The cerebrum, outer surface of the four lobes of the brain.

The Three Stages of an Activated Stress Response

*Our nervous system consists of two components: the **central nervous system** and the **peripheral nervous system**. The central nervous system consists of the brain and the spinal cord. The peripheral nervous system, nerves outside of outside of the brain and spinal column, consists of the **somatic nervous system** and the **autonomic nervous system**.*

The somatic nervous system, which is concerned with voluntary control of the body, consists of **sensory nerves** (**afferent**), which send signals/information from our senses to our spinal cord and brain, and **motor nerves** (**efferent**), which send signals/information from our spinal cord and brain to the skeletal muscle system in regards to body movement.

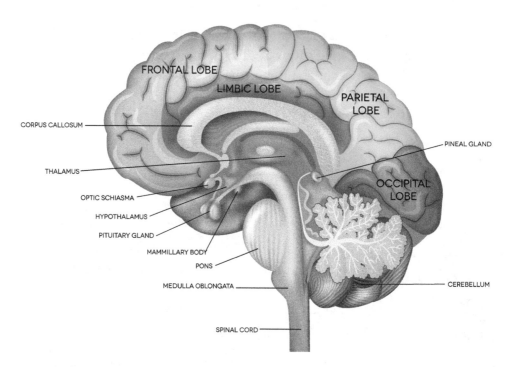

Limbic system and pituitary gland

The autonomic nervous system, which is essentially unconscious and lies beyond our conscious control, enables the brain to monitor and regulate our **visceral organs**. It consists of the **sympathetic nervous system** along with the **parasympathetic nervous system**.

The sympathetic nervous system causes changes in the body to address various demands placed on it by interacting with the environment. The parasympathetic nervous system reverses those demands when they have been addressed and resolved. The sympathetic nervous system, along with the **endocrine system,** make up the activation and maintenance component of the fight/freeze/flee or stress response.

There are three stages involved in the activation of the stress response. The first two stages make up the short-term response of stress response while the third stage represents the long-term response.

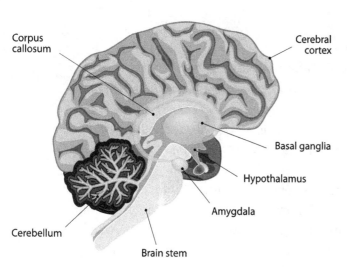

Limbic system and amygdala

Stage One

*Upon reception of information from the amygdala indicating a threat, the hypothalamus stimulates the sympathetic nervous system, which releases from its axon terminal the neurotransmitters **epinephrine (adrenaline)** and **norepinephrine (noradrenaline)**, resulting in the changes shown in **Table 2.1** such as heart rate increasing, blood pressure rising, muscles tensing, and so on. This activation lasts for approximately a few seconds, alerting and preparing the individual to respond to the threat.*

Stage Two

*The hypothalamus also stimulates, via the release of the neurotransmitter acetylcholine from the nerve end or axon terminal, the adrenal medulla to synthesize and release the hormones **epinephrine (adrenaline)** and **norepinephrine (noradrenaline)** into the blood stream. This extends the initial activation of the stress response up to approximately a few minutes.*

Stage Three

*If the threat has not been addressed and resolved, the hypothalamus releases the hormone **corticotrophin-releasing factor (CRF)**, which stimulates the **pituitary gland** to release **adrenocorticotropic hormone (ACTH)**, which stimulates the adrenal cortex to release glucocorticoids, such as **cortisol**, into the blood stream. Cortisol extends, by keeping the energy supply elevated and suppressing energy functions in areas not needed, the activation of the stress response by such activities as increasing the production and release of glucose, by the liver, into the blood stream, suppressing the immune system, inhibiting inflammation, and suppressing appetite. This process is known as the **hypothalamic-pituitary-adrenal (HPA) axis**.*

In addition to releasing ACTH, the pituitary gland releases the antidiuretic hormone **vasopressin** into the blood, which decreases fluid loss, thus keeping blood volume and blood pressure elevated. The pituitary gland also releases **thyrotopic hormone (TTH)** into the blood, which stimulates the thyroid gland to release the hormones **thryroxine** and **triiodothyronine**. This results in an increase in energy production that is necessary for maintaining the stress response. This third stage can extend the activation of the stress response for a longer period of time, minutes and hours, in order to address and resolve the threat. Once the threat is resolved the stress response is deactivated. Thus, in acute situations, as long as acute situations are not yoyoed throughout the day, the activation of the stress response is usually quite beneficial.

However, if the threat is not resolved in a timely manner the stress response can be extended in this third stage to days, weeks, months, and so on. This moves the activation of stress response out of the acute stage to the chronic stage. At this point its chronic activation can be quite detrimental to one's physical and psychological health and well-being.

Hans Selye's **general adaptation syndrome (GAS)** attempted to describe this process of moving from an acute activation of the stress response to its chronic activation and the subsequent physical and psychological damage done to the individual (Selye, 1978). The three stages of GAS are **alarm**, **resistance**, and **exhaustion**. The alarm stage was essentially Cannon's fight or flight response, that of an acute threat. The resistance stage is the body's coping with the threat, allowing the body to adapt and return to the pre-threat state. The third and final stage, that of exhaustion, occurs when the body is unable to cope with or adapt to the threat during the resistance stage. This being the case, the individual is essentially chronically stressed. This chronic stress leads to a depletion of the stress hormones, which, in turn, leads to illness, disease, and possible death. Sapolsky (2004, 2010), however, posits that Selye was wrong regarding the depletion of hormones as being the cause of illness, disease, and death in the exhaustion stage. Instead, he argues it is the ongoing activation of the stress response that wears down the body's ability to rest and recover that does the damage.

Not only did evolution provide us with the stress response and how it is turned on and maintained until the threat is resolved, but it also provided a mechanism for turning it off once the threat is resolved, known as the relaxation response (Benson, 2001).

DEACTIVATION OF THE STRESS RESPONSE

The Relaxation Response

Once a threat has been addressed and resolved, the relaxation response turns off the stress response. The relaxation response is the activation, by the hypothalamus, of the parasympathetic nervous system. The primary nerves in this system are the vagus nerves. The relaxation response essentially performs the opposite actions of the sympathetic nervous system by slowing down heart rate, lowering blood pressure, decreasing respiration, relaxing muscles, and so on. While the sympathetic nervous system is concerned with mobilizing and expending energy, the parasympathetic nervous system is concerned with conserving and storing energy, growth, digestion, rest, and repair. Many stress-management techniques such as mindfulness, the relaxation response, taijiquan, qigong, yoga, meditation, and various breathing exercises activate the relaxation response through controlled breathing.

It is clear the chronic activation and yoyoing of the stress response is detrimental to one's physical and psychological health and well-being. In addition, the chronic turning off of the relaxation response (because they both cannot be on at the same time) compromises the relaxation response, making it more difficult to perform its function of reversing the effects of the stress response. In addition, its ability to support the body to recover, rest, grow, digest, conserve and store energy, and repair itself is significantly hampered.

NEUROSCIENCE AND THE STRESS RESPONSE

Neural Activity

The overall neuroscience and the stress response have, essentially, already been introduced and described in the last number of sections. The underlying mechanisms of neural function will be described in this section.

The neuron is essentially the basic building block of behavior. It processes information, via **neurotransmitters**, from other neurons and sends it onward to still other neurons linked together, via **synapses**, in the neural networks of the brain. The average estimate of neurons in the human brain is 86 billion: 16 billion in the **cerebral cortex**, 69 billion in **cerebellum**, and less than a billion in the rest of the brain, with each neuron having 10,000 to 100,000 **synaptic con nections** to other neurons in neural networks (Herculano-Houzel, 2009, 2016).

In addition to the 86 billion neurons in the brain there is an average of 85 billion **glial cells** in the brain, which is approximately a 1-to-1 ratio (Azevedo et al., 2009; Herculano-Houzel, 2009, 2016; Jabar, 2012). The glial cells are traditionally viewed as providing support, nourishment, oxygen, insulation, and stabilization to neurons while also removing dead neurons. More recently, research indicates the role of the glial cells in the brain is much broader than originally thought and it is argued that they need to be viewed as being of equal importance as neurons (Jauregui-Huerta et al., 2010). Glial cells are believed to be involved with such additional areas as the immune response, monitoring and adjusting homeostasis, learning, memory, and synaptic activity (Jauregui-Huerta et al., 2010; Pearson, Osborne, & McNay, 2016).

TABLE 2.4   **Structure of a neuron and synapse**

COMPONENT	FUNCTION
DENDRITE	Receives chemical information, neurotransmitters, from axon terminals/tips/branches of other neurons.
CELL BODY	Processes neurotransmitter information received by dendrites and sends electrical signal or action potential, via the axon, to the axon terminal/tips/branches.

COMPONENT	FUNCTION
CELL NUCLEUS	Contains genetic material, chromosomes, which provide blueprints and instruction for cell behavior.
AXON	Conducts electrical messages from cell body.
MYELIN	Forms sheath around axon in order to help speed electrical impulse down axon.
SCHWANN CELLS	Glial cells that nourish and protect neurons; forms myelin.
NODE OF RANVIER	Gaps in the myelin sheath between Schwann cells of the axon that assist in speeding electrical message.
AXON TERMINAL/ TIPS/BRANCHES	Releases chemical information, neurotransmitters, into synapses in order for them to be received by dendrites of other neurons.
SYNAPSE	Space between dendrites and axon terminal/tips/ branches of neurons across which neurotransmitters are carried.
NEUROTRANSMITTER	Chemical messages/information released by axon terminal/tips/branches and sent to other neurons.

TABLE 2.5

MAJOR NEUROTRANSMITTERS	ASSOCIATED FUNCTION
EPINEPHRINE OR ADRENALINE	Excitatory/stimulating, released during stress response, arousal, alertness, glucose metabolism/energy. Also a stress hormone.
NOREPINEPHRINE OR NORADRENALINE	Excitatory/stimulating, mood, released during stress response, arousal, alertness, eating.
GLUTAMATE	Brain's main excitatory/stimulating neurotransmitter; memory, learning, neuroplasticity.
GAMA AMINOBUTYRIC ACID (GABA)	Brain's main inhibitory/calming neurotransmitter; mood, anxiety, memory, learning.
SEROTONIN	Mood, anxiety, appetite, sleep, sexuality, sensory perception, learning, muscle control.

DOPAMINE	Inhibitory/calming, mood, cognitive functioning, learning, movement, attention, motivation, pleasure, reward.
ENDORPHINS	Pleasurable feelings, relieving pain.
ACETYLCHOLINE	Excitatory/stimulating, voluntary muscle control; memory, learning, sleep, released during relaxation response.
OXYTOCIN	Social bonding, recognition, sexual behavior. Also a hormone.

Brain Function

*The **cerebral cortex, cerebrum**, is the most recent and outer layer of the brain. It consists of the **occipital, parietal, temporal**, and **frontal lobes**. It is associated with the higher-order functioning of the brain. The **cerebellum** is an older component of the brain and is traditionally viewed as being involved with adjusting balance, coordinating movement, and posture. More recently, however, research suggests its function is much broader and now includes executive function, cognition, language, attention, memory, and emotion (Beaton & Marien, 2010; Koziol et al., 2013; Ratey, 2008; Schmahmann & Caplan, 2006). Chronic stress compromises functioning in the prefrontal cortex and the cerebellum (Ansell, Rando, Tuit, Guarnaccia, & Sinha, 2012; Caulfield & Servatius, 2013).*

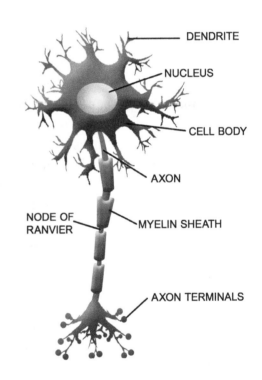

Neuron cell

Chronic stress, with special attention to the **glucocorticoid hormones,** especially **cortisol,** significantly compromises the functioning of neurons and damages them, depletes certain glial cells (NG2) while increasing certain other glial cells (oligodendrocytes), causes brain shrinkage and shortening of **dendrites**, dysregulates the HPA axis, compromises neuroplasticity and hampers neurogenesis, and is linked to short-term depression and long-term vulnerability to psychological disorders such as depression, anxiety, and PTSD (Birey et al., 2015; Chetty et al., 2014; Epel, Daubenmier, Moskowitz, Folkman, & Blackburn, 2009; Jauregui-Huerta et al., 2010; Pearson,

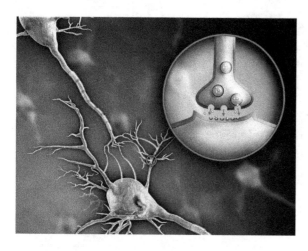

Neuron synapse

Osborne, & McNay, 2016; Ong et al., 2016; Puga et al., 2015; Ratey, 2008; Sapolsky, 2004).

Research (American Institute of Stress (AIS), 2016; Epel et al., 2004; Epel et al., 2009; Lu, 2014; Mitchell et al., 2014; Norris, 2011; Verhoeven et al., 2015) in **telomeres**, the caps at the ends of chromosomes (which prevent their unraveling but tend to shrink with chronological aging) and the enzyme **telomerase** (which extends telomeres and thus impedes the unraveling of chromosomes) has found that perceived and chronic stress shrinks telomeres and causes the supply of telomerase to decrease in adults (care givers) and causes telomeres to shrink in children (in non-advantageous environments). When telomeres shrink past a certain point, the ability of cells to increase and restock tissue in the body is significantly compromised (Blackburn, 2001; Norris, 2011; Verhoeven, 2015). In addition, this research has linked chronic stress and telomere shrinkage with such chronic diseases as cardiovascular disease, Alzheimer's, cancer, depression, anxiety, atherosclerosis, osteoporosis, arthritis, Type 2 diabetes, and dementia.

TABLE 2.6   Areas of brain function

COMPONENT	FUNCTION
FRONTAL LOBE	Decision making, problem solving, planning, regulation of complex behavior, judgment, motor skills, impulse control, executive function.
TEMPORAL LOBE	Auditory processing, speech, language, memory.
PARIETAL LOBE	Tactile processing, vestibular processing, proprioception, sensory motor integration.
OCCIPITAL LOBE	Visual spatial processing.
CEREBELLUM	Adjusting balance, coordinating movement, posture, executive function, cognition, language, attention, memory, and emotion.

INDIVIDUAL FACTORS
RELATED TO CHRONIC STRESS

That chronic stress is a significant problem simply cannot be denied. A number of factors that are potential stressors themselves and/or have a direct impact on the development and sustaining of chronic stress are addressed.

Impact of Age

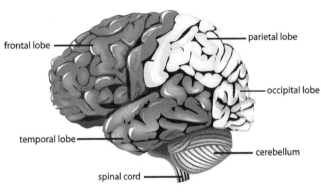

Lobes of the brain

*The results of the 2015 Stress in America Survey (American Psychological Association (APA), 2016) survey (N = 3,361 adults 18 years old or older), conducted in August of 2015 (and performed annually since 2007) indicated that (a) reported stress levels were higher than **their accepted health rate of 3.8/10** by the respondents in the 18–36-year-old (6.0), 37–50-year-old (5.8), and 51–69-year-old (4.30) age groups when compared to the 70 years or older (3.5) age group; and (b) 34% of those surveyed reported an increase in stress from the previous year with the 18–36-year-old group (45%) and 37–50-year-old group (39%) being highest.*

The results of the 2013 *Stress in America Survey* (APA, 2014), conducted in August of 2013 notes that for teenagers (N = 1018) (a) their reported, during the school year, average stress levels (5.8) were higher than **their average accepted health rate of 3.9/10**; (b) their reported, for the previous month, stress levels (4.6) were higher than **their accepted health rate of 3.9/10**; (c) 31% indicated their stress levels had increased from the previous year; (d), 34% expected, for the coming year, that their stress levels would increase; and (e) girls (5.1) reported, for the previous month, a higher stress level than boys (4.1).

Impact of Ethnicity/Race

The results of the Stress in America Survey (APA, 2016) indicate that (a) 62% of Whites, 77% of Hispanics, 78% of Blacks, 70% of Asians, and 70% of American Indians/Alaskan Natives view money as a significant stressor; and (b) 62% of Whites, 74% of Hispanics, 69% of Blacks, 71% Asians, and 59% of American Indians/Alaskan Natives view work as a significant stressor.

The report further notes 48% of Whites, 58% of Hispanics, 56% of Blacks, 56% of Asians, and 57% of American Indians/Alaskan Natives view personal health as a significant stressor. Sixty-nine percent of Whites, 61% of Hispanics,

67% of Blacks, 49% of Asians, and 72% of American Indians/Alaskan Natives report having at least one chronic illness. Twenty-three percent of Whites, 33% of Hispanics, 29% of Blacks, 31% of Asians, and 21% of American Indians/Alaskan Natives responded that they did not have access to a medical doctor in non-emergency situations.

Impact of Discrimination

The results of the Stress in America Survey (APA, 2016) indicates that (a) 69% of those surveyed have been discriminated against while 61% note daily discrimination; (b) 71% of Blacks, 64% of Asians, 56% of Hispanics, and 36% of American Indians/Alaskan Natives believe race is the source of daily discrimination, while 33% of Whites attribute discrimination to age; (c) 30% of women and 8% of men report that gender is the basis for daily discrimination; (d) LGBTs indicate they have been discriminated against by police (23%) and employers by not hiring them (33%) and 24% note that teachers or advisors discriminated against them by discouraging them from further education; (e) the reported stress level for those LGBTs (6.4) who acknowledge being discriminated against is higher than non-LGBTs (5.5) who reported discrimination against them; and (f) those who do not have a disability (18%) were less likely to regard discrimination toward them as a stressor than individuals with disabilities (26%).

Impact of Sexual Identity and Orientation

According to the Stress in America Survey (APA, 2016), there is (a) a one-point difference regarding average stress levels between LGBTs (6.0) and non-LGBTs (5.0), (b) a 15% difference between LGBTs (49%) and non-LGBTs (34%) regarding stress levels increasing from the previous year, and (c) a difference in job stability as a source of stress for LGBTs (57%) as compared with non-LGBTs (36%).

Impact of Disability

The Stress in America Survey (APA, 2016), regarding the disabled, notes that (a) when compared against those who are not disabled (4.8) individuals with disabilities have a higher average reported stress rate (5.5), and (b) those with disabilities also note that money (75%), work (73%), personal health concerns (69%), and their health problems affecting family members (60%) are their major stressors.

Impact of Developmental Stages

Although the brain changes throughout an individual's lifespan and is subject to being compromised by chronic stress, there are, in addition, critical periods of development where the individual's brain is more vulnerable to chronic stress. It is at these points that stress management is particularly vital.

At the prenatal stage of development, the embryo/fetus and its environment is completely vulnerable to the mother's physical and psychological states. If the mother is chronically stressed during pregnancy the normal process of gestation is compromised and may lead to lower birth rate, cognitive and behavioral problems during childhood, and enduring problems with the stress response, cognitive processing, social interactions and psychological disorders during adulthood (Koenig, Walker, Romeo & Lupien, 2011; Lupien, McEwen, Gunnar, & Heim 2009).

During the neonatal period, the newborn is now directly interacting with the external environment. A chronically stressful environment and inadequate nutrition may lead to subsequent problems down the road with the stress response, metabolism, pain sensitivity, food choices, and, in adulthood, susceptibility to addictive behaviors (Koenig, Walker, Romeo & Lupien, 2011).

The Adverse Childhood Experiences (ACE) study (Felitti et al., 1998) found a strong association between childhood physical abuse, psychological abuse, sexual abuse, and/or dysfunctional family behavior and environment (in other words, being subject to chronically stressful experiences) and subsequent dysfunctional health risk behaviors and chronic illnesses as adults. Felitti (2009) notes that these chronically stressful experiences occur often, are not usually identified, and can negatively affect behavior and health/well-being in childhood itself. McEwen (2011) links these chronically stressful experiences to compromising brain development and function, which in turn connects to health risk behaviors, psychological disorders, and chronic diseases.

Adolescence is clearly designated by the onset of puberty, and chronic stress significantly compromises this transition period. Lupien, McEwen, Gunnar, and Heim (2009) link chronic stress during this time period to possible issues with the frontal cortex and the upsurge of psychological disorders such as anxiety and depression. Koenig, Walker, Romeo, and Lupien (2011) note that chronic stress during adolescence may compromise turning off the HPA axis.

During the aging process the adult brain becomes more susceptible to the impact of stress hormones. It is also during this adult aging process that the damage done to the brain during earlier periods of the developmental process begin to manifest physically, psychologically, and behaviorally.

Impact of Gender

Taylor and colleagues (2000), while acknowledging that the fight/flight response is probably physiologically similar across males and females, says it's important to note that research on stress has been primarily focused on the behavioral responses of males to stress and that the fight/flight/freeze response does not really represent the *evolutionary-based behavioral responses, "**tend-and-befriend**," of females to stress, which are thought to be oriented to protecting their children, (**tending**) and protecting themselves (**befriending**) by linking to others via social behavior. These behaviors are seen as enhancing the survival and reducing the stress of both mother and child. They also suggest that these responses, mediated by the hormone **oxytocin**, which is linked to maternal and social behavior, reduce the occurrence of the fight/flight/freeze response to stress in females.*

The number-one cause of death (2013) for both males (24.6%) and females (22.4%) in the United States is heart disease (Centers for Disease Control and Prevention (CDC), 2015a, 2015b). The number-two cause of death for both males (23.5%) and females (21.5%) is cancer (CDC, 2015a, 2015b). Both heart disease and cancer have been clearly linked to lifestyle and chronic stress. The third leading cause of death for males (6.3%) is unintentional injuries (traffic accidents, accidental falls, accidental poisoning) and for females (6.1%) chronic obstructive pulmonary disease (CDC, 2015a, 2015b). Both are quite distant from the two leading causes of death and both can be easily linked to lifestyle and chronic stress. When examined from the perspective of race/ethnicity for both males and females across Hispanic, White, Black, American Indian/Alaska Native, and Asian/Pacific Islanders, the number-one and number-two causes of death are either heart disease and cancer or cancer and heart disease (CDC, 2015c, 2015d).

The results of the *Stress in America Survey* (APA, 2016) indicate, where 3.8 is considered healthy by the respondents, that (a) women note higher average levels of stress (5.3/10) than men (4.9/10); (b) both view money and work respectively as the number-one and number-two sources of stress; and (c) 37% of women and 31% of men when compared to the previous year reported an increase in stress.

Two areas intimately linked to chronic stress are alcoholism and depression. The ratio of women to men regarding depression is 2 to 1 (Culbertson, 1997; Depression and Bipolar Support Alliance (DBSA), 2016). The ratio of men to women regarding alcohol abuse is 1.8 to 1 (CDC, 2016; Esser et al., 2014).

Impact of Physical and Mental Health

As noted previously in this chapter, chronic stress has a significant impact on physical and mental health. The Stress in America Survey (APA, 2016) indicates that (a) 42% of respondents reported feeling anxious/nervous, 37% reported feeling depressed/sad, 33% reported chronic worrying, 16% reported receiving a diagnosis of depression, and 13% reported receiving a diagnosis of anxiety; and (b) 32% of participants noted high blood pressure, 58% noted being overweight or obese, 39% noted not eating healthy or eating in excess during the past month, 32% reported headaches, 27% noted concentration problems, and 46% reported problems getting to sleep, all within the past month.

Impact of Socioeconomic Status/Environment

The evidence is quite clear that low socioeconomic status and deprived social environments are significant stressors and thus detrimental to the physical and psychological health/well-being of individuals (APA, 2016; Marmot, 2005; McEwen, 2012; Mitchell et al., 2014). Mitchell and colleagues (2014) have noted that these environments cause telomeres to shrink in both adults and children. McEwen (2012) indicates that low SES is linked to problematic changes in the hippocampus, amygdala, and prefrontal cortex. Marmot (2005) notes that fundamental to low socioeconomic status, deprived social environments, and the chronic stress associated with them is the lack of and perceived lack of control over one's life.

The *Stress in America Survey* (APA, 2016) shows (a) that the average reported stress level is higher for those living in an urban environment (5.6) when compared to suburban (5.0) and rural (4.7) environments; (b) that crime and violence are more of major concerns for the those living in an urban (46%) environment when compared to rural (19%) and suburban environments (17%); (c) obtaining healthy food is more of an issue for those living in an urban environment (34%) when compared to rural (20%) and suburban (13%) environments; and (d) unemployment is reported as more of a problem in the urban (48%) and rural (43%) environments than the suburban (22%) environment.

Impact of Substance and Alcohol Abuse

Substance abuse and alcohol abuse are both dysfunctional behaviors. They both are attempts to cope with the physical and psychological symptoms associated with chronic stress. The problem is that while the excessive use of substances and alcohol may give individuals temporary relief from the symptoms and the stressors in their life, the abuse ends up as an additional stressor to both the brain and the body. As a result, in addition to the original stressors, the individual now has an additional stressor. As long as the individual continues to engage in this dysfunctional behavior, the neural networks associated with it become stronger and more readily accessible, thus, the difficulty associated with becoming alcohol or drug free.

Research regarding drug use and health, performed annually by the Substance Abuse and Mental Health Services Administration (SAMHSA), for the year 2013 indicates that that not only is there a chronic alcohol and drug problem in the United States, there is a significant problem with not receiving treatment for drug and alcohol abuse or dependence. Their report (U.S. Department of Health and Human Services. 2014) notes,

> In 2013, an estimated 24.6 million Americans aged 12 or older were current (past month) illicit drug users, meaning they had used an

illicit drug during the month prior to the survey interview. This estimate represents 9.4 percent of the population aged 12 or older. Illicit drugs include marijuana/hashish, cocaine (including crack), heroin, hallucinogens, inhalants, or prescription-type psychotherapeutics (pain relievers, tranquilizers, stimulants, and sedatives) used nonmedically (1).

Slightly more than half (52.2 percent) of Americans aged 12 or older reported being current drinkers of alcohol in the 2013 survey, which was similar to the rate in 2012 (52.1 percent). This translates to an estimated 136.9 million current drinkers in 2013 (3).

In 2013, an estimated 21.6 million persons aged 12 or older (8.2 percent) were classified with substance dependence or abuse in the past year based on criteria specified in the Diagnostic and Statistical Manual of Mental Disorders, 4th edition (DSM-IV). Of these, 2.6 million were classified with dependence or abuse of both alcohol and illicit drugs, 4.3 million had dependence or abuse of illicit drugs but not alcohol, and 14.7 million had dependence or abuse of alcohol but not illicit drugs (7).

The annual number of persons with substance dependence or abuse in 2013 (21.6 million) was similar to the number in each year from 2002 through 2012 (ranging from 20.6 million to 22.7 million) (7).

Treatment need is defined as having substance dependence or abuse or receiving substance use treatment at a specialty facility (hospital inpatient, drug or alcohol rehabilitation, or mental health centers) within the past 12 months. In 2013, 22.7 million persons aged 12 or older needed treatment for an illicit drug or alcohol use problem (8.6 percent of persons aged 12 or older). Of these, 2.5 million (0.9 percent of persons aged 12 or older and 10.9 percent of those who needed treatment) received treatment at a specialty facility. Thus, 20.2 million persons (7.7 percent of the population aged 12 or older) needed treatment for an illicit drug or alcohol use problem but did not receive treatment at a specialty facility in the past year (7).

Of the 20.2 million persons aged 12 or older in 2013 who were classified as needing substance use treatment but did not receive treatment at a specialty facility in the past year, 908,000 persons (4.5 percent) reported that they felt they needed treatment for their illicit drug or alcohol use problem. Of these 908,000 persons who felt they needed treatment, 316,000 (34.8 percent) reported that they made an effort to get treatment. Based on combined 2010-2013 data, the most commonly reported reason for not receiving treatment among this group of persons was a lack of insurance coverage and inability to afford the cost (37.3 percent) (7).

PRACTICAL APPLICATION

The Relaxation Response

*The medical doctor Herbert Benson (2001) coined the term **relaxation response** to indicate the physiological system that reverses the effects of the fight/freeze/flight response and also to indicate a specific type of meditation (there are many variations of it) practice that activates this physiological system. Everything that applied to the counting-of-your-breath meditation, with one exception, applies to practicing the relaxation response.*

The one exception is that instead of counting your breaths when you exhale, you instead say a meaningful word or meaningful short phrase to yourself. **You do not count.** Select a word or short phrase before you start and stay with the same word or phrase throughout the duration. **Remember to be nonjudgmental while you practice.** Begin with 5 minutes (you of course can do more), and as you progress and feel more comfortable with this meditation practice, gradually add more time, with the suggested goal being 20 minutes.

It is recommended that you practice at least once a day. The morning when you first awake before breakfast is considered the best time. It is important to note, however, that you do have a life and it often gets in the way when you are adding new practices to your lifestyle. In other words, you need to be flexible and find what time frame and how often best works for you so that you receive its benefits. For something to wire into your brain (think neuroplasticity) you need to practice in a consistent and regular manner. The bottom line for all of these various techniques is practice!

- Take a comfortable, relaxed sitting position where your head and body are properly aligned, in other words, no slouching, hunching, leaning sideways or backwards, and so on.
- Make sure you have decided on your word or phrase and stick with it throughout the exercise.
- Inhaling and exhaling though your nose, take a deep breath and as you exhale say your word or phrase silently to yourself.
- Continue for your set time.
- If your mind wanders, don't make any judgments about it, just return to saying your word or phrase as you exhale.

Upon finishing the relaxation response, note how you feel physically, mentally, and emotionally. Is there a difference between how you felt before you started it and how you feel after you finished? What did you notice? Did your mind wander? If so, how did you respond to its wandering? Now compare the results of when you engaged in the counting-your-breath meditation, which activates the physiological relaxation response, with the relaxation response meditative technique. What did you discover? Which one worked better for you? Same results? Preference? As there are numerous techniques that activate the physiological relaxation response, the goal is to find which ones work best for you.

Zhanzhuang: Position Two

Beginning from the wuji position, described in chapter 1, simply let your arms arc slightly forward, staying thigh-width apart, until your hands, palms facing each other, are at

waist level, which is about 3 or so inches below your bellybutton. Visualize you are holding a large beach ball with your hands, arms, and lower abdomen/pelvic area gently holding it in place. Staying in this position, slowly and gently inhaling and exhaling through your nose, simply nonjudgmentally observe what you are feeling. If your mind wanders, simply return to your breath to re-anchor, and return to observing what you feel. After 5 minutes let your hands naturally arc back to the beginning position. Take a deep breath, let it out, and open your eyes.

What did you notice? How are you feeling? Did you feel any discomfort? Did you notice certain parts of your body were tight or sore? Did you find yourself swaying side to side or backward or forward? Was your balance an issue? Did your mind wander? If so, were you able to easily refocus? Do you notice a difference between what you felt upon completing the *wuji* position and what you felt after completing this second position? If so, what? Was one position easier for you? If so, why?

Yoga: Reclined Pigeon Pose (*Supta Kapotasana*)

Find a comfortable place on the floor. For this position, start by lying flat on your back with your feet, bottom of feet flat on the floor, pulled up about 6 inches from your buttock. The back of your head rests on the floor. Your neck is gently extended. Breath naturally through your nose.

- Take your right leg and cross it over your left thigh. Your right ankle is a few inches above your left knee.
- Lift your left foot off the floor and circle your lower left thigh with your fingers clasped together.
- Gently pull your left leg toward your chest.
- You should feel a stretch on the back of your thigh running up your right buttock.
- Hold for 30 seconds or about 10–12 slow, complete breaths.
- Release and return to original position.
- Repeat on the opposite side.

What did you notice while you were doing the reclined pigeon pose? How does your lower back, back of your thigh, and buttock feel? How is your mind? Agitated? Still? Did your mind wander? If so, what did you do to address it? How does this posture compare with the mountain pose? What do you notice?

KEY TERMS

normal stress
threat-based thinking
fight, freeze, or flight response
chronic stress
neuroplasticity
adaptive problem
adaptive solution

allostasis
allostatic load
negativity bias
sympathetic nervous system
adrenal medulla
adrenal gland
epinephrine/adrenaline

parasympathetic nervous system
cardiovascular system
pulmonary system
glycogen
glucose
humoral branch of immune system

amygdala

hippocampus

prefrontal cortex

thalamus

hypothalamus

sensory cortex

central nervous system

peripheral nervous system

somatic nervous system

autonomic nervous system

sensory nerves (afferent)

motor nerves (efferent)

visceral organs

endocrine system

norepinephrine/ noradrenaline

corticotrophin-releasing factor (CRF)

pituitary gland

adrenocorticotropic hormone (ACTH)

glucocorticoids

cortisol

hypothalamic-pituitary-adrenal axis (HPA)

vasopressin

thyrotopic hormone (TTH)

thryroxine

triiodothyronine

general adaptation syndrome (GAS)

alarm stage

resistance stage

exhaustion stage

neurotransmitters

synapses

cerebral cortex

cerebrum

cerebellum

synaptic connections

glial cells

occipital lobes

parietal lobes

temporal lobes

frontal lobes

dendrites

telomeres

telomerase

tend and befriend

oxytocin

EXERCISES

1. During the past week, pick one occasion when your stress response was appropriately activated. Describe the situation. What happened? What was the adaptive problem/threat? How did the appropriate activation of your stress response assist you in generating an adaptive solution and resolving the problem?

2. During the past week, pick one occasion when your stress response was inappropriately activated. Describe the situation. What happened? Why was the activation of your stress response in this situation inappropriate? Did it make things worse? Explain.

3. During the past week, describe three situations of normal stress. What happened in each of them? What did your body do to adapt?

4. Select a situation in your life where you felt you were discriminated against. What was it due to? Age? Skin color? Gender? Ethnicity? Did you feel your stress response kicking in? How did you feel physically? Psychologically? How did your resolve the situation?

5. Describe a situation where the short pathway to the activation of the stress response occurred. Did it help you address a threat? Explain.

6. Describe a situation where the short pathway and the long pathway to the activation of the stress response occurred. Did it help you address a threat? Explain.

7. When you are stressed, what physical and psychological changes do you notice in yourself?

8. Think about the psychosocial threats in your life. Which ones are appropriate and which ones are inappropriate? How do you know?

REFERENCES

American Institute of Stress (AIS). (2016). Seniors. Retrieved from http://www.stress.org/seniors/

American Psychological Association (APA). (2014). Stress in America: Are teens adopting adults' stress habits? Stress in America Survey. Retrieved from https://www.apa.org/news/press/releases/stress/2013/stress-report.pdf

American Psychological Association (APA). (2018). Stress in America press room. Retrieved from http://www.apa.org/news/press/releases/stress/index.aspx

Ansell, E. B., Rando, K., Tuit, K., Guarnaccia, J., & Sinha, R. (2012). Cumulative adversity and smaller gray matter volume in medial prefrontal, anterior cingulate, and insula regions. Biological Psychiatry, 72(1), 57–64. Retrieved from http://europepmc.org/articles/PMC3391585

Arnsten, A. F. T. (2009). Stress signaling pathways that impair prefrontal cortex structure and function. Nature Reviews Neuroscience, 10(6), 410–422.

Azevedo, F. A., Carvalho, L. R., Grinberg, L. T., Farfel, J. M., Ferretti, R. E., Leite, R. E., ... & Herculano-Houzel, S. (2009). Equal numbers of neuronal and nonneuronal cells make the human brain an isometrically scaled-up primate brain. Journal of Comparative Neurology. 513(5), 532–541.

Beaton, A., & Marien, P. (2010). Language, cognition and the cerebellum: Grappling with an enigma. Cortex, 46(7), 811–820.

Benson, H. (2001). The relaxation response. New York, NY: Harper.

Benson, H., & Casey, A. (Eds.). (2013). A Harvard Medical School special report: Stress management. Boston, MA: Harvard Medical School.

Birey, F., Kloc, M., Chavali, M., Hussein, I., Wilson, M., Christoffel, D. J., ... & Aguirre, A. (2015). Genetic and stress-induced loss of NG2 glia triggers emergence of depressive-like behaviors through reduced secretion of FGF2. Neuron, 88(5), 941–956.

Blackburn, E. (2001). Switching and signaling at the telomere. Cell, 106(6), 661–673.

Boyd, L. (2015). After watching this your brain will not be the same [Video file]. Retrieved from https://www.bing.com/videos/search?q=lara+boyd+ted+talks&view=detail&mid=5908B6ECA70A1A86CCE95908B6ECA70A1A86CCE9&FORM=VIRE

Caulfield, M. D., & Servatius, R. J. (2013). Focusing on the possible role of the cerebellum in anxiety disorders. In F. Durbano (Ed.), New insights into anxiety disorders. Retrieved from http://cdn.intechopen.com/pdfs-wm/41031.pdf

Centers for Disease Control and Prevention (CDC). (2015a). Leading causes of death in females United States, 2013. Retrieved from https://www.cdc.gov/women/lcod/2013/index.htm

Centers for Disease Control and Prevention. (2015b). Leading causes of death in males United States, 2013. Retrieved from https://www.cdc.gov/men/lcod/2013/index.htm

Centers for Disease Control and Prevention. (2015c). Leading causes of death by race/ethnicity, all females-United States, 2013. Retrieved from https://www.cdc.gov/women/lcod/2013/womenrace_2013.pdf

Centers for Disease Control and Prevention. (2015d). Leading causes of death by race/ethnicity, all males-United States, 2013. Retrieved from https://www.cdc.gov/men/lcod/2013/race_ethnicitymen2013.pdf

Centers for Disease Control and Prevention. (2016). *Fact sheets - Excessive alcohol use and risks to men's health.* Retrieved from https://www.cdc.gov/alcohol/fact-sheets/mens-health.htm

Chetty, S., Friedman, A. R., Taravosh-Lahn, K., Kirby, E. D., Mirescu, C. M., Guo, F., ... & Kaufer, D. (2014). *Stress and glucocorticoids promote oligodendrogenesis in the adult hippocampus.* Molecular Psychiatry, 19(12), 1275–1283.

Culbertson, F. M. (1997). *Depression and gender: An international review.* American Psychologist, 52(1), 25–31.

de Gelder, B., van Honk, J., & Tamietto, M. (2011). *Emotion in the brain: Of low roads, high roads and roads less travelled.* Nature Reviews Neuroscience, 12(7), 425.

Depression and Bipolar Support Alliance (DBSA). (2016). *Depression statistics.* Retrieved from https://www.dbsalliance. org/education/depression/statistics/

Epel, E., Daubenmier, J., Moskowitz, J. T., Folkman, S., & Blackburn, E. (2009). *Can meditation slow rate of cellular aging? Cognitive stress, mindfulness, and telomeres.* Annals of New York Academy of Science, 1172(1), 34–53.

Epel, E. S., Blackburn, E. H., Lin, J., Dhabhar, F. S., Adler N. E., Morrow, J. D., & Cawthon, R. M. (2004). *Accelerated telomere shortening in response to life stress.* Proceedings of the National Association of Science, 101(49), 17312–17315.

Esser, M. B., Hedden, S. L., Kanny, D., Brewer, R. D., Gfroerer, J. C., & Naimi, T. S. (2014). *Prevalence of alcohol dependence among US adult drinkers, 2009–2011.* Preventing Chronic Disease 11(206), 1–11. Retrieved from https://www.cdc.gov/pcd/issues/2014/pdf/14_0329.pdf

Felitti, V. J. (2009). *Adverse childhood experiences and adult health.* Academic Pediatrics, 9(3), 131–132.

Felitti, V. J., Anda, R. F., Nordenberg, D., Williamson, D. F., Spitz, A. M., Edwards, V., Koss, M. P., & Marks, J. S. (1998). *Relationship of childhood abuse and household dysfunction to many of the leading causes of death in adults: The adverse childhood experiences (ace) study.* American Journal of Preventive Medicine, 14(4), 245–258.

Fuchs, E., & Flugge, G. (2014). *Adult neuroplasticity: More than 40 years of research.* Neuroplasticity, 2014. Retrieved from https://www.hindawi.com/journals/np/2014/541870/

Ganzel, B. L., Morris, P. A., & Wethington, E. (2010). *Allostasis and the human brain: Integrating models of stress from the social and life sciences.* Psychological Review, 117(1), 134–174.

Goldstein, D. S., & Kopin I. J. (2007). *Evolution of the concept of stress.* Stress, 10(2), 109–120.

Guo, Q. F. (1956). *A concordance to Chuang Tzu. Cambridge, MA: Harvard University Press.*

Hanson, R., & Mendius, R. (2009). *Buddha's brain: The practical neuroscience of happiness, love and wisdom. Oakland, CA: New Harbinger.*

Herculano-Houzel, S. (2009). *The human brain in numbers: A linear scaled up primate brain.* Frontiers in Human Neuroscience, 3, 1–11. Retrieved from http://journal.frontiersin.org/article/10.3389/neuro.09.031.2009/full

Herculano-Houzel, S. (2016). *The human advantage: A new understanding of how our brain became remarkable. London, UK: MIT Press.*

Jabar, F. (2012). *Know your neurons: What is the ratio of glia to neurons in the brain?* Scientific American. Retrieved from https://blogs.scientificamerican.com/brainwaves/know-your-neurons-what-is-the-ratio-of-glia-to-neurons-in-the-brain/

Jauregui-Huerta, F., Ruvalcaba-Delgadillo, Y., Gonzalez-Castañeda, R., Garcia-Estrada, J., Gonzalez-Perez, O., & Luquin, S. (2010). *Responses of glial cells to stress and glucocorticoids.* Current Immunology Reviews, 6(3), 1–15. Retrieved from http://europepmc.org/articles/PMC2924577

Joja, D. O. (2013). *Learning experience and neuroplasticity: A shifting paradigm.* NOEMA, XII 159–170.

Juster, R. P., McEwen, B. S, & Lupien, S. J. (2010). *Allostatic load biomarkers of chronic stress and impact on health and cognition.* Neuroscience and Biobehavioral Reviews, 35, 2–16.

Kabat-Zinn, J. (2005). *Full catastrophe living: Using the wisdom of your body and mind to face stress, pain, and illness. New York, NY: Random House.*

Karatsoreos, I. N., & McEwen, B. S. (2011). *Psychobiological allostasis: Resistance, resilience and vulnerability.* Trends in Cognitive Neuroscience, 15(12), 576–584.

Kays, J. L., Hurley, R. A., & Taber, K. H. (2012). *The dynamic brain: Neuroplasticity and mental health.* Journal of Neuropsychiatry and Clinical Neuroscience, 24, *118–124. Retrieved from http://neuro.psychiatryonline.org/ doi/full/10.1176/appi.neuropsych.12050109*

Koenig, J. I., Walker, C. D., Romeo, R. D., & Lupien, S. J. (2011). *Effects of stress across the lifespan.* Stress, 14(5), *475–480.*

Koziol, L. F., Budding, D., Andreasen, N., D'Arrigo, S., Bulgheroni, S., Imamizu, H., ... & Yamazaki, T. (2013). *Consensus paper: The cerebellum's role in movement and cognition. Cerebellum. Retrieved from http://www.leonardkoziol. com/publications/Cerebellum_consensus_paper_2013.pdf*

Ledoux, J. (2002). Synaptic self: How our brains become who we are. *New York, NY: Viking.*

Ledoux, J. (2015). Anxious: Using the brain to understand and treat fear and anxiety. *New York, NY: Viking.*

Logan, J. G., & Barksdale D. J. (2008). *Allostasis and allostatic load: Expanding the discourse on stress and cardiovascular disease.* Journal of Clinical Nursing, 17(7B), *201–208.*

Lu, S. (2104). *How chronic stress is harming our DNA: Elissa Epel is studying how personality, stress processes and environment affect our DNA—and how we might lessen damaging effects.* Monitor on Psychology, 45(9). *Retrieved from http://www.apa.org/monitor/2014/10/chronic-stress.aspx*

Lupien, S. J., McEwen, B. S., Gunnar, M. R., & Heim, C. (2009). *Effects of stress throughout the lifespan on the brain, behavior, and cognition.* Nature Reviews Neuroscience, 10(6), *434–445.*

Marin, M. F., Lord, C., Andrews, J., Juster, R. P., Sindi, S., Arsenault-Lapierre, G., Fiocco, A. J., & Lupien, S. J. (2011). *Chronic stress, cognitive functioning and mental health.* Neurobiology of Learning and Memory, 96(4), *583–595.*

Marmot, M. (2005). The status syndrome: How social standing affects our health and longevity. *New York, NY: Henry Holt and Company.*

McEwen, B. S. (1993). *Stress and the individual. Archives of Internal Medicine, 153(18), 2093–2101.*

McEwen, B. S. (2000). *Allostasis and allostatic load: Implications for neuropsychopharmacology.* Neuro psychopharmacology, 22(2), *108–124.*

McEwen B. S. (2004). *Protection and damage from acute and chronic stress: Allostasis and allostatic overload and relevance to the pathophysiology of psychiatric disorders.* Annals of New York Academy of Sciences, 1032, *1–7.*

McEwen, B. S. (2011). *Effects of stress on the developing brain. Cerebrum. Retrieved from http://www.dana.org/ Cerebrum/Default.aspx?id=39467*

McEwen, B. S. (2012). *The brain on stress: How behavior and the social environment "get under the skin."* Proceedings of the National Academy of Sciences, 109(43), *17180–17185.*

McEwen, B. S. (2015). *Recognizing resilience: Learning from the effects of stress on the brain.* Neurobiology of Stress, 1, *1–11.*

McEwen, B. S., & Gianaros, P. J. (2011). *Stress-and allostasis-induced brain plasticity.* Annual Review of Medicine, 62, *431–445.*

McEwen, B. S., & Lasley, E. N. (2002). The end of stress as we know it. *Washington, DC: Joseph Henry Press.*

McEwen, B. S. & Morrison, J. H. (2013). *Brain on stress: Vulnerability and plasticity of the prefrontal cortex over the life course.* Neuron, 79(1), *16–29.*

McEwen, B. S., Nasveld, P., Palmer, M., & Anderson, R. (2012). *Allostatic load: A review of the literature. Retrieved from http://www.dva.gov.au/sites/default/files/files/consultation%20and%20grants/healthstudies/allostatic/ allostatic.pdf*

McGrady, A. (2007). *Psychophysiological mechanisms of stress. In P. M. Lehrer, R. L. Wolfolk, & W. E. Sime (Eds.)* Principles and practices of stress management (3rd ed.) (pp. 16–37). *New York, NY: Guilford.*

Mitchell, C., Hobcraftb, J., McLanahanc, S. S., Rutherford, S., Siegeld, A. B., Brooks-Gunne, J., Garfinkelf, I., & Nottermand, D. (2014). *Social disadvantage, genetic sensitivity, and children's telomere length.* Proceedings of the National Academy of Sciences, 111(16), *5944–5949. Retrieved from http://www.pnas.org/content/111/16/5944.full*

Norris, J. (2011). *Aging, chronic disease and telomeres are linked in recent studies. University of California, San Francisco. Retrieved from https://www.ucsf.edu/news/2011/02/9353/aging-telomeres-linked-chronic-disease-and-health*

Ong, L. K., Zhao, Z., Kluge, M., TeBay, C., Zalewska, K., Dickson, P. W., ... & Walker, F. R. (2016). *Reconsidering the role of glial cells in chronic stress-induced dopaminergic neurons loss within the substantia nigra? Friend or foe?* Brain,

Behavior, and Immunity. *Retrieved from https://www.researchgate.net/publication/308957981_Reconsidering_the_role_of_glial_cells_in_chronic_stress-induced_dopaminergic_neurons_loss_within_the_substantia_nigra_Friend_or_foe*

Pearson-Leary, J., Osborne, D. M., & McNay, E. C. (2016). *Role of glia in stress-induced enhancement and impairment of memory.* Frontiers in Integrative Neuroscience, 9, *1–14. Retrieved from http://journal.frontiersin.org/article/10.3389/fnint.2015.00063/full*

Pessoa, L., & Adolphs, R. (2010). *Emotion processing and the amygdala: From a "low road" to "many roads" of evaluating biological significance.* Nature Reviews Neuroscience, 11(11), *773–783.*

Puga, D. A., Tovar, C. A., Guan, Z., Gensel, J. C., Lyman, M. S., McTigue, D. M., & Popovich, P. G. (2015). *Stress exacerbates neuron loss and microglia proliferation in a rat model of excitotoxic lower motor neuron injury.* Brain, Behavior, and Immunity, 49, *246–254.*

Ratey, J. (2008). *Spark:* The revolutionary new science of exercise and the brain. *New York, NY: Little, Brown and Company.*

Santee, R. (2005, October 11–15). *Cultivating emptiness: The practice of Xinzhai, an ancient Daoist solution for the problem of chronic stress. Paper presented at the International Conference of Daoist Cultivation and its Modern Value, Sichuan University, Chengdu. China.*

Santee, R. (2007). An Integrative Approach to Counseling: Bridging Chinese Thought, Evolutionary Theory, and Stress Management. *Copyright © 2007 by SAGE Publications. Reprinted with permission.*

Sapolsky, R. M. (2004). Why zebras don't get ulcers: An updated guide to stress, stress-related diseases, and coping. *New York, NY: W. H. Freeman.*

Sapolsky, R. (2010). Stress and your body. *Chantilly, VA: The Great Courses.*

Schmahmann, J. D., & Caplan, D. (2006). *Cognition, emotion and the cerebellum.* Brain, 129(2), *288–292.*

Schulkin, J. (2010). *Social allostasis: Anticipatory regulation of the internal milieu.* Frontiers of Evolutionary Neuroscience, 2. *Retrieved from https://www.ncbi.nlm.nih.gov/pmc/articles/PMC3037529/*

Seligman, M. (2006). Learned optimism: How to change your mind and your life. *New York, NY: Random House.*

Selye, H. (1978). The stress of life. *New York, NY: McGraw-Hill.*

Stefano, G. B., Fricchione, G. L., Slingsby, B. T., & Benson, H. (2001). *The placebo effect and relaxation response: Neural processes and their coupling to constitutive nitric oxide.* Brain Research Reviews, 35(1), *1–19.*

Sterling, P. (2004). *Principles of allostasis: Optimal design, predictive regulation, psychopathology and rational therapeutics. In J. Schulkin (Ed), Allostasis, homeostasis and the costs of physiological adaptation, (pp. 17–64). Cambridge, UK: Cambridge University Press.*

Sterling, P., & Eyer, J. (1988). *Allostasis: A new paradigm to explain arousal pathology. In S. Fisher & J. Reason (Eds.)* Handbook of life stress, cognition, and health (pp. 629–649). Hoboken, NJ: Wiley.

Stuart, E. M., Webster, A., & Wells-Federman, C. L. (1993). *Managing stress. In H. Benson & E. Stuart (Eds.), The* wellness book: The comprehensive guide to maintaining health and treating stress-related illness (pp. 177–188). New York, NY: Simon & Schuster.

Taylor, S. E., Klien, L. C., Lewis, B. P., Gruenwald, T., Gurung, R. A. R., & Updegraff, J. A. (2000). *Biobehavioral responses to stress in females: Tend-and-befriend, not fight-or-flight.* Psychological Review, 107(3), *411–429.*

Tripitaka. (n.d.). Sutra of distinguishing the Four Noble Truths. Retrieved from *http://tripitaka.cbeta.org/mobile/index.php?index=N12n0005_015*

U.S. Department of Health and Human Services. (2014). *Results from the 2013 National Survey on Drug Use and Health: Summary of national findings. Retrieved from https://www.samhsa.gov/data/sites/default/files/NSDUHresultsPDFWHTML2013/Web/NSDUHresults2013.pdf*

Verhoeven, J. E., Revesz, D., van Oppen, P., Epel, E. S., Wolkowitz, O. M., & Penninx, B. W. J. H. (2015). *Anxiety disorders and accelerated cellular ageing.* British Journal of Psychiatry, 206(5), *371–378.*

Author name, X. (2011). *The Yijinjing. Journal of Traditional Eastern Health and Fitness, 21(2), 34–43).*

American Psychological Association (2016). Stress in america: the impact of discrimination. Stress in America Survey. Retrieved July 10, 2016 from http://www.apa.org/news/press/releases/stress/index.aspx

CREDITS

CHAPTER 3

Daoism, Confucianism, Buddhism, and Stress Management

After finishing this chapter, you will be able to do the following:

- Understand how Buddhism, Daoism, and Confucianism can be understood within the context of evolutionary theory (adaptive problem, adaptive solution, changing environment) and stress management
- Compare Buddhist, Daoist, and Confucian approaches to managing stress
- Describe how the culturally diverse approaches of Buddhism, Daoism, and Confucianism can be integrated into a holistic approach to managing stress
- List and describe the three fundamental components of the Daoist path to managing stress
- Describe the interpersonal/moral approach of Confucianism to managing stress
- Explain Buddha's concepts of interdependence, non-substantiality, and impermanence
- List and describe Buddha's four noble truths
- Compare the Daoist concepts of *wuwei* and *wushi*
- Explain the Confucian concept of *ren*

Although Buddhism, Daoism, and Confucianism are traditionally seen in the context of religion and/or philosophy, if they are put into the context of evolutionary theory, ever-changing environment, adaptive problems, adaptive solutions, and stress management, it can be easily seen that their teachings are essentially *adaptive solutions—stress management, in other words—for the adaptive problem of chronic stress*. Their teachings are fundamentally concerned with how to live life in the least stressful manner possible.

This being the case, in this chapter students will be introduced to the contexts that gave rise to these three teachings. Students will explore the fundamental concepts and practices of these teachings within the context of evolutionary theory, chronic stress, and stress management.

Because it is not a Western approach, the information regarding Buddhism, Daoism, and Confucianism in this chapter might be quite new; look at this new approach as a challenge that will allow you to expand your perspective on living life. Because this text integrates culturally diverse approaches to managing stress, fundamental Pali, Sanskrit, and Chinese terms are included to further introduce you to their respective contexts. They are, of course, all translated so that you can integrate them into a holistic, culturally diverse approach to managing stress.

It must be pointed out that while this chapter provides the foundation and context, the specific application and integration of the various techniques and practices will be woven through the subsequent chapters of this text along with Western approaches to managing chronic stress and the findings from neuroscience.

BUDDHISM

The ultimate reality for Hinduism is called Brahman. Brahman is absolute, unchanging, and the creator of everything. **Brahman** is the universal soul. In all living things, there is a drop or spark of Brahman called **Atman**. Atman is the absolute, unchanging, individual soul. The goal of Hinduism is to reunite the individual's Atman with Brahman—a return to an absolute, unchanging oneness.

Hinduism was the dominant religion/way of life in India during the lifetime of Siddhartha of the Shakya clan, who was later known as the Buddha (6th–5th century BCE). According to tradition, there are some variations in his story, Siddhartha was born into the lap of luxury. He lived in a palace. All his material and sensual needs were more than met. He was a member of the warrior class. His father was a king. He was married and had a son. Nonetheless, he was not satisfied.

As the story goes, one day Siddhartha left the palace and saw sickness, old age, and death. In other words, he saw the physical and psychological pain and suffering due to the ravages of ongoing stress. For whatever reason, he decided he was going to put an end to all of it. He thus gave up all of his wealth, luxury, social status, power, control, destiny to become king, and his family, including his wife and child, and left the palace. He became an ascetic; apparently, he saw someone who appeared at peace, denying everything to himself but the bare minimum to survive. He wandered for 6 years saying he would not stop until he resolved the problem of, essentially, the human condition of *dukkha* (*ku*苦). That is, "life is extremely stressful!"

As the story continues, one day he became tired and decided he was going to sit under a tree and not move until he found a solution to the human condition. At the time of the morning star (Venus), just before sunrise, his awakening experience occurred. He had solved the problem. As a result of his experience he came to be known as the Buddha or the one who has awakened.

Buddha experienced existence as impermanent, interdependent, and non-substantial, clearly in contradiction to the teachings regarding Brahman and Atman in Hinduism. His experience was not due to faith, reason, or logic. It was not due to scriptures. It was due to his direct, nonjudgmental awareness of the present via mindfulness. He clearly saw the adaptive problem of the human condition, the cause, the release, and the adaptive solution. It was not the extreme of self-denial/asceticism or the extreme of self-indulgence/hedonism. Instead he presented the middle way of his **four noble truths**. It is the middle way of **moderation**.

It must be noted that Buddha did not write anything. His teachings were passed down orally, both in Pali and Sanskrit, by his disciples, in turn to their disciples, and so on until finally at the Fourth Council of the Pali tradition (late 1st century BCE) the Pali Canon was written down and at the Fourth Council of the Sanskrit tradition (1st century CE), the Sanskrit Canon, was written down (Access to Insight, 2005; Buddhist Society, 2017; Pali, 2017). The Pali Canon is associated with the Theravada (Doctrine of the Elders) tradition of Buddhism while the Sanskrit Canon is associated with the more well-known Mahayana (Greater Vehicle) tradition. So, for over 400 years, since the death of Buddha, his teachings survived in an oral tradition that was contingent on a monk's ability to memorize.

The Theravada and the Mahayana schools of Buddhism differ in a number of areas. The role model for the Theravada school is the *arhat/arhant*, who is essentially focused on one's own individual enlightenment/release from dukkha. The *bodhisattva*, the role model for the Mahayana school, puts off one's own individual enlightenment/release from *dukkha* until everyone else is enlightened/released from *dukkha*. Not everyone can be enlightened/released from *dukkha* in the Theravada tradition. Everyone can be enlightened/released from *dukkha* in the Mahayana school. For the Theravada school

Dukkha
Chronic stress

enlightenment/release from *dukkha* requires consistent effort, discipline, practice, and hard work. For the Mahayana school, there are exceptions such as Chan/Zen, and salvation can be obtained by faith and chanting.

Sometime during the turn of the millennium, most likely late 1st century BCE or early 1st century CE, Buddhism entered China. Buddhism's assimilation into Chinese culture is considered one of the major cross-cultural events in the history

of the world. It took approximately 500 years before Buddhism was fully assimilated into Chinese culture. The Buddhist texts that were translated into Chinese were primarily from the Sanskrit and represented the Mahayana tradition. The four-major distinct Chinese Buddhist schools that developed in China were Tiantai (天台), Huayan (華嚴), Jingtu (淨土) or Pure Land, and Chan (禪), which is known as Zen in Japan.

The translation of the Sanskrit Buddhist texts into Chinese took well over 1,000 years. The texts from the Chinese Buddhist schools were combined with the Sanskrit translations and the Chinese Canon of Buddhism was created. The Chinese Canon in turn was translated into Korean and Japanese (Buddhist Society, 2017). All three canons or Tripitaka, Pali, Sanskrit, and Chinese, consist of three sections: the sutras, the monastic rule (*Vinaya*), and the philosophical/psychological analyses (*Abhidharma*).

Four Noble Truths

For Buddha, the adaptive problem is that of chronic stress (*dukkha*). *His treatment plan, if you will, to being released from chronic stress is his adaptive solution.* Utilizing what appears to be a medical/counseling format, Buddha links them together with the cause of the adaptive problem and the goal of the adaptive solution. This results in the four noble truths. In the *Larger Sutra of the Simile of the Elephant's Footprint*, Sariputra offers a simile regarding what is contained in the four noble truths:

> Fellow students! Just as all the varieties of footprints of living things which walk in the jungle can be contained within the footprint of an elephant, the elephant's footprint is said to be, amongst them all, the foremost. Namely, it is the most encompassing. In a similar sense, Monks, all the skillful truths and teachings, everything is

absorbed within the Four Noble Truths (*si sheng di* 四聖諦). Within what Four? Within the Noble Truth of Stressfulness (*dukkha*). Within the Noble Truth of the Origination of Stressfulness. Within the Noble Truth of Extinguishing of/Being Released from (*Nirvana, mie* 滅)) Stressfulness. Within the Noble Truth of the Path Leading to the Extinguishing of/Being Released from Stressfulness. (Agama, 2018)

In the *Sutra of Turning of the Dharma Wheel* (*zhuan falun jing* 轉法輪經) Buddha expands on the meaning of each of the four noble truths. It becomes quite clear that he is referring to chronic stress and that he has a specific, holistic, and integrative treatment/intervention to eliminate it. He states,

Monks! This is the Noble Truth of Stressfulness (ku苦). Birth is stressful. Aging is stressful. Sickness is stressful. Dying is stressful. Being associated with what/who you do not like is stressful. Being apart from what/who you like is stressful. Not attaining that which you seek/desire is stressful. Essentially, the human condition (the five components of the person) is stressful.

Monks! This is the Noble Truth of the Origin of Stressfulness. This is the bringing about of future becoming, following pleasure and greed, everywhere thirsting after and craving pleasure: thirsting after and craving sense pleasures, existence, and oblivion.

Monks! This is the Noble Truth of the extinguishing of/release from (nirvana) stressfulness. It is the complete, total, extinguishing, giving up, abandoning, releasing oneself, and being without craving and thirsting after anything.

Monks! This is the Noble Truth of the Path Leading to the Extinguishing of/Release from Stressfulness. This is the **Eightfold Noble Path:** Correct Seeing, Correct Thinking, Correct Speech, Correct Action, Correct Livelihood, Correct Effort, Correct Mindfulness, and Correct Concentration. (Agama, 2017)

> **Four noble truths**
> 1. **Adaptive problem**
> 2. **Cause**
> 3. **Goal**
> 4. **Adaptive solution**

Fundamental Teachings of Early Buddhism

While there is controversy (after all it was 400 years or so before Buddha's teachings were actually written down) regarding what exactly constitutes early Buddhism, there appears to be agreement on the fundamental teachings regarding the extreme stressfulness of life (Sanskrit *duhkha* or Pali *dukkha*, of Buddha). These fundamental teachings are **conditioned arising/interdependence** (Sanskkrit *pratītyasamutpāda* or Pali *paṭiccasamuppāda*), **ignorance** (Sanskrit *Avidyā* or Pali: *avijjā*), **thirst/craving** (Pali *taṇhā* or Sanskrit *tṛṣṇā/trishna*), **impermanence** (Sanskrit *anitya* or Pali *anicca*), **non-substantiality/non-self** (Sanskrit **anātman** or Pali **anattā**), **five aggregates/components of an individual** (Sanskrit *Skandhas* or Pali *khandhas*), **mental dispositions/beliefs/biases/thinking** (Sanskrit *Samskara* or Pali *sankhara*), and the four noble truths.

The Nature of Existence: Everything Is Interdependent

For Buddha, based on his direct, nonjudgmental observational experience of existence, everything is interdependent. There is no separation or independent state of existence. We are dependent on the sun for our existence. We and other living beings are dependent on the plants and trees to produce the oxygen we breathe. Plants and trees are dependent on the carbon dioxide we and other living beings exhale to make oxygen. We have a symbiotic relationship with the various friendly bacteria that live in our bodies. We are simply part of an ongoing interdependent process in all aspects of our lives. There is no separation.

Ignorance

The problem, according to Buddha, is that we are ignorant of the fact that everything is interdependent This ignorance leads to the false belief that existence consists of separate, independent components that we can possess. This being the case, we crave after, thirst after, and cling to what we believe to be permanent, independent, and substantial. Since this is not the case, we suffer from chronic stress (*dukkha*).

Conditioned Arising/Interdependence

In the *Large Sutra on the Complete Destruction of Craving* (*ke'ai de mie jin da jing* 渴愛的滅盡大經), the issue of the nature of consciousness is misinterpreted by a disciple named Sati/Shadi (沙低). His fellow monks tell him, to no avail, that he is incorrect regarding his interpretation of what Buddha said about consciousness. They repeat what Buddha said, but Sati is not convinced. Finally, the monks seek out the Buddha. Buddha explains to Sati that consciousness, like everything else, is conditioned and does not have separate existence. During the process of the interaction between Buddha, Sati, and the other monks regarding the issue of consciousness, Buddha describes conditioned arising/ interdependence (*yuanqi* 緣起) and links his fundamental teachings together.

Monks! Good! Monks! It is in this way. You all speak in this way. I also speak in this way. Should this exist, then that will exist. If this arises, then that will arise.

That is, conditioned (*yuan*緣) by ignorance (*wuming* 無明) there are mental dispositions, beliefs, and world views (*xing*行, *samskara*). Conditioned by mental dispositions, beliefs, and world views there is consciousness (*shi*識). Conditioned by consciousness there is mental and physical phenomena (*mingse*名色, *nāmarūpa*). Conditioned by mental and physical phenomena there are the six senses/dwellings (*liuchu*六處). Conditioned by the six senses/dwellings there is contact/sensations (*chu*觸). Conditioned by contact/sensations there is feeling/perception/reception (*shou*受 *vedana* (pleasant, neutral, and unpleasant). Conditioned by feeling/perception/reception there is craving/thirst (*ke'ai*渴愛, *taṇhā*). Conditioned by craving/thirst there is possessing/clinging (*qu*取). Conditioned by possessing/clinging there is becoming. Conditioned by becoming there is birth. Conditioned by birth, aging, dying, worry/grief (*chou*愁), depression (*bei*悲), suffering (*ku*苦), obsession/anxiety/depression (*you* 憂), and hopelessness/despair (*juewang*絕望) all rise up. In such a way is the entirety of stressfulness (*ku*苦). (Agama, 2019).

Once Buddha, the World Honored One, has laid out the interdependent causal process leading to chronic stress, he then shows that by eliminating ignorance the individual's false beliefs, biases, problematic thinking, faulty dispositions, and incorrect world view/perspective, the individual will see and experience existence/reality as impermanent, interdependent, and non-substantial. This being the case, craving/thirst/clinging will be eliminated, leading to the extinguishing of chronic stress. The selection from the *Large Sutra on the Complete Destruction of Craving* continues.

But, if ignorance is completely and totally extinguished, then the conditioning of the mental dispositions, beliefs, and world views will be extinguished. If the conditioning of mental dispositions, beliefs, and world views are extinguished, then the conditioning of consciousness will be extinguished. If the conditioning of consciousness is extinguished, then the conditioning of mental and physical phenomena will be extinguished. If the conditioning of mental and physical phenomena is extinguished, then the conditioning of the six senses/dwellings will be extinguished. If the conditioning of the six senses/dwellings is extinguished, then the conditioning of contact/sensations will be extinguished. If the conditioning of contact/sensations is extinguished, then conditioning of feeling/perception/reception will be extinguished. If the conditioning of feeling/perception/reception is extinguished, then craving/thirst will be extinguished. If craving/thirst is extinguished, then possessing/clinging will be extinguished. If possessing/clinging is extinguished, then the conditioning of becoming will be extinguished. If the conditioning of becoming is extinguished, then the conditioning of birth is extinguished. If the conditioning of birth is extinguished, then aging, dying worry/grief, depression, suffering, obsession/anxiety/depression, and hopelessness/despair will be extinguished. In such a way, the accumulation of all stressfulness (ku苦) will be extinguished.

Monks! Good! Monks! In such a way, you all say this and I also say this: Should this not exist, then that would not come to exist. If this is extinguished, then that is extinguished. If ignorance is extinguished, then ... the accumulation of all stressfulness (ku苦) will be extinguished. (Santee, 2007, Agama, 2019)

**Interdependence
Impermanence
Non-substantiality**

The essential point of this sutra is that everything is conditioned and interdependent. Ignorance of the nature of existence/reality is linked to craving/thirst, which in turn is linked to *dukkha*. In other words, if you view and act as if existence/reality consists of independent, permanent, and substantial components you will crave/thirst after them and as such you will always be stressed (*dukkha*). In order to be released from *dukkha* (stressfulness) you must remove your ignorance and craving. To do so, you must change how you perceive, think about, believe, and interact in the world such that reality/existence is seen and experienced as impermanent, interdependent, and non-substantial. The importance of conditioned arising for Buddha is succinctly summed up in the following quote:

> This is what the World Honored one said: "All who see conditioned arising (緣起) truly see truth/reality (fa 法, dharma). All who see the dharma see conditioned arising. (Agama, 2018)

Dukkha or Chronic Stress

In the *Larger Sutra of the Simile of the Elephant's Footprint* (*xiang bu zuji piyu jing* 象足跡譬喻大經), Sariputra, one of Buddha's two chief disciples and second only to Buddha in regards to the ability to teach, explains to the monks the meaning of first noble truth of *dukka* (stressfulness). He also indicates that essentially the human condition, the five components of the holding on to of the person, is stressful. He states,

> Friends. What is the noble truth of *dukkha* (*ku* 苦) or chronic stress? Birth is stressful, aging is stressful, dying is stressful, worry, grief, depression, suffering, obsession, anxiety, and hopelessness/despair are stressful. Not getting what one seeks/desires is stressful. In general, the human condition, the five components (*skandha*) of the holding on of the person, is stressful. Fellow students! What are the five components of holding on to of the person? Holding on to form, holding on to contact/sensation, holding on to feelings/perceptions/receptions, holding on to dispositions, beliefs and world views, and holding on to consciousness. (Agama, 2018)

Impermanence and Non-Substantiality

For Buddha, the nature of reality is impermanent. Everything is continually changing. The problem arises when an individual, due to ignorance, believes (a) that which is in fact impermanent, is permanent; (b) that there is an underlying, unchanging, absolute substance to it; and (c) then attempts to identify with it (me) and/or becomes attached to it/possess it (mine). When this occurs, and the individual is not able to prevent it from changing, it is quite stressful (*dukkha*) for the individual. When things do not go the way you expect them to or you anticipate them not to go the way you want them to, the results are stressful. Worrying about the future, obsessing and grieving about the past, and not obtaining what you desire are all stressful. Because of these absolute beliefs, our judgments and our very thinking can result in the activation and maintaining of our stress response. Again, this is because you identify all of it with an absolute, independent sense of yourself (Hanson & Mendius 2009), a belief that also incorporates the notion of an unchanging, underlying substance or stuff, all of which leads to a chronic thirst and craving to obtain and possess.

Moderation

Buddhism and Evolutionary Theory

From the perspective of evolutionary theory, everything is a continual process of change, and that life is about, at the most basic level, generating adaptive solutions for adaptive problems in this everchanging process. Your body, and all the wonderful things it is able to do, is on loan to you via the evolutionary process (Nisker, 2000). Both evolutionary theory and the teachings of Buddha recognize a relative, continually changing self that is necessary for adapting to an ever-changing environment. Unfortunately, at least as far as the Buddha was concerned, we don't see life this way as we tend to view it as consisting of a separate, independent, and permanent I and me—an I and me that is believed to rest on an underlying and unchanging substance (Epstein, 1995). We view everything else, when we so choose, as mine. This absolute, independent, substance-based, subjective, and objective dichotomy is not consistent with the world described by evolutionary theory or Buddha. According to Buddha, because we have these absolute beliefs and demands about how the world, others, and our selves must exist and behave, when they do not, everything is subject to change and thus impermanent and non-substantial, we become chronically stressed as life is not behaving to our satisfaction. This chronic stress interferes with our ability to generate functional adaptive solutions for the multitude of adaptive problems presented to us by our ever-changing, interdependent, and non-substantial environment, and thus is detrimental to our physical and psychological health and wellbeing. For Buddha, existence is marked by three fundamental characteristics: *anicca* or impermanence, *anatta* or non-substantiality, and *dukkha* or chronic stress.

In the *Discourse on Impermanence Sutra* (*shuo wuchang jing* 說無常經), Buddha describes the human condition with these three marks or characteristics of existence.

> Thus, I have heard. There was an occasion when Buddha was traveling in the district of Shravasti, staying at Jeta grove in Anàthapindika's monastery. At that time, the World Honored One told all the monks, "Form is impermanent (wu chang 無常). Impermanence is stressful (ku 苦). It is stressful as it is non-substantial (wu wo 無我). Sensation is impermanent. Impermanence is stressful. It is stressful as it is non-substantial. Perception is impermanent. Impermanence is stressful. It is stressful as it is non-substantial. Mental dispositions, beliefs, and world views are impermanent. Impermanence is stressful. It is stressful as it is non-substantial. Consciousness is impermanent. Impermanence is stressful. It is stressful as it is non-substantial." (Agama, 2019a)

For Buddha, as noted earlier, the person or relative self consists of five components/aggregates or *skandha*. They are form, which is essentially the physical body, sensations, perceptions, mental dispositions, and consciousness. They are all interdependent, impermanent, and without any underlying substance or stuff. When you hold on to them, however and identify with them (I, me, and mine), it results in chronic stress. Buddha is not saying, however, that impermanence and non-substantiality are inherently stressful. It is because we view and hold on to existence as being permanent and substantial. When change does occur that contradicts this viewpoint, we become chronically stressed as it is a threat to our worldview and sense of self.

This holding on to existence as being permanent and absolute, and the consequences that occur as the result of it, is concretely described in the River Sutra (he jing (河經/Nadi suttam). Buddha addresses his disciples and describes a river flowing rapidly down a mountain in to the distance. Growing and hanging over on both sides of the river are reeds, various grasses, and trees. A man who being pulled along by the current reaches out and grasps and hold onto to some of the reeds. The reeds snap and break loose from his grip. As a result, he has misfortune and hardship. As he continues flowing down the river he grasps and holds on to various grasses and to trees. The results are the same in all instances. They all snap and break loose from his grip. Misfortune and hardship ensue. He then uses this example to compare to the fate of masses who have not received his teaching, instructions and guidance, are not skilled in his teachings and have not practiced his teachings. He notes

> "He who thinks form is the self or the self possess form, form is within the self, or the self is within form, his form is torn away. What comes to him is misfortune and hardship. So it is with sensation, perception, dispositions, and consciousness. Monks! What do you think? Is form permanent or impermanent?" "Impermanent, Virtuous One!" "How about sensations, perceptions, dispositions and consciousness, are they permanent or impermanent?" "Impermanent, Virtuous One!" (Agama, 2017a).

Buddha's teachings from well over 2,000 years ago are quite consistent with how the nature of chronic stress is viewed today as being primarily psychological and psychosocial in nature. As you journey through subsequent chapters in this text, his teachings, along with the various methods of intervention/treatment from the eightfold path, will be woven into the overall approach of managing chronic stress. It is important that you note that although you may have heard of Buddhism as a religion and/or a philosophy, first and foremost in its origins and in some of its later developments (Chan/Zen), it is a lifestyle that is contingent on the removal of chronic stress.

Wuwei
Non-interference

Wushi
Non-entanglement

DAOISM/TAOISM

The Daodejing or the Way and Its Internal Power

According to tradition, Daoism is over 2,500 years old. Tradition focuses on the text the *Daodejing* and its purported author Laozi, said to be an older contemporary

of Confucius (551–479 BCE) as the beginning point/foundation of Daoism. The *Daodejing* was written to provide an adaptive solution to the adaptive problem of ongoing political, social, and military strife and instability between the various kingdoms/states during China's Zhou Dynasty (1046–256 BCE).

The *Daodejing* was written for the aristocracy, the primary ones who were literate, and focused on teaching the ruler how to rule and people how to live. The overall goal was establishing social harmony. The text views the contrived, artificial values, norms, beliefs, and behaviors of society and its government as giving rise to an agitated mind, self-centeredness, excessive desires and greed, and problematic interpersonal relationships, thus precluding people from interacting in a natural, harmonious, and humanistic manner. In order to address these concerns and establish social harmony, its focus is on moderation, reducing desires, non-interference (**wuwei 無為**) and non-entanglement in the activities of the world (**wushi 無事**), simplifying life, self-discovery, self-actualization, and stilling and emptying the mind and body of agitation. For all intents and purposes, the *Daodejing* is a manual on reducing chronic stress.

Carl Rogers (1902–1987) one of the founders of the humanistic approach to counseling/psychotherapy and the founder of a specific approach to counseling/psychotherapy known as person/client-centered therapy notes in his article, "My Philosophy of Interpersonal Relationships and How it Grew," an affinity for the Daoist practice of *wuwei*, its notion of an ideal leader, and how it relates to an effective, non-interfering therapist in a group counseling context and its perspective on interpersonal relationships and how it relates to his own perspective (Rogers 1973; Santee 2005b). The teachings of the *Daodejing* are, for the most part, quite consistent with the humanistic approach to psychotherapy and counseling as can be easily seen in the end of chapter 57:

> Thus, the Sage says
> I do not interfere (wuwei, 無為)
> And the people transform themselves.

I appreciate stillness (*jing*, 静)
And the people correct themselves.
I am not entangled in the affairs
of the world (wushi, 無事)
And the people enrich themselves.
I am without controlling desires (*wuyu*, 無欲)
And the people simplify their lives (*pu*, 樸). (Santee, 2005b; Yang, 1972;
Wang, 1993)

The Zhuangzi

The second major figure in Daoism is Zhuangzi (4th–3rd century BCE). Unlike Laozi, who many researchers doubt even existed and who suggested that the *Daodejing* is a compilation of many authors, Zhuangzi did exist and wrote at least part of the text. Agreement is fairly strong for Chapters 1 to 7, known as the *Zhuangzi*. Unlike the *Daodejing,* which is quite poetic in nature, the *Zhuangzi* consists of stories, fables, philosophical analysis, satire, existential inquiry, folk tales, practical guidance, and instruction oriented toward freeing oneself from self-imposed and society-imposed restrictions. Unlike the *Daodejing*, the *Zhuangzi* is not really concerned with establishing social harmony or teaching the ruler how to rule. In fact, it is quite clear, as is the *Daodejing*, that it is the artificial, contrived values, norms, beliefs, and behaviors imposed by the government and society on the individual that results in an agitated mind, self-centeredness, excessive desires, greed, and problematic interpersonal relationships and is the source of the restrictions and shackles that result in what we today call chronic stress. In chapter 2 of the *Zhuangzi*, the author notes,

> When people are asleep their spirits are knotted up. When they are awake, their form is scattered. Interacting in the world creates entanglements. Daily their mind/hearts battle, plodding, concealing, and tentative. Their small fears result in apprehensiveness. Their large fears result in being overwhelmed. In their judging of right and wrong their words shoot out as if an arrow was released from a bow. They hold onto their judgments as if they were sacred oaths. Guarding what they call their victory, they are executed like autumn moving into winter. (Santee, 2004, pp. 10–12; Guo, 1974; translations mine)

It is apparent that whether awake or asleep, people are chronically stressed by the fears and threats generated by and imposed on them by their social interactions. They become entangled with the artificial, contrived values, norms, beliefs, and behaviors of society and the government. Once they become entangled, their very thinking, perspectives, and beliefs alone can generate and maintain their ongoing stress. For the *Zhuangzi*, participation in government essentially kills the spirit and suppresses one's natural freedom. It notes in chapter 17,

> Zhuangzi was fishing at Pu waters. The king of Chu sent an envoy of two senior officials who came before Zhuangzi and said, "We wish for you to come and work for our kingdom. Zhuangzi holding the fishing pole and not turning around said, "I hear the Chu has a spiritual tortoise. It has been dead for over 3,000 years. The king conceals it in a basket and a cloth in the imperial temple. Would this tortoise prefer to be dead having its bones saved and honored or would it prefer to be alive dragging its tail in the mud? The two senior officials replied, "It would prefer to be alive and dragging its tail in the mud." Zhuangzi said, "Go away!" I will drag my tail in the mud." (Santee, 2005a, pp. 81–84)

Like the *Daodejing*, the *Zhuangzi* also focuses on simplifying life, reducing desires, and stilling and emptying the mind and body of agitation. Unlike the *Daodejing*, its focus is not on establishing social harmony. Its focus is on freedom: to live out one's natural lifespan free from self-imposed and **Simplicity and naturalness** society-imposed restrictions, which result in chronic stress. It does this in quite a different format than the *Daodejing* as it weaves together a tapestry that many have found to be the most profound literary text to ever come out of China. Given its reoccurring themes surrounding death, meaning, and freedom, it appears that it shares an affinity with existential counseling/psychotherapy (Santee, 2004).

The Liezi

The third major text in what is known as early/philosophical Daoism is the *Liezi* and is attributed to a man named Lie Yukou or Liezi. Like Laozi, his existence and authorship is questioned. Little is known about him. There are stories about him in the *Zhuangzi*. He is believed to have been a contemporary of Zhuangzi (4th–3rd century BCE). The *Liezi*, like the *Zhuangzi*, primarily consists of stories, fables, and tales. It is, however, much more practical and down to earth in nature than both the *Daodejing* and the *Zhuangzi*. In most cases, it is quite straightforward and an easier read. It is an important piece of Daoist literature, though far less well known than both the *Daodejing* and the *Zhuangzi*.

The focus of the *Liezi* is on how one's absolute, restrictive judgments, beliefs, attitudes, and biases can compromise our emotions and behaving. In this sense it has a strong affinity with modern-day cognitive therapy. The following quote from chapter 8 of the *Liezi* demonstrates this to be the case. It shows how one's absolute beliefs and biases can result in stress and significantly compromise one's emotions and behaviors:

> There was a man from the East who was called Yuan Jingmu. He was traveling and fell starving on the road. A thief from Hufu called Qiu, saw him on the ground and got a bowl of food to feed him. After Yuan Jingmu ate three mouthfuls, he was able to look about. He said, "Who are you?" Qiu said, "I am Qiu from Huli." Yuan Jingmu screamed. "Are you not a thief? Why did you give me food? I am a moral person and I will not eat your food." He grabbed the ground with both hands and opened his mouth. Nothing came out. Coughing and coughing he fell face first onto the ground and died. The man from Huli was indeed a thief. Yet the food was not stolen. Although the man was a thief, to not dare eat the food because it is associated with a thief, is to mistake an abstract label for concrete reality. (Santee, 2005b; Zhang, 1972, p. 97)

Freedom

It might interest the reader to know that these three texts, the *Daodejing,* the *Zhuangzi,* and the *Liezi,* make up, primarily, what came to be known, from a Western perspective, early/philosophical Daoism. This was not, however, an organized structure or entity. This grouping, from a Chinese perspective, became known as the Dao family or **Daojia** (道家) during the 2nd century BCE (Littlejohn, 2016). It has been argued that Daoism as an organized entity first occurred during the 2nd century CE with the creation, by Zhang Daoling, of the *Tianshi* (天師) or Heavenly Masters Sect. Over the next 1,000 years or so, Shangqing (上清), or Highest Clarity (4th century CE), Lingbao (靈寶) or Numinous Treasure (4th century CE), and Quanzhen (全真) or Complete Reality (11th–12th century CE) schools/sects were created. During the 5th century CE the early schools/sects were grouped together and referred to as **daojiao** (道教) or the teachings of Dao (Komjathy 2013). From a Western perspective, this movement/grouping was clearly a religion and became known as later/religious Daoism. While the early Western scholars in Daoism separated out *daojia* and *daojiao* to distinct and, for all intents and purposes, separate entities known as early/philosophical and later/

religious Daoism, modern scholarship does not accept and argues against this separation (Komjathy, 2013).

The *Zuowanglun* or A Discussion on Sitting in Forgetfulness/Oblivion

There are a number of commonalities across both *daojia* and *daojiao*. Utilizing a selection from chapter 6 of the *Zhuangzi* regarding the meditative technique **zuowang** (坐忘) or sitting in oblivion, the sixth patriarch of Shangqing Daoism, Sima Chengzhen (647–735 CE), wrote a text that not only expanded on the *Zhuangzi* reference, explained and taught the technique, and linked together *daojia* and *daojiao* across three fundamental components, but also provided a step-by-step process, an adaptive solution if you will, to the removal of what we today call chronic stress. For Sima, the removal of chronic stress, a healthy body and mind, is a necessary step before returning to the *Dao*. The text is called the *Zuowanglun* (坐忘論) or *A Discussion on Sitting in Oblivion*. The practice of *zuowang* is a core, if not the primary core, meditative practice of Daoism (Kohn, 2010).

Sima recognizes the link between our agitated, threat-based thinking, chronic stress, and illness. He describes this link, respectively, in the *Shouxin* section and the *Shūyì* section or appendix of this text:

> When you obsessively think about something and hold on to it, the mind/heart is strained. This is not only irrational, it causes the individual to become ill (*bing* 病). (Saohua, n.d.)

> If the mind/heart is restrained by excessive distress, the distress will lead to illness (bìng 病). Frenzied, erratic and unstable breath is symptomatic of this. (Santee, 2010a)

Sima delineates the three fundamental components of the path to the removal of chronic stress and the eventual return to the Dao in the *Shūyì* section or appendix of the *Zuowanglun*; while listed as three separate guidelines, they are in fact all part of an interrelated, integrative mind and body, holistic, and reciprocal process.

> If you intend to return to the Dao, a deep and vivified faith (xin 信) must first receive three guidelines. ... The first one is simplifying your circumstances/life. The second one is to be without desires, and the third one is to still and empty the mind/heart. (Santee, 2010a)

A fundamental practice found throughout all aspects of Daoism is that of moderation. In the *Jian Shi* section of the *Zuowanglun*, the author states,

If you strive for that which is excessive, then you bring harm to the body and spirit. … That which is not beneficial for life is excessiveness. (Saohua, n.d.)

This focus on moderation, albeit in the frame of keeping life simple, and its importance in eliminating stressfulness is found, respectively, in chapter 67 of the *DaodeJing* and chapter 29 of the *Zhuangzi*.

Simplify life.
Reduce desires.
Still and empty your mind.

I have three treasures that I maintain and protect. The first is compassion (*ci*慈). The second is simplicity (*jian*儉). The third is not daring to be prior to the world. (Wong, 1993)
Moderation is happiness. Excessiveness is harmful. There is no activity in life where this is not so! (Guo, 1956, pp. 92–93)

The connection between moderation, lifestyle, physical and psychological well-being, health, and the elimination of chronic stress is found in the Daoist-related medical text the *Huangdi Neijing* or the *Yellow Emperor's Discourse on Internal Medicine*. In chapter 1, the Yellow Emperor asks his Minister Qi Bo to explain why the people of ancient times lived so long. Qi Bo replied,

Moderation

People of ancient times understood the pathway (dao 道) and modeled themselves on yin and yang. They were in harmony with the art, skill, and assessment of living life. They practiced moderation in eating and drinking. Throughout their daily life their behavior was consistent. They did not overwork. Thus, their body and spirit were not fragmented. They completed their natural lifespan of 100-plus years before dying. (Chinese Text Project, n.d.)

CONFUCIANISM

Confucius (551–479) offered an adaptive solution to the adaptive problem of ongoing political, social, and military strife and instability between the various kingdoms/states during China's Zhou Dynasty (1046–256 BCE). His goal was social harmony. The primary cause was self-centeredness and self-benefit at the expense of others. Individuals were out for their own gain. Because of this interpersonal conflict, people were chronically stressed as they competed for their own individual needs, benefits, and desires while behaving inappropriately with others. The solution of appropriate, respectful, interpersonal behavior with the harmony of society as a whole, not the individual, as the focus

Authenticity
Empathy
Respect
Trust

is found in the *Lunyu* (論語) or *Analects* of Confucius. Like the *Daodejing*, the *Analects* was written for the aristocracy in order to teach the ruler how to rule and people how to live. Confucius, however, did not write the *Analects*. The *Analects* was compiled by his disciples and their disciples.

The Confucian Path

The Confucian path to the removal of chronic stress focuses on teaching and learning morally appropriate, contextual interpersonal behavior. The foundation of the teachings of Confucius regarding interpersonal relationships is based in the family. It is in the family where people learn about filial piety/respect (*xiao* 孝), trust (*xin* 信), appropriate contextual behavior (*li* 禮), choosing appropriate contextual behavior (*yi* 義), the wisdom to choose the appropriate contextual behavior (*zhi* 知), authenticity/coming from the center of one's heart (*zhong* 忠), empathy (*shu* 恕), and interpersonal selfless relationships (*ren* 仁).

The Morally Integrated Person or *Junzi*

For Confucius, there was a clear distinction between his role model, the morally integrated person or **junzi** (君子), and the morally fragmented person, the **xiaoren** (小人). The *junzi* were free from chronic stress while the *xiaoren*, essentially everybody else, were chronically stressed. In Books 12 and 13, respectively, of the *Analects* this distinction is quite apparent:

> The Master said, "The *junzi* is composed and at peace. The *xiaoren* is chronically agitated and distressed." (Santee, 2007, p. 205; Chinese Classic, n.d.)
> The Master said, "The *junzi* is calm and not arrogant. The *xiaoren* is arrogant and not calm." (Santee, 2007, p. 205; Chinese Classic, n.d.)

Confucianism, like Buddhism and Daoism, link chronic stress to illness. In Book 12, the *Analects* looks at the relationship between chronic stress and illness. In this case the *junzi* is viewed as being free from both chronic stress and illness.

Interpersonal
selfless

Si Maniu (a disciple of Confucius) asked about the *junzi*. The Master replied, "The *junzi* is not chronically stressed (*bu you* 不憂) nor fearful (*buju* 不懼). Si Maniu said, "If a person is not chronically stressed and not fearful, it then can be said the person is a *junzi*? The Master said, "Finding neither fault nor illness within himself, why should he be chronically stressed or fearful?" (Santee, 2007, p. 50; Chinese Classic, n.d.)

Ren: Interpersonal, Selfless Relationships

In order to address the issue of self-centeredness, self-benefit, self-gain, and the chronic stress associated with those attitudes, Confucius focuses on appropriate interpersonal relationships and his highest virtue, *ren*, and all that it entails. It is important to note that for Confucius, *ren* is not something that is found in the individual. It is only manifest in contextually appropriate, interpersonal relationships. In Book 12 of the *Analects*, a discussion between his favorite disciple, Yan Yuan, and Confucius is presented regarding *ren*:

> Yan Yuan/Yan Hui (a disciple of Confucius) asked about interpersonal selfless relationships (*ren* 仁). The Master said, "Overcoming your self-centeredness and returning to appropriate, contextual moral behavior (*li* 禮) is *ren*. If for one day people overcame their self-centeredness and returned to *li,* then the whole world would come together in *ren*. This is because *ren* is due to the relationship between yourself and other people." Yan Yuan said, "May I ask about what this entails?" The Master said, "If it is not appropriate contextual behavior (*li*) do not look. If it is not *li*, do not listen. If it is not *li,* do not speak. Do not do anything contrary to *li.*" Yan Yuan said, "Although I am not very smart, I will engage in what you have said." (Santee, 2007, p. 197; Chinese Classic, n.d.)

Moderation

Fundamental to the practice of *ren*, which only occurs in interpersonal selfless relationships, and eliminating chronic stress is the practice of moderation: staying within the bounds of appropriate contextual behavior and not being excessive or deficient. In Book 2 and Book 6, respectively, of the *Analects* the importance of incorporating, holistically, moderation into one's lifestyle is presented:

> Confucius said, "The 300 Odes in the *Shijing* (*Book of Songs*), can be summed up in single phrase. He said, "Your thinking and behavior remain healthy by not going astray. (Santee, 2007, p. 191; Chinese Classic, n.d.)
>
> Confucius said, "Practicing moderation (*zhongyong* 中庸) is supreme moral excellence (*de* 德). It has been rarely seen amongst the people for a long time." (Santee, 2007, p. 207; Chinese Classic, n.d.)

PRACTICAL APPLICATION

Meditation: Mindfulness

Jon Kabat-Zinn (2003) defines mindfulness, operationally, as "The awareness that arises, by paying attention, on purpose, in the present moment, and nonjudgmentally" (p. 145). This practice is one of the components of the Eight-Fold Path of Buddha. For Buddha, mindfulness is the path to awareness of conditioned arising,

and thus seeing existence as it really is: interdependent, impermanent, and non-substantial (Santee 2007). Mindfulness is the solution to mind wandering in the past or the future (Mrazek, Franklin, Phillips, Baird, & Schooler, 2013). It pulls you out of your default network. It suspends your negativity bias. Being nonjudgmental, not distracted, and simply aware of the task you are engaged in, in the present, your chronic stress will dissipate for that moment. The problem, of course, is that once you return to judging and negativity, which is inevitable, your chronic stress will return. It takes considerable practice to change old habits and current brain wiring. Practice is the secret. As you continue to practice on a regular basis, your brain will begin rewiring such that the new neural network will be more readily accessible than the old problematic one that initiated and maintained your chronic stress, thus, the importance of a holistic approach to stress management as there are many behaviors, neural networks, that activate and maintain your chronic stress.

Essentially mindfulness is being in the present with your focus on what you are doing without any distractions or judgments. For example, when you are eating you are just eating. You are not watching TV, playing or texting on your phone, reading a book, engaged in a conversation, listening to music, and so on. You are simply focused on/aware of all aspects of eating. All of your senses are involved. You are not making any judgments about the process. You are simply paying attention to all aspects of eating. Mindfulness can be practiced in just about any situation such as following your breath, taking a shower, washing the dishes, taking a walk and observing your surroundings, playing with your children, playing with your pet, listening to music, and so on.

Pick a task and spend 5 minutes practicing mindfulness with it. If you get distracted while engaged with the task and find your mind wandering, which is normal, simply refocus on the task and continue. Remember no judging or editorializing!

Upon completion of the task, reflect on what happened. How do you feel? What did you notice? Did your mind wander? Where did it go? Did you find yourself making judgments? Where you able to refocus back on the task and continue on? Do you notice a difference between before starting the exercise and after you completed it? If so, what is it?

Zhanzhuang: Position Three

As this is the third position in the practice of *Zhan Zhuang*, a short sequence of all three positions (see chapters 1 and 2) can performed. Hold each position for 1 minute; you can of course hold it longer. Breathing naturally through your nose, simply observe, without making any judgments, what you feel in your body. The Daoists refer to this as *guan* (觀) or nonjudgmental awareness, without any distractions, of the present (Cheng, 2003). If your mind wanders, as it usually does, don't make any judgments; just refocus on your breath for a moment to reenter awareness and then observe what you are feeling in your body. Your eyes can be either closed or open. If you mind wanders simply return your focus to holding the beach ball.

1. Start with the *wuji* position and just stand.

2. After 1 minute, simply let your arms arc slightly forward, staying thigh-width apart, until the palms of your hands are facing each other at waist level, which is about 3 or so inches below your bellybutton. Visualize you

are holding a large beach ball with your hands, arms, and lower abdomen/pelvic area gently holding it in place.

3. After 1 minute, you can now move into the third position. Simply raise your arms up until they are at shoulder level. Once the arms are shoulder high, curve the fingers in toward each other until the tips of the finger are touching. You are still holding the beach ball. There should be a distinct sense of an inward twisting of both the arms and hands toward the center of the circle/ball as if the beach ball is actually being held. Hold for 1 minute.

Upon completion of the third position, let your hands arc down to your sides and return to the *wuji* position. Hold this position for 1 minute. After 1 minute take a deep breath and simply do a short walk.

Upon completion, how do you feel? What did you notice? Was there a difference between doing the positions/postures individually as opposed to doing them in a sequence? Did your mind wander? If so, were you able to easily refocus? Was one position easier for you? If so, why?

Yoga: Warrior One Pose (*Virabhadrasana*)

Begin by standing in the mountain pose (which was presented in chapter 1). Upon completion of the mountain pose, breathing naturally, inhaling and exhaling through your nose, step straight forward with your left foot such that your left leg is bent in a 45-degree angle and your left knee is directly over your left ankle. *Make sure your knee does not jut out past your toes.* Your rear leg is straight but not locked. Your legs are shoulder-width apart. Your back is straight. Your shoulders and hips are squared and you are facing straight forward. Your eyes are level. Lower your hips slightly while maintaining this alignment. Your feet are flat on the floor. Your left foot is straight forward, while your right foot is turned in at about 45-degree angle. Push both feet into the ground as if you are pushing them apart. It is important to feel grounded and rooted. Your weight is evenly distributed.

Slowly raise and extend both of your arms straight forward, bringing your palms together, continuing upward until your hands are pressed together over the top of your head with your fingers pointing and pushing straight up, extending but not locking your arms. Continue to breathe in a natural manner. Nonjudgmentally observe your body and mind.

This pose requires your body to be going in many directions at once. Your arms are pushing straight up while your feet are pushing down and apart. Your hips are sinking. You should have a sense of your entire body being opened up and stretched out. Hold for 30 seconds. Step up with your rear leg, lower your arms to your sides, and return to the mountain pose. Pause for a moment, take a breath, let it out, and then perform the warrior one pose on the other side, stepping forward with your right leg.

How do you feel upon completion of the warrior one pose? What did you notice while you were in the pose? Was one side easier than the other side? Does your body feel relaxed and stretched out? How does you mind feel? Did you get distracted while performing it? If so, were you able to easily return to your focus on it?

KEY TERMS

Brahman
Atman
dukkha/duhkha
Four Noble Truths
moderation
Arhat/Arhant
Bodhisattva
conditioned arising/
interdependence

ignorance
thirst/craving
impermanence
non-substantiality/
non-self
anātman or *Pali anattā*
five aggregates/compo-
nents of an individual

mental dispositions/
beliefs/biases/thinking
eightfold noble path
wuwei
wushi
Jing
Wuyu

Pu	Zhong	Xiaoren
Daojia	Shu	
Daojiao	Ren	
Zuowang	Li	
Xiao	Junzi	

EXERCISES

1. Why is it important to understand Buddhism, Daoism, and Confucianism within the context of the stress response and stress management?

2. Why are the evolutionary theory concepts of the adaptive problem and the adaptive solution important for understanding *how* Buddhism, Daoism, and Confucianism can be incorporated into a stress-management program?

3. Why is an understanding of culturally diverse approaches to managing stress important for managing your own and others' stress?

4. Compare the adaptive solutions of Buddha, Daoism, and Confucianism for the adaptive problem of chronic stress.

5. Based on your reading, why is moderation a fundamental practice for eliminating chronic stress?

6. Compare *wuwei* and *wushi*.

7. For Buddha, ignorance refers to ignorance of what? How is ignorance connected to craving/thirst?

8. What is *Ren*? Why is this concept so important to Confucius?

REFERENCES

Access to Insight (2005). *What is Theravada Buddhism*? Retrieved from http://www.accesstoinsight.org/theravada.html

Agama. (2017). Kindred sayings. Translated from agama.buddhason.org/SA/SA0379.htm

Agama (2017a). Kindred sayings. Translated from http://agama.buddhason.org/SN/SN0611.htm

Agama. (2018). *The middle length sayings.* Translated from http://agama.buddhason.org/MN/MN028.htm

Agama (2019). Middle length sayings. Translated from agama.buddhason.org/MN/MN038.htm

Agama. (2019a). Translated from http://agama.buddhason.org/MA/MA120.htm

Buddhist Society (2017). *Scriptures and texts.* Retrieved from http://www.thebuddhistsociety.org/page/scriptures-texts

Cheng, C. Y. (2003). Philosophy of change. In A. S. Cua (Ed.), *Encyclopedia of Chinesep Philosophy* (pp. 517–524). New York, NY: Routledge.

Chinese Classic. (n.d). *Analects*. Retrieved from http://www.chineseclassic.com/13jing/LeungYu/LeungYu01.htm

Chinese Text Project. (n.d.). *Yellow Emperor's discourse on internal medicine*. Translated from https://ctext.org/huangdi-neijing/zh

Epstein, M. (1995). *Thoughts without a thinker*. New York, NY: Basic Books.

Guo, Q. F. (1956). *A concordance to Chuang Tzu*. Cambridge, MA: Harvard University Press.

Hanson, R., & Mendius, R. (2009). *Buddha's brain: The practical neuroscience of happiness, love, and wisdom*. Oakland:, CA New Harbinger.

Kabat-Zinn, J. (2003). Mindfulness-based interventions in context: Past, present, and future. *Clinical Psychological Science and Practice, 10*(2), 144–156.

Kabbat-Zinn (2013). Jon Kabbat-Zinn defines mindfulness [Video file]. Retrieved from https://www.bing.com/videos/search?q=Jon+Kabbat-Zinn+definition+of+mindfulness&view=detail&mid=06804A1EA889633DC55406804A1EA889633DC554&FORM=VIRE

Kohn, L. (2010). *Sitting in oblivion: The heart of Daoist meditation*. Dunedin, FL: Three Pines.

Komjathy, L. (2013). *The Daoist tradition: An introduction*. New York, NY: Bloomsbury Academic.

Littlejohn, R. (2016). Daoist philosophy. *Internet Encyclopedia of Philosophy*. Retrieved from http://www.iep.utm.edu/daoism/

Mrazek, M. D., Franklin, M. S., Phillips, D. T., Baird, B., & Schooler, J. W. (2013). Mindfulness training improves working memory capacity and GRE performance while reducing mind wandering. *Psychological Science, 24*(5), 776–781.

Nisker, W. (2000). *Buddha nature: A practical guide to discovering your place in the cosmos*. New York, NY: Bantam Books.

Novella, S. (2012). What is traditional Chinese medicine. *Science-Based Medicine*. Retrieved from https://www.sciencebasedmedicine.org/what-is-traditional-chinese-medicine/

Pali. (2017). *The origin of the Pali canon*. Retrieved from http://www.palicanon.org/

Rogers, C. R. (1973). My philosophy of interpersonal relationships and how it grew. *Journal of Humanistic Psychology, 13*(2), 3–15.

Santee, R. (2003). An inquiry into the Dao of the Dao de Jing. *World Hong Ming Philosophical Quarterly*.

Santee, R. (2004, July 22). *A Daoist and an existential psychotherapist: A comparative study*. Paper presented at the 1st World Hong Ming Philosophy Conference. Honolulu, HI.

Santee, R. (2005a, October 12–15). *Cultivating emptiness: The practice of xin zhai, an ancient Daoist solution to the problem of chronic stress*. Paper presented at the International Conference of Daoist Cultivation and its Modern Value. Chengdu, China.

Santee, R. (2005b, May 20–23). *Carl Rogers and the Dao de Jing: A comparative study*. Paper presented at the International Conference on Daoism Mt. Tiantai And Zhejiang. Zhejiang, China.

Santee, R. (2007). *An Integrative Approach to Counseling: Bridging Chinese Thought, Evolutionary Theory, and Stress Management*. Copyright © 2007 by SAGE Publications. Reprinted with permission.

Santee, R. (2010a, June 2–6). Sitting in forgetfulness and the relaxation response: An inquiry into managing the physical and psychological symptoms of chronic stress. Paper presented at the 6th International Daoist Studies Conference, Daoism Today: Science, Health and Ecology. Los Angeles, CA.

Santee, R. (2010b). The Liezi: The forgotten Daoist text? *The Empty Vessel, 17*, 9–13.

Saohua. (n.d.). *A discussion on sitting in oblivion*. Retrieved from http://www.saohua.com/shuku/zongjiao/daojiao/011.htm

Yang, J. L. (zhu bian) (1972). *Lao Zi Ben Yi, Lao Zi Xin Kao Shu Lue*. Taipei, Taiwan: Shi Jie Shu Ju.

Wang, K. (1993). *Laozi Daodejing He Shanggong Zhang Zhu*. Beijing, China: Zhong Hua Shu Ju.

Zhang Zhan. (1972). *Liezi zhu*. Taipei, Taiwan: Shijie Shuju Yinxing.

CREDITS

CHAPTER 4

Meditation

After finishing this chapter, you will be able to do the following:

- List the common components of the various types of meditation
- Describe meditation in the context of research in neuroscience
- Indicate why meditation is an important component for managing chronic stress
- Describe how meditation is related to enhanced learning
- Compare Buddhist, Daoist, and Confucian meditation practices
- Demonstrate how Buddhist, Daoist, and Confucian meditation practices can be understood from the perspective of neuroscience and evolutionary theory
- Specify how meditation can be utilized within the context of mind wandering
- Indicate how the autobiographical self, social self, and self-referential threat-based thinking is related to chronic stress and how meditation can be used to address concerns with it
- Briefly describe Samadhi, Sati, Zuowang, Xinzhai, and Jingguo
- Indicate why an understanding of neuroplasticity is an important factor regarding the effectiveness of meditation practices

THE WESTERN PERSPECTIVE ON MEDITATION: NEUROSCIENCE

In this chapter, the practice of meditation and its relationship to neuroscience, evolutionary theory, and stress management will be explored. In addition, meditation practices will be examined in the Buddhist, Daoist, and Confucian traditions. In order to give you a more concrete and contextual feel for meditation practices in these traditions, translations, from the original texts, regarding meditation practices are presented. The relationship between these ancient traditions, neuroscience, and evolutionary theory are examined.

As indicated in previous chapters, the stress response is primarily activated by threat-based, self-referential psychosocial thinking. This type of self-referential threat-based thinking reflects an evolution-based negativity bias (Ito, Larsen, Smith, & Cacioppo, 1998; Rozin & Roysman, 2001). Ongoing self-referential obsessing and rumination about threat-based psychosocial occurrences from the past and ongoing, self-referential anticipation and worrying about threat-based psychosocial occurrences in the future maintains the activation of the stress response and results in chronic stress (Sood & Jones, 2013).

> **Cost-benefit analyses indicate** mind wandering significantly compromises reading comprehension, attention, concentration, aptitude measurement, mood, and working memory.

From the perspective of neuroscience, ongoing self-referential moving back and forth between the **psychosocial past** and the **psychosocial future** occurs in the **default network** and establishes, via **neuroplasticity** and thus memory, a continuous sense of a **social self** or an **autobiographical self** (Andrews-Hanna, 2012 Buckner & Carroll, 2006; Northoff et al., 2006; Schacter et al., 2012; Spreng & Andrews-Hanna, 2015; Stawarczyk, Cassol, & D'Argembeau, 2013). While this continuous social and autobiographical self is certainly adaptive, the tendency of the self to mind wander and be susceptible to self-referential negativity bias leaves it prone to psychosocial threat-based thinking and judgments, which lead to chronic stress (Sood & Jones, 2013).

Considerable research has found, although there are adaptive benefits, that mind wandering, past and future, can be quite detrimental to one's physical and psychological well-being (Mrazek, Broadway, et al., 2014; Mrazek, Franklin, Phillips, Baird, & Schooler, 2013; Mrazek, Smallwood, & Schooler, 2009; Sood & Jones, 2013; Szpunar, 2017). Research (Mrazek et al., 2013; Smallwood, Fishman, & Schooler, 2007; Sood & Jones, 2013) has demonstrated that mind wandering compromises learning and performance. Cost-benefit analyses (Mooneyham & Schooler, 2013; Schooler et al., 2014) indicates mind wandering significantly compromises reading comprehension, attention, concentration, aptitude measurement, mood, and working memory. Killingsworth and Gilbert (2010) and Killingsworth (2011) note that people spend, while awake, almost half their time mind wandering and, as a result, are unhappy. Research (Smallwood & O'Connor, 2011; Smallwood et al., 2009) indicates that individuals with a negative mood tend to mind wander and that their mind wandering tends to focus on the past. Jazaieri and colleagues (2015) found that mind wandering can compromise caring for oneself and others. What makes this even more troublesome is that, for the most part, people are quite often not aware that they are mind wandering (Schooler et al., 2011; Smallwood & Schooler, 2009; Zedelius, Broadway, & Schooler, 2015).

Considerable research has indicated that an adaptive solution to the adaptive problem of mind wandering and its associated problems is **meditation** (Brandmeyer & Delorme, 2016; Brewer et al., 2011; Lutz, Slagter, Dunne, & Davidson, 2008; Mooneyham & Schooler, 2013; Mrazek, Mooneyham, & Schooler 2014; Mrazek et al., 2013; Mrazek, Broadway, et al., 2014; Sood & Jones, 2013; Zanesco et al., 2016). There is an extensive body of research indicating the physical and psychological benefits of meditation on such areas as anxiety, depression, anger, blood pressure, heart disease, cancer, chronic stress, self-regulation, executive functioning, cognitive performance, attention, pain management, fatigue, and substance abuse (Chang, Casey, Dusek, & Benson, 2010; Chang, Dusek, & Benson, 2011; Chen et al., 2012; Davis & Hayes, 2011; Dimidjian & Segal, 2015; Dusek & Benson, 2009; Esch, Fricchione, & Stefano, 2003; Farb et al., 2010; Grossman, Niemann, Schmidt, & Walach, 2004; Harrington & Dunne, 2015; Kohn, 2008; Sedlmeier et al., 2012; Tang et al., 2007; Walsh, 2011; Walsh & Shapiro, 2006a; Zeidan, Johnson, Diamond, David, & Goolkasian, 2010).

> **Considerable research has** indicated that an adaptive solution to the adaptive problem of mind wandering and its associated problems is **meditation.**

Chronic, problematic psychosocial past- and future-focused thinking is associated with both the negative aspects of mind wandering and chronic stress. Addressing both of them requires, in part, focusing and maintaining one's attention on the present. The practice of meditation is one such way of focusing and maintaining one's attention on the present. Thus, meditation needs to be included as a component in your holistic and integrated personal stress-management program (PSMP).

THE WESTERN PERSPECTIVE ON MEDITATION: CHARACTERISTICS AND TYPES

Doing research on meditation, issues of methodology, conceptualization, consensus, agreeing on a definition of what constitutes meditation, and then operationalizing the definition so it can be measured to determine what exactly it does, how it does it, where and what precisely is occurring in the brain and the body as a result of meditation, and thus explain it and make predications regarding it, is an ongoing issue in the research world (Chen et al., 2012; Davidson & Kaszniak, 2015; Esch, Fricchione, & Stefano; Lutz, Jha, Dunne, & Saron 2015; Walsh & Shapiro, 2006a). Definitions of meditation may include such practices as being nonjudgmental; focused on, observing, and staying in the present; counting breaths; focused attention/concentrating on a single stimulus, such as breath, a sound, a word or phrase, an object, an image, and so on; not mind wandering in the past or present; gaining insight; self-regulation; not dwelling on or attempting to consciously stop the thoughts of the mind; a flexibly focused attention/ awareness of the present; being detached; nonjudgmentally monitoring and refocusing drifting attention; scanning/being aware of sensations/energy in the body; immersion; nonjudgmentally observing body movement; immediacy; letting go of everything; visualization; paying attention; being aware of awareness; restful alertness; integrating mind, body and environment; stilling and emptying the mind; and so on (Benson, 2000; Chen et al., 2012; Davidson & Kaszniak 2015; Goyal et al., 2014; Kabat-Zinn, 2005; Kohn, 1989, 2008, 2010; Rahula, 1959; Sedlmeier et al., 2012; Tang, Posner, & Rothbart, 2014; Wallace & Shapiro 2006; Walsh & Shapiro, 2006.

In general, research suggests that there are two fundamental types of meditation. A laser like, nonjudgmental focus or concentration on a single object and a more insight-based, flexibly focused, nonjudgmental awareness and attention to various phenomenal fields (Dakwar & Levine, 2009; Kohn, 2008; Sedlmeier et al., 2012; Walsh, 2000; Walsh & Shapiro, 2006). The prime example of this distinction can be found in two components of the Buddha's Eight-Fold Path:

Samadhi or one-point concentration and *Sati* or mindfulness (Kohn, 2008). Mindfulness needs to be seen in the context of the actual meditative technique known as **vipassana/vipasyana** or insight meditation (Kohn, 2008; Kristeller, 2007; Rahula, 1959). On the other hand, Kohn (2008), looking at meditation from a somewhat different perspective, classifies meditation in the following six ways: visualization, mantra practice, body awareness, observation, immediacy, and body energetics.

Meditation can be performed while the body is still or while it is moving. **Mindfulness (*Sati*), one-point concentration (*Samadhi*), the relaxation response, transcendental meditation, yoga, sitting in oblivion/forgetfulness (*Zuowang*坐忘), quiet/still sitting (*Jingzuo*靜坐), mind/heart fasting (*Xinzhai* 心齋), standing like a stake/post (*Zhan Zhuang* 站樁), sit in meditation (*Zazen* 座禅), and just sit (*Shikantaza* 只管打坐) are all examples of still meditation.** Mindful walking, qigong (氣功), taijiquan (太極拳), Japanese archery/the way of the bow (*Kyudo* 弓道), and Japanese quick sword drawing/the way of being present and prepared (*Iaido* 居合道) are all examples of **moving meditation**. For many people today, moving meditation may be a more comfortable, preferred, and practical approach to meditating.

It is necessary to point out that some of the still meditations such as *Zhan Zhuang* and yoga have transition movements as the practitioner moves from one posture to the next posture. In the same sense, some styles of moving meditations such as qigong, Kyudo, and Iaido may incorporate postures that are still and held, by the practitioner for a certain period of time, before moving. The integration of still and moving meditation can also be found in such practices as the Daoist tea ceremony and the Japanese tea ceremony. Mindfulness and the relaxation response can be performed while moving. Thus, the distinction between still meditation and moving meditation is more fluid than concrete.

> **Meditation can be** performed while the body is still, moving, standing, sitting, or lying down or as an integration of these various types of meditation.

DAOIST, CONFUCIAN, AND BUDDHIST APPROACHES

Specific techniques of meditation will now be explored in the Buddhist, Daoist, and Confucian traditions. Their creation and utilization of meditation contributed significantly to the adaptive challenge of living life without what we today refer to as chronic stress.

Buddhism

During the time of the Buddha, various ascetics and Brahmans (the Hindu caste, that of the priests) traveled about from town to town, offering, to the inhabitants, their theories, practices, and solutions to living life while at the same time criticizing the theories, practices, and solutions of those who had visited before them. This state of affairs is the context for the *Kalama Sutra*. The Buddha, whose positive reputation preceded him, enters the town of Kesaputta and finds a place to rest. The Kalamas, citizens of the town of Kesaputta, seek out the Buddha. They explain to him their frustration and confusion regarding these ascetics and Brahmans. They note that these individuals offer their own solution while demeaning and criticizing the solutions offered by those who have visited before them. They ask the Buddha how they should go about separating truth from falsehood. Who should they believe? Given what has transpired, Buddha tells them it is natural they should be uncertain and have doubt. He then provides them some guidelines to help them separate truth from falsehood.

> You do not want to depend upon oral instruction. You do not want to depend upon tradition. You do not want to depend upon legend. You do not want to depend upon the teachings of the sutras. You do not want to depend upon logic. You do not want to depend upon reasoning. You do not want to depend upon pondering deeply on theory. You do not want to depend upon thinking about the viewpoints of others. You do not want to depend upon the power of images. You do

not want to depend upon the notion that "This monk is our honored and respected teacher." Furthermore, abide Kalamas, be in accord with, resolute and accept, what you yourselves are directly aware of, realize, experience: "If these methods are not good, if these methods produce further suffering, if these methods the wise reprimand against, when completing and believing in these methods they lead to that which is detrimental and chronically stressful (dukkha), Kalamas, at that time you should abandon them."

Come Kalamas. You do not want to depend upon oral instruction. You do not want to depend upon tradition. You do not want to depend upon legend. You do not want to depend upon the teachings of the sutras. You do not want to depend upon logic. You do not want to depend upon reasoning. You do not want to depend upon pondering deeply on theory. You do not want to depend upon thinking about the viewpoints of others. You do not want to depend upon the power of images, you do not want to depend upon the notion that "This monk is our honored and respected teacher." Furthermore, abide Kalamas, be in accord with, resolute and accept, what you yourselves are directly aware of, realize, experience: "If these methods are good, if these methods are without further suffering, if these methods the wise praise, when completing and believing in these methods they lead to benefit, peacefulness, and happiness, Kalamas, at that time you should enter and therein abide." (Agama, 2019)

It is important to note, at this point, that the Kalamas are not disciples of Buddha and have not been transmitted his teachings. He has simply given them guidelines, based on direct experience in the here and now, on how to separate truth from falsehood when engaging in the various practices offered by any teacher. If the results of the practices are experienced as good, do not produce further suffering, are praised by the wise, and lead to benefit, peacefulness, and happiness then the practitioner will have separated truth from falsehood. All of the components are required to validate the teachings. Having heard his guidelines, the Kalamas decide to follow the Buddha.

One of Buddha's most fundamental guidelines was that you must directly experience for yourself what he is talking about. The release from *dukkha* or chronic stress can only be accomplished by determining (read direct experience) for yourself that his pathway results in the release from chronic stress or *dukkha*. The practitioner is free to follow other paths and determine if they are valid. But he is quite clear: Do not depend on anything other than your own experience—not reason, logic, tradition, scriptures, tradition, oral instruction, legend, theory, the viewpoint of others, faith, images or the fact that this person is your teacher.

Of fundamental importance in putting the teachings of Buddha into practice is to focus on the present. Focusing on the present is essential for reducing mind wandering and eliminating chronic stress. In the *Sutra of One Night of the Good and Wise Person*, the Buddha (the World Honored One) is essentially discussing, with his disciples, what neuroscientists today refer to as the default mode and the mind wandering associated with it. Although not defining it as such, it is quite clear he is referring to mind wandering when he refers to "not being inattentive and slacking off." In other words, stay focused in the present and do not become distracted.

> **Of fundamental importance** in putting the teachings of Buddha into practice is to focus on the present. Focusing on the present is essential for reducing mind wandering and eliminating chronic stress.

Buddha specifically indicates the necessity of not getting entangled and agitated by wandering in the past and in the future. Being entangled, agitated, and craving for that which is already long gone and cannot be undone is threat-based, psycho-social-focused thinking and leads to *dukkha* or chronic stress. Being entangled, agitated, and craving for that which has not yet come is threat-based, psychosocial-focused thinking and leads to *dukkha* or chronic stress. He is clear that the attention of the monks needs to be focused on the present in a nonjudgmental manner, such that they are tranquil, calm, and still. This is skillful observation or mindfulness. He is also quite clear that for one to become tranquil, calm, still, and free from *dukkha* or chronic stress requires consistent, around-the-clock practice. From the perspective of neuroscience, this consistent, around-the-clock practice results in learning. This learning is represented by structural and functional changes in the brain, in other words, neuroplasticity.

> One time, the World Honored One, was staying outside of Sravasti city at Jeta grove in
>
> Anàthapindika's monastery. The World Honored One informed all the monks, "All monks!"
>
> The monks responded, "World Honored One!" The World Honored One thus said, "All
>
> monks! I will speak to you analyzing and summarizing the One Night of a Good and Wise
>
> Person. You should listen attentively and consider it. I shall speak of it." All the monks
>
> responding to the World Honored One said, "Proceed." The World Honored One thus said,

Do not chase after the past. Do not wish for what has not yet come.

Regarding everything in the past, all of it is already gone.

Regarding the future, it has not arrived. Regarding what is in the present,

in all respects, it is skillfully observed, not agitated and not moved.

Knowing that this is so, cultivate it through practice. Work on this now!

You must be enthusiastic and work on it with zeal.

Who knows, you may be dead tomorrow. The truth is there is nothing you can do about it.

You cannot negotiate with the great forces of death.

Thus, stay enthusiastic! Day and night [do] not be[] inattentive and slacking off.

This one night of the good and wise person is called one who is tranquil, calm and still. (Tripitaka, 2016).

Correct effort: For meditation to be effective, it requires commitment, motivation, enthusiasm, determination, and consistent regular practice. You cannot practice haphazardly. In other words, you have to put forward the appropriate effort. This is not only the case for all aspects of Buddha's Eight-Fold Path, it is also the case for an effective stress-management program. In other words, for learning to take place, for the new behaviors to wire in/neuroplasticity, regular and consistent practice is required. Fundamental to the implementation of the Buddha's adaptive solution, the Eight-Fold Path, for the removal of *dukkha* or chronic stress is the component correct effort. In the *Analysis of the Noble Truths Sutra* it states,

Friends, now what is Correct Effort? Friends, monks are determined, are energetic, are devoted and industrious, are enthusiastic, and are motivated for not allowing the arising of evil unskilled methods that have not arisen and for abandoning evil unskilled methods that have already arisen. They are determined, are energetic, are devoted and industrious, are enthusiastic, and are motivated for the arising of all the skilled methods that have not arisen. They are determined, are energetic, are devoted and industrious, are enthusiastic, and are motivated for continuing, not confusing, increasing, expanding and cultivating all the skilled methods that have already arisen. Friends this is the meaning of Correct Effort. (Santee, 2007, p. 102; Agama, 2019a)

The fourth noble truth, the path to the release from *Dukkha*, is Buddha's adaptive solution, treatment plan if you will, for resolving the adaptive problem of *dukkha* or chronic stress. The two components or folds of the Eight-Fold Path treatment plan that directly relate to meditation are correct concentration (*zheng ding* 正定, *Samadhi*) and correct mindfulness (*zheng nian* 正念, *Sati*). Correct concentration is the basis of the counting of breaths and the relaxation response exercises you were previously introduced to and taught how to practice. In the *Analysis of the Noble Truths Sutra*, correct concentration is described.

Correct concentration: Let's open with another quote from a master:

> Friends, now what is Correct Concentration? Now monks, it is being separate from all sensory desire, apart from all evil and unskilled methods, it has discovery and analysis, it is born due to detachment, and it is happy and joyful. This is the place of the initial meditation (*chan* 禪, *dhyana*). Causing discovery and analysis to stop, entering where the mind is peaceful, still, focused on one point, without discovery and analysis, it is born due to concentration (*ding* 定, *samadhi*), happy and joyful. It is the second meditation. (Santee, 2007, p. 122)

Research has shown one-point concentration or Samadhi to be beneficial physically and psychologically and be effective in reducing stress and stress-related illnesses (Chang, Dusek, & Benson, 2011; Dusek & Benson, 2009; Esch, Fricchione, & Stefano, 2003). *Samadhi* must be seen, however, as part of an interrelated, holistic approach, the Eight-Fold Path, to the elimination of *dukkha* or chronic stress.

Buddha's journey to being released from *dukkha* or chronic stress is described in the *Noble Quest Sutra* where he addresses and overcomes the final barrier of the conception of a permanent, independent, and substantial sense of self or I and where *Samadhi* or one-point concentration is shown to be a necessary step in the journey (Agama, 2019b, c). In the *Analysis of the Boundaries Sutra*, Buddha addressed the sense of an absolute, independent, substantial and permanent sense of self or I. He notes,

> In this way, it is said, where one is at peace, all thinking about pleasure and happiness do not continue on. When all thinking about pleasure and happiness do not continue on, the Buddha is still and tranquil. So, what does this mean? Monk! To say "I have an I," this is wishful thinking. To say "I am that," this is wishful thinking. To say "I will exist," this is wishful thinking. To say that "I will not exist," this is wishful thinking. To say "I will be and have form," this is

wishful thinking. To say that "I will be and not have form," this is wishful thinking. "I will be and think," this is wishful thinking. "I will not be and not think," this is wishful thinking. "I will be not thinking and not not thinking," this is wishful thinking. Monk, wishful thinking is an illness. Wishful thinking is an abscess. Wishful thinking is foreign body embedded in you. Monks! Thus, getting past and beyond all the wishful thinking, the Buddha is still and tranquil. (Santee, 2007, p. 116; Agama, 2019c.)

While Buddha certainly acknowledges a relative, transitory sense of an I or self that is impermanent, inter-dependent, non-substantial, and engages in the present, his concern is with the judgmental, conceptual sense of I or self that is the focus of attention as one's mind wanders in the past and present and with which the individual identifies. It is this sense of I or self that is viewed as being permanent, substantial, and independent, which leads to *dukkha* or chronic stress. It is this sense of I or self that is the final barrier to the removal of *dukkha* or chronic stress.

> **Do not chase** after the past. Do not wish for what has not yet come.
> **Regarding everything in** the past, all of it is already gone.
> **Regarding the future,** it has not arrived. Regarding what is present, in all respects, it is skill-fully observed, not agitated and not moved.
> **Knowing that this** is so, culti-vate it through practice.

Interestingly enough, research in neuroscience appears to have come to the same conclusion, as a distinction is made between a continuous, autobiographical sense of self, narrative sense of self, and a schema-based sense of self that wan-ders, in the default network, back and forth between past and future engaging, primarily, in self-referential thinking, and thus temporally connecting and rein-forcing this, essentially viewed as permanent, conceptual sense of self and the self that is experienced fleetingly and momentarily in the present (Brewer et al., 2011; Damasio, 2010; Farb et al., 2007; Gusnard, Akbudak, Shulman, & Raichle, 2001). In addition, research (Farb et al., 2007 has suggested that disengagement from the negative self-referential judgments associated with the conceptual sense of self or I in the default network and focusing more on the present may be beneficial for addressing psychologically based concerns. Mindfulness is one such method for disengagement.

Correct mindfulness: Even though the fourth noble truth, Buddha's adaptive solution or treatment plan to address the adaptive problem of *dukkha* or chronic stress, is called the Eight-Fold Path and thus consists of eight components, the component of mindfulness is necessary for the successful implementation for each of the other seven folds or components. Buddha makes this quite clear in *The Dwellings of Mindfulness Sutra* where he states,

Then the Buddha said, "Monks. To purify all sentient beings, to over-come anxiety and depression, to eliminate bitterness and worry, to arrive at the correct path, to realize nirvana, there is this one dharma (teaching/truth): the four dwellings of mindfulness." (Santee, 2007, p. 103; Agama, 2019d)

It is quite clear from this quote that the focus of *The Dwellings of Mindfulness Sutra* is, from a Western perspective, psychological in nature and on issues associated with chronic stress or what Buddha calls *dukkha*. Given mindfulness is utilized to attend to the present, awareness is directed, by its practice, away from the conceptual self or I, the default network, the negativity bias, threat-based thinking, and mind wandering in the past and the future. The practice of mindfulness is defined in the *Analysis of the Noble Truths Sutra*:

Friends, now what is Correct Mindfulness? Friends, a monk follows along non-judgmentally observing the body as the body. Enthusiastic, there is correct knowing and mindfulness. Controlling and subduing the greed and anxiety in the world. Then moving on to sensations, feelings, and then arriving at mental objects. The monk follows along non-judgmentally observing mental objects as mental objects. Enthusiastic, there is correct knowing and mindfulness. Controlling and subduing the greed and anxiety in the world. Friends this is Correct Mindfulness. (Santee, 2007, p. 103)

The primary barrier to the release from *dukkha* or chronic stress is the sense of a permanent, independent, non-substantial, conceptual sense of a self or I. This being the case, in *The Dwellings of Mindfulness Sutra,* the practice of mindfulness is addressed, in the present, individually toward each of the components that constitute the sense of self. Through the practice of mindfulness, the practitioner observes and experiences, this is the key, the components that make up the self as transient and fleeting, in other words, as impermanent, non-substantial, and interdependent. There is no permanent, substantial, and independent self!

The components that make up the self are the body, sensations, feelings/emotions, mental objects, and consciousness. Consciousness is not addressed because consciousness arises from contact between a sense and its object. It is clearly impermanent, non-substantial, and interdependent. Thus, there are six types of consciousness. For Buddha, your mind is simply another sense, all of which are interdependent, impermanent, and non-substantial. Close your eyes and keep them closed. Is the room/space you are in still there? You will of course answer yes. But this is not due to visual consciousness as your eyes are closed. It is due to your mental consciousness where the thought "I am in this room/space" is in contact with your mind. Now open your eyes. The room/space returns because there is contact between your visual sense and the objects that are in your visual field.

In *The Dwellings of Mindfulness Sutra* Buddha elaborates further on the application of mindfulness to the four dwellings of the self:

> What are these four? The Buddha said, "Monks, it is to follow along non-judgmentally observing the body as the body, enthusiastic and attentive, maintaining mindfulness very deeply to eliminate the world of greed and anxiety. It is to follow along non-judgmentally observing sensations as sensations, enthusiastic and very attentive, maintaining mindfulness to eliminate the world of greed and anxiety. It is to follow along non-judgmentally observing feelings/emotions as feelings/emotions, enthusiastic and very attentive, maintaining mindfulness to eliminate the world of greed and anxiety. It is to follow along non-judgmentally observing mental objects as mental objects, enthusiastic and very attentive, maintaining mindfulness to eliminate the world of greed and anxiety." (Santee, 2007, p. 106)

Mindfulness is applied, in *The Dwellings of Mindfulness Sutra,* to the body, sensations, feelings/emotions, and mental objects. In order to give you some sense of the actual practice of mindfulness in the context of how Buddha taught it, two sections from this Sutra regarding how mindfulness is applied to the body will be presented. The first section refers to breathing and in this section the specifics for seated meditation is described. The second section applies mindfulness to various behaviors associated with the body such as walking, sitting, standing, lying down, defecating, and urinating. In all cases the goal is being in the present while observing and experiencing, not thinking about or judging, all aspects of the behavior of the body. You are simply observing and experiencing the body as the body while being, for all intents and purposes, disengaged from the autobiographical self I. As such, the goal is to simply experience, via direct, unfiltered observation or awareness, that the body is impermanent, non-substantial, and interdependent.

Practice mindfulness

The practice of mindfulness is not restricted to sitting in some type of formal meditational practice. In fact, it is actively engaged in all aspects of the Eight-Fold Path.

Mindful Breathing

Monks! How does a monk follow along non-judgmentally observing the body as the body? Monks! By this! A monk walked into a forest, he walked to the base of a tree, he walked to an empty place, folded his legs, sat cross-legged, and straightened his body, in the present, mindfully. At that point, mindful he exhales, mindful he inhales. Perhaps it is a long exhalation. Being aware he says, "I am breathing out a long breath." Perhaps it is a long inhalation. Being aware he says, "I am breathing in a long breath." Perhaps it is a short exhalation. Being aware he says, "I am breathing out a short breath." Perhaps it is a short inhalation. Being aware he says, "I am breathing in a short breath." Perhaps he cultivates himself non-judgmentally observing, "I am aware of my entire body when I exhale." Perhaps he cultivates himself non-judgmentally observing, "I am aware of my entire body when I inhale." Again cultivating himself he non-judgmentally observes, "I am making the actions of my body tranquil and still when I exhale." Cultivating himself he non-judgmentally observes, "I am making the actions of my body tranquil and still when I inhale. ... In this way he follows along non-judgmentally observing the body in the body internally, the body in the body externally, the body in the body internally and externally. (Santee, 2007, pp. 106–107)

Mindfulness and the Body

In this way he follows along non-judgmentally observing things arising in the body, in this way he follows along observing things ceasing in the body, in this way he follows along observing things arising and ceasing in the body. In the present, mindfully, he says, "The body is this." Thus is the establishment of his wisdom and his remembrance. In the world, he is without dependency or attachments. This, monks, is following along non-judgmentally observing the body in the body.

Monks, again! Perhaps a monk is walking, knowing this he says, "I am walking." Perhaps he is standing, knowing this he says, "I am standing." Perhaps he is sitting, knowing this he says, "I am sitting." Perhaps he is lying down, knowing this he says, "I am lying down." Whatever aspect of the body is indicated, he knows it is such. In this way, he follows along non-judgmentally observing the body ... without dependency or attachments. This monks, is non-judgmentally observing the body as the body. Monks, again! A monk is going off, returning, truly aware, non-judgmentally observing the front and the back, truly aware, desiring to bend or stretch, truly aware, desiring to hold his top coat, robe or alms bowl, he is truly aware. Eating, drinking, chewing, tasting, he is truly aware. At the time of defecating or urinating, he is truly aware. (Santee, 2007, pp. 107–108)

Daoism

Meditation is fundamental to the practice of Daoism (Kohn, 1989, 2008, 2010), be it still and/or moving, sitting and/or not sitting. The focus is on a direct awareness and experience of the here and now. In early Daoist texts, such as the *Daodejing* and the *Zhuangzi*, prior to the introduction and development of Buddhism in China, there is a type of awareness or observation, developed through meditation practices, known as **guan**. *Guan* is a flexibly focused, nonjudgmental, detached, unfiltered, tranquil observation or awareness of the here and now (Cheng, 2003).

When Buddhism began to flourish in China during the Tang dynasty (618–907), insight meditation, *Sati* or mindfulness, became integrated into later Daoism and was known as "inner observation or *neiguan*, concentration and observation or *dingguan*, and true observation *zhenguan*" (Kohn, 2008, p. 85). The *guan* of early Daoism and *sati* or mindfulness of Buddhism seem to have developed independent from each other. There does not appear to be any evidence to suggest otherwise.

> **Nonjudgmentally and without** any bias observe (*guan*, 觀) the body as the body.

The concept of *guan*, within the context of traditional early Daoist texts, is first mentioned in the first chapter of the *Daodejing*.

> Being without desire nonjudgmentally (*guan*觀) observe the subtleness. Being with desire, nonjudgmentally observe (*guan*觀) the boundaries. The two of these are produced together yet differently named. Together they are called the mystery (*xuan*玄). The mystery, moreover, of the mystery, is the gate to all wonder (*miao* 妙). (Wang, 1993; Yang, 1972)

Guan is being utilized to gain a direct, unfiltered, unbiased, nonjudgmental experience and awareness of or insight into the nature of reality from essentially an intentional and non-intentional perspective. For this to occur, the individual needs to be focused, without any distractions, in the present. There can be no mind wandering. There can be no agitation. The negativity bias for psychosocial threats cannot be present. There can be no sense of an autobiographical or continuous self. The individual cannot be stressed. For the Daoist practitioner, the mind is still and empty. The practitioner is tranquil, centered, and at peace.

The non-intentional or being-without-desire–based aspect of *Guan* is clearly presented in chapter 16 of the *Daodejing*:

> To bring about utmost emptiness (*xu ji*, 虛 極),
> Seriously maintain (*shou* 守) stillness (*jing*, 靜)
> All things acting together
> I am nonjudgmentally aware (*guan*, 觀) of their cycles (fu, 復)
> As much as there are numerous things
> All cycles return (*gui,* 歸) to their root (gen,根)
> Returning to the root (gen, 根) is called stillness (jing, 靜) (Santee, 2003, 2005a; Wang, 1993; Yang, 1972)

In this case, the mind of the individual has been stilled and emptied. As a result, the nature of existence is observed, nonjudgmentally and without any bias, in the here and now. Without any intention or desire the subtleness of existence is revealed as the individual observes things working together as they work through their cycles.

The intentional, being with desire, or having a specific focus, allowing for relative distinctions, aspect of *guan* still requires the same stillness and emptiness of the individual's mind. In this case, whatever your specific focus, you observe it as it is in the here and now. There are no judgments or biases. This is made quite clear in chapter 54 of the *Daodejing*:

> That which is properly established cannot be uprooted. That which is properly embraced cannot be disconnected … non-judgmentally and without any bias observe (*guan*, 觀) the body as the body. Non-judgmentally and without any bias observe (*guan,* 觀) the family as the family. Non-judgmentally and without any bias observe (*guan*, 觀) the hometown as the hometown. Non-judgmentally and without any bias observe (*guan*, 觀) the kingdom as the kingdom. Non-judgmentally and without any bias observe (*guan*, 觀) the world as the world. How do I know the world is so? By this! (Santee, 2007; Wang, 1993; Yang, 1972)

To be properly established is to have a mind that is still, empty, and rooted in the present. This being the case, to be properly embraced is to observe things, people, interactions, and situations as they really are without bias or judgement in the present. What is this? *Guan*!

The problem is that there is no clear indication in the *Daodejing* of any specific type of meditative process. How does one be still and empty the mind? How does one develop and cultivate *guan*? There certainly appear to be guidelines oriented toward what we call meditation and what needs to be done to implement it.

Ames and Hall (2003) indicated that numerous chapters in the *Daodejing* can be interpreted as referring to meditative breathing exercises, with chapter 10 being a prime example. For instance, the first three lines of chapter 10 state

> Are you able to be whole by integrating your body and mind?
> Are you able to focus on your breath (*qi* 氣) to become soft and flexible like an infant?
> Are you able to be without judgments and biases by cleansing your mind? (Santee, 2005b, 200c; Wang, 1993; Yang, 1972)

These three lines certainly are indicative of becoming physically and psychologically integrated and relaxed, with a strong focus on breathing. Clearly these are components of a path to removing chronic stress. In chapter 6 of the *Zhuangzi*, there is a comparison between the authentic person or ***zhenren*** (真人), who is free from chronic stress, and those, essentially everyone else, who are not free from chronic stress. A primary focus is on how they differ regarding breathing:

> The authentic person of ancient times slept without dreaming, was not chronically stressed (you 憂) when awake, ate without relishing, and breathed very deeply. The authentic person breathes from the heels. All other people breathe from their throats. Being restricted, their words are like a throat retching. Their desires long standing and deep, their essential nature is shallow. (Santee, 2004; Guo, 1956)

The authentic person is not chronically stressed when asleep, when awake, or when eating. This freedom from chronic stress is clearly indicated by the deep breathing of the authentic person. All other people are chronically stress as indicated by their shallow, throat breathing, the manner in which they speak, and the fact that they are restricted by their unresolved desires and expectations. They are agitated physically and psychologically. The commentary of Guo Xiang (252–312) to this passage regarding why the authentic person does not dream states, "He does not have expectations" (Santee 2011, p. 45; Guo, 1974, p. 124). Cheng Xuanying (631–652), adding on to this commentary of Guo, notes,

Those who dream have vain hopes and unsatisfied wishes. The authentic person is without emotions and has cut off deliberation. Therefore, when he sleeps he is anchored in a quiet place and does not dream. (Santee, 2011, p. 45; Guo, 1974, p. 124)

Regarding the authentic person not being chronically stressed while awake, Guo Xiang comments "Accepting whatever is encountered, he is at peace." (Santee, 2011, p. 45; Guo, 1974, p. 124). Cheng adds, "To the extent that you realize that everything is what it is, you will be without chronic stress (*you* 憂)" (Santee, 2011, p. 45; Guo, 1974, p. 124). Realizing that everything is what it is and accepting it requires a direct experience of the present that is nonjudgmental and unbiased. This clearly alludes to *guan*.

Xinzhai or mind/heart fasting: For *guan* to arise appears to require some type of training in meditation. Given what has been previously explored, it seems this training is somehow linked to stilling and emptying the mind, with a focus on breathing. In chapter 19 of the *Zhuangzi* a link between stilling and emptying the mind, breathing, *guan*, a meditative experience, and creativity is established:

Carpenter Qing was carving wood to make a bell stand. After the stand was completed those who looked at it were startled as it appeared supernatural. Marquis Lu saw it and asking a question said, "Is there an art by which you make this?" Answering, Carpenter Qing said, "Your subject is a worker. What art could I have? However, there is one thing. Before I make a bell stand, I do not dare to compromise my breath (*qi* (氣). I must fast in order to still (jìng, 靜) my mind/heart (xīn, 心). After 3 days of fasting I do not feel compelled to think of approval, admiration, rank or salary. After fasting for five days, I do not feel compelled to think of not having a reputation, being skillful or clumsy. After 7 days of fasting I am still. I forgot about having four limbs and a body. At this moment, there are no official duties or royal court. I am focused on my skills and outside distractions disappear. After this I enter the mountain forest, unbiased and nonjudgmentally observing (guān, 觀) with my natural instincts (tiān xìng, 天性) until a form appears such that I can see the completed bell stand. I then begin my work. There is nothing else. Thus, take the natural to unite with the natural. That is the reason why people suspect the bell stand is supernatural. That is it!" (Santee, 2005a; Guo, 1956)

Mind/heart fasting
Xinzhai (心齋)

In this story about Carpenter Qing, the reference to fasting refers to a meditative technique known as mind/heart fasting or *xinzhai* (心齋). The early rendering of the character *xin* (心) was a picture of a heart, which integrated both cognitive (mind) and emotional (heart) processes. Just think about what is entailed when you make a decision, especially one that is very important to you. It is, for most, people not just cold reason or logic that is involved. There is a feeling or emotional component. The character *xin* captures both, hence the translation/interpretation of mind/heart.

Cheng, in his commentary to the consequences of fasting for 3 days, notes, "The true state of the mind/heart is to be fasting" (Guo, 1974 p. 340). Kohn (2011) indicates that the term "fasting" often refers to and is used to indicate meditation. Given the story, it is quite clear that *xinzhai* is a meditative process about stilling and emptying the mind/heart. It is a gradual process that frees Carpenter Qing from both cognitive and emotional restrictions, allowing him to create without any self-imposed or society-imposed restrictions. He has essentially returned to his true or natural state of mind/heart.

The first step in this meditative process is to unify, calm, and stabilize the breath so that Carpenter Qing can focus and concentrate in the present. In the commentary on the written character's section for the previous quote for "fasting" it states, "If the breath (*qi*) is compromised, then the mind/heart is agitated and wanders (*xindong* 心 動). If the mind/heart is agitated and wanders, then the spirit is not focused" (Guo, 1974, p. 340). In order to prevent this agitation and mind wandering, Carpenter Qing must still and empty his mind/heart. All psychosocial threat-based thinking is eliminated, hence the focus on the breath and the cultivation of *guan*.

Thus, what neuroscience has discovered and is addressing today is an adaptive problem well over 2,000 years old from the Daoist perspective. The practice of *xinzhai* is oriented toward, from the perspectives of neuroscience and stress management, eliminating the psychosocial negativity bias, the elimination of psychosocial threat-based thinking, stopping agitation, stopping mind wandering in the past and future, and disengaging from the default network. It allows one to return to the present.

There is one other component, from the perspective of neuroscience, that is not visibly addressed in the story of Carpenter Qing. This component is that of the autobiographical or permanent sense of self. The absolute I! In chapter 4 of the *Zhuangzi*, the practice of *xinzhai* is described and the issue of the autobiographical self is clearly addressed.

Throughout the *Zhuangzi* there are numerous stories involving Confucius and his favorite student Yan Hui (顏回). These stories are satirical in nature as they put the early Daoist perspective and teachings into the mouths of Confucius and Yan Hui. The story surrounding the practice of *xinzhai* is one such story. In the story, Confucius is trying to impress upon Yan Hui that he needs ask himself why he wants to go to the kingdom of Wei to teach the ruler how to govern his kingdom. There is then a series of interactions between Yan Hui and Confucius regarding how Yan Hui is going to approach the ruler of Wei, with Confucius indicating none of the ways will work. Yan Hui is at a loss what to do next and asks Confucius for guidance. Confucius finally tells Yan Hui he needs to fast. Yan Hui mistakes this to mean refraining from eating meat and drinking wine. Confucius tells him that is not mind/heart fasting (*xinzhai*). Yan Hui asks for an explanation of mind/heart fasting (*xinzhai*):

> Zhongni (Confucius) said, "Your attention and will are unified. Do not listen with the ear, listen with the mind/heart. Do not listen with the mind/heart, listen with your breath (*qi*氣). Listening is stopped by the ear. The mind/heart is stopped by symbols. This is emptiness (xu虛) interacting with things. Dao (道) is a gathering of emptiness. Emptiness is mind/heart fasting." Yan Hui said, "Having not yet reached a point of applying this to myself (Hui回), my self (Hui 回) was real. Having applied it, I do not begin to have a self (Hui回)." Is it possible to call this emptiness?" Fuzi said, "That is it!" (Santee, 2004; Guo, 1956)

The first step in the practice of *xinzhai* is to focus one's attention and will so that the individual is not externally and internally distracted. This is clarified by not listening with the ear (this essentially means all of the senses) such the individual is not being controlled and/or distracted by the objects in one's sensory fields. The next step is not listening with the mind/heart such that the individual is not being controlled and/or distracted by thoughts and emotions. Finally, one interacts internally and externally by being grounded in the breath. As the breath has no object to cause one to be fragmented and distracted, it is emptiness interacting with things. There are no self-imposed or society-imposed psychosocial restrictions. There is no psychosocial threat-based thinking. There are no biases or judgments. There is no mind wandering in the past or the future. There is no agitation.

You are disengaged from the default network. You are fully engaged in the ever-changing present.

In the Chinese culture, the surname (Yan) is given first, followed by the given name Hui (回). When Yan Hui says he does not have a self, he is referring to his given name or autobiographical self—a self that he previously viewed as being permanent. After practicing *xinzhai* he comes to the realization that there is no absolute autobiographical self. The realization that there is no permanent autobiographical self is reinforced in the quote by referring to Confucius by his courtesy name Zhongni and his given title of Fuzi or master. His surname is Kong.

The realization that not having a permanent sense of self is emptiness, along with the awareness that Dao is a gathering of emptiness, is essentially the same awareness that Carpenter Qing had when he noted, as a result of practicing *xinzhai*, "take the natural to unite with the natural." In both cases, there is no separation as everything is an interacting, continual process of change.

Given that mind wandering in the past and future, agitation, psychosocial threat-based thinking, a psychosocial negativity bias, a permanent sense of an autobiographical self, absolute judgments and biases, and being excessively engaged in the default network are all overcome by the practice of *xinzhai*, it should be quite clear that this meditative practice is beneficial in addressing and eliminating chronic stress.

Zuowang or sitting in oblivion/forgetfulness: In chapter 6 of the *Zhuangzi* the meditative practice of *zuowang* (坐忘) or sitting in forgetfulness/oblivion is presented in the context, once again, of a discussion between Confucius and his favorite student Yan Hui. The satire is more intense than the story of Carpenter Qing as the fundamental Confucian concepts of *ren* (benevolence), *yi* (morally appropriate choice), *li* (morally appropriate behavior), and *yue* (music) are viewed as barriers and restrictions that must be discarded. In this story, the roles are reversed as Confucius requests, at the end, to become a follower of Yan Hui. Like the story of Carpenter Qing and the story about how to practice *xinzhai*, there is a removal of biases, self-imposed and society-imposed psychosocial restrictions, and the psychosocial negativity bias. Like the Carpenter Qing story and the story about how to practice *xinzhai*, there is a disengagement from the default network and the sense of the permanent autobiographical self associated with it. Like the story about how to practice *xinzhai* there is a specific focus on the given name or autobiographical self, but in this case, instead of Yan Hui and Confucius, the sole focus is on the given name Qiu and the courtesy name Zhongni of Confucius. The point about the autobiographical self is still the same.

> **Sitting in forgetfulness/ oblivion**
> *Zuowang* (坐忘)

Yan Hui said, "I succeeded." Zhongni (Confucius) said, "What do you mean?" Hui said, "I forgot/am oblivious of (wang 忘) benevolence (ren 仁) and morally appropriate choice (yi 義)." Confucius said, "That is possible, yet you are still not there." Later on, they saw each other again. Hui said, "I succeeded." Confucius said, "What do you mean?" Hui said, "I forgot/am oblivious of morally appropriate behavior (li 禮) and music (yue 樂)." Confucius said, "That is possible, yet you are still not there." Later on, they saw each other again. Hui said, "I succeeded." Zhongni (Confucius) said, "What do you mean?" Hui said, "I sit in forgetfulness/oblivion (zuowang 坐忘)." Zhongni, somewhat startled, said, "What do you mean sit in forgetfulness/oblivion?" Yan Hui said, "I let my body (limbs and trunk) fall away. I dismissed my senses. I separated from form and got rid of knowledge. I am the same as the great passageway (da tong 大通). This is the meaning of sitting in forgetfulness/oblivion." Zhongni said, "Being the same, thus you are without partiality. Transformed, thus without absolutes. The results are quite worthy." Qiu (Confucius) then requested to become his disciple. (Santee, 2005a; Guo, 1956) (Historically translators have translated/interpreted zuowang as sitting in forgetfulness. Kohn (2010) makes a strong case why it should be translated/interpreted as sitting in oblivion. Given that most earlier translations have used sitting in forgetfulness and Kohn's insights, I felt it would be best to combine both of them.)

This story in the *Zhuangzi* does not provide any real guidelines on how to practice *zuowang*. During the Tang dynasty, the Daoist Shangqing priest Sima Chengzhen (647–735) wrote an entire text that was generated from the *zuowang* story in the Zhuangzi. The text is called *Sitting in Oblivion/Forgetfulness* (*Zuowang lun* 坐忘論). In the "Respect and Belief" (*jingxin* 敬信) section of the *Zuowanglun*, the author provides the basic requirements for practicing *zuowang*.

Belief (xìn 信) is the root of Dao (道). Respect (jing 敬) is the stem of internal, gentle power (de 德). If the root is deep, then the Dao will grow. If the stem is unwavering, then the *De* will be profuse. … If a person hears talk of sitting in forgetfulness (zuowang 坐忘), believes (xin 信) that it is essential to cultivating the Dao, is respectful of its value, is without any doubt, and practices diligently and consistently, he/she will certainly attain Dao. (Santee, 2010; Saohua, n.d.)

Essentially the practitioner is being asked to be totally committed to engaging in *zuowang*. Once the basic requirements are clear and established, the next step is how to practice *zuowang*. The guidelines on how to practice *zuowang* are found in the in the "Gathering the Mind/Heart" (*Shouxin* 收心) section

> When you begin to study the Dao, it is essential to sit peacefully, gather your mind and focus your attention, let go of all concerns, and not dwell on anything. Because you are not dwelling on anything, you are not affected by a single thing. You will naturally enter into emptiness. The mind/heart merges with Dao. If you completely eliminate the obstructions of the mind/heart and open up to recognize the root of the spirit, this is called cultivating Dao. When you do not repeatedly drift with the waves, are joined with Dao, and are at peace in Dao, it is called "returning to the root." Maintaining the root and not being separate, it is called "the establishment of stillness" (*jingding* 靜定). Stillness being established, in the course of time, illness (*bing* 病) disappears and life is restored. … When you dwell on something, the mind/heart is strained. This is not only irrational, it causes the individual to become ill (*bing* 病). But if the mind/heart is not affected by anything, then it will not be moved. This is authentic stabilization and the correct foundation. (Santee, 2010; Saohua, n.d.)

In this selection from the *Zuowanglun*, it is quite clear that dwelling or holding on to your thoughts and/or emotions compromises your physical and psychological well-being. You get ill! The solution is to not dwell on anything. Do not do not repeatedly drift with the waves. In other words, don't let your mind wander. Do not become distracted. This being the case you will not become chronically stressed and then ill. This is clearly consistent with present-day research regarding chronic stress and research in neuroscience regarding mind wandering and the negative consequences associated with it. So, what does "sit peacefully" entail? In the appendix (*shūyì* 樞翼) to the *Zuowanglun* the process of sitting peacefully is described:

> If you desire to cultivate the Dao to bring about authenticity, you must first get rid of unhealthy practices, detach from external affairs, and be without an interfering mind/heart. After that, sit properly and straight (*duanzuo* 端坐), without bias, non-judgmentally

observing inwardly (***nei guan*** 內觀) with correct perception. If you perceive a single thought rising up, then you must extinguish it. If following thoughts arise, then continue to extinguish them. This practice will bring about a peaceful and still mind/heart. Next, although you do not have any insatiable desires, wandering, random thoughts will float up. These thoughts must also be removed and extinguished. Day and night you must diligently practice. Not for a single moment should you stray from this practice. ... Do not be attached to a single thing, and the mind-heart will always be unaffected. (Santee, 2010; Saohua, n.d.)

The Chinese characters *duan* (端) provide a picture of what exactly "proper" refers to in the phrase "sit properly and straight." The right side (duan 耑) of the character *duan* (端) is a picture of a plant, with its roots descending deeply into the Earth seeking nutrients and stability, while with the top part of plant reaches upward, seeking the energy from the sun. Thus, proper sitting links the sky, the human being, and the Earth into a single, interrelated process. Descending downward and reaching upward allows the spine to naturally align. The left side (*li* 立) of the character *duan* (端) means to stand, be upright or vertical, thus reinforcing the notion of the bi-directional aspect of the plant.

Sit properly and straight (*duanzuo* 端坐), without bias, nonjudgmentally observing inwardly (***nei guan*** 內觀) with correct perception.

Thus, to sit in forgetfulness/oblivion is to sit up straight with your neck gently pushing upward and your tailbone gently pulling downward. Breathe naturally. Do not dwell on anything. If you mind wanders, and it will, don't judge or dwell on the thoughts or feelings that arise and they will naturally fade away or extinguish. Let your mind/heart be naturally still and empty. For this practice to be effective, for neuroplasticity to occur such that your brain and body learn, you must practice on a regular and consistent basis.

Confucianism

The two most important members of the Confucian tradition, Confucius (551–479 BCE) and Mencius (371–289 BCE), do not really discuss any specific type of meditation. It is not until Song dynasty (960–1279) that there is a reference to a specific meditation practice. It is with the Neo-Confucians, during this time period, that a particular type of meditation, known as quiet/still sitting (*jingzuo* 靜坐) is clearly specified and practiced. The Neo-Confucian teachings, while consistent with the learning-driven, moral, family, and society-based and focused teachings of Confucius and Mencius, needed, in order to stay relevant, to adapt to and address the issues and concerns, such as the mind, nature of the universe, and nature of the human being and their linking together, raised and explored by both the Buddhist and Daoist contemporary worldviews. While Buddhism, Daoism, and Neo-Confucianism practice meditation as a way to learn how to adapt to their various environments, the Neo-Confucian approach, while necessarily removing chronic stress and agitation, is specifically focused on enhancing the ability to learning and adapt to society.

The Neo-Confucian Zhuxi (1130–1200), the most prominent member of the Confucian tradition after Confucius and Mencius, gathered and integrated the teachings of various Confucian and Neo-Confucian thinkers before him to address these ontological (nature of the human being) and cosmological (nature of the universe) issues. The practice of meditation, specifically quiet/still sitting (*jingzuo* 靜坐) was used to understand and control one's mind in order for the individual to learn how make appropriate moral decisions and be in harmony with society and the universe wherein it rested.

Zhu Xi's *Collection of Similar Thinking* (*Jinsilu* 近思錄), compiled (1175) by Zhu and Lu Zuqian (1137–1181) is a gathering of the teachings and conversations of various Neo-Confucians who preceded him such as Zhou Dunyi (1017–1073), Zhang Zai (1020–1077), and the brothers Cheng Yi (1033–1107) and Cheng Hao (1032–1085), both of whom were students of Zhou Dunyi and cousins of Zhang Zai. *The Sayings of Master Zhu on Various Topics* (*Zhuzi yu lei* 朱子語類) is a collection of his sayings written by, gathered by, and compiled, in 1270, by his students.

Quiet/still sitting
Jingzuo (靜坐)

In order to place the meditative practice of quiet/still sitting (*jingzuo*) in context, it is necessary to indicate the adaptive problem for which it is being used to resolve. The adaptive problem is that students are having difficulties learning how to internalize and put into practice, in all situations, the characteristics, qualities, and behavior of the Confucian role model: the sage. This adaptive problem has to do with students learning, paying attention, self-monitoring, and mind wandering and the resulting agitation and confusion (chronic stress) that compromises them from progressing on the Confucian path. The following selections from both *Collection of Similar Thinking* and *The Sayings of Master Zhu on Various Topics* present the adaptive problem:

> The moral way (dao 道) of the Sage (shengren 聖人) enters through the ear, exists in the heart-mind (xin 心), accumulates through the individual's moral conduct (dexing 德行) and is practiced in all activities. (Guoxue, n.d.)
>
> Zhu Xi said, "When the sage moves about, there is not an instance when his mind is not quiet/still/calm (*jing* 靜). On the other hand,

when everybody else moves, their minds are agitated and confused. Nowadays, when people desire to work on one activity, they are not able to be focused on that one single activity without being agitated and confused. When they begin to think and consider something, they then desire to do this and desire to do that. When their minds wander like this that is why their mind is not quiet or still." (National Center University, n.d.)

Cheng Yi said, "The minds of students are agitated and confused. They are not able to be tranquil and still. This is a common problem everywhere. If the student merely grounds/roots their mind, then it will end up being free." (Guoxue, n.d.)

The adaptive problem being clearly defined, the next step is to stop the mind wandering and the agitation, confusion, and chronic stress associated with it. It was clear, the mind needed to be calmed down and focused to stop the mind wandering.

Just control/gather the mind by not letting it wander with frivolous thinking. Then this mind will become calm without any distractions. It will naturally (ziran 自然) be single-minded and focused. Then when a concern arises, you will engage with and respond to it. When the concern is resolved, then your mind will return to its natural calmness. You do not want to generate a second or third concern while dealing with the initial concern. If so, your mind will become confused without any boundaries. How could you attain focus and single-mindedness? (National Center University, n.d.)

The adaptive solution to stop the mind wandering, eliminate agitation, confusion, and chronic stress, to reintegrate, become single-minded, and focused, and to get back on track to learning is to practice quiet/still sitting (jingzuo 靜坐).

A student, Xie Xiandao (1050–1103), was with Master Cheng Hao in Fugou (a county in Henan province). Cheng Hao, one day, said, "Your generation that comes along with me to this place, has only studied and learned to make showy speech. Thus, in their learning their minds and their mouth do not correspond. Why don't you practice?" "Practice what?" Master Cheng Hao said, "Just practice quiet/still sitting (jingzuo 靜坐). Each time Cheng Yi saw people practicing quiet/still sitting (jingzuo 靜坐), he exclaimed, with admiration, they were engaged in proficient studying and learning. (Guoxue, n.d.)

Zhu Xi was quite clear that the practice of quiet/still sitting (*jingzuo*) was not like the Chan Buddhist practice of sitting in meditation (*zuochan* 坐禪). His concern was that the goal of this practice was a one-point concentration or *samadhi* (*ding* 定) where all thought and deliberation was eliminated. This contradicted, for him, the Confucian perspective of being fully engaged in the world around you. Quiet/still sitting was to assist the individual in learning the way of the sage, and thus morally interacting and engaging with members of the social structure. He viewed the Chan Buddhist practice of sitting in meditation as an attempt to escape from learning about and morally interacting and engaging with members of the social structure. He notes,

> When quiet/still sitting (jingzuo 靜坐), you do not want it to be like the *samadhi* (*ding* 定) of the Chan Buddhist practitioner sitting in meditation (*zuochan* 坐禪) which cuts off and eliminates all thought and careful consideration. (National Center University, n.d.)

Fundamental to the practice of quiet/still sitting was eliminating mind wandering. Mind wandering was a barrier to and compromised still/quiet sitting itself and learning in general and resulted in agitation, confusion, and chronic stress. Serious attentiveness (jing 敬) addresses and prevents mind wandering. To be successful in quiet/still sitting the practitioner needed to develop, nourish, and practice serious attentiveness. Serious attentiveness was not only for quiet/still sitting. It was fundamental for all aspects of life.

> Zhuxi said, "Sitting quietly/still (jingzuo 靜坐) yet not able to stop your mind wandering (banish your thoughts and deliberations) simply means you are not being seriously attentive (jing 敬) when you are quiet/still sitting (jingzuo 靜坐). Serious attentiveness is simply being seriously attentive." (National Center University, n.d.)
>
> Zhu Xi said, "Serious attentiveness (jing 敬) is to contain, nourish and manage one's mind so that it does not go wandering off." (National Center University, n.d.)
>
> Serious Attentiveness (jing 敬) is merely being single-minded. Single Mindedness is not going east nor going west. It is merely being centered. It is neither this nor that. (Guoxue, n.d.)
>
> Serious Attentiveness (jing 敬): do not consider it to be a single activity. It merely is gathering your mental vitality/spirit (jing shen 精神) and being single-minded. (National Center University, n.d.)

Zhu Xi said, "Serious attentiveness (jing敬) is to contain, nourish and manage one's mind so that it does not go wandering off."

> If you are seriously attentive (*jing*敬), then you will be empty (*xu* 敬) and quiet/still (*jing*靜). (Guoxue, n.d.)
>
> Zhu Xi said, "When the Sage moves about, there is not an instance when the mind of the Sage is not calm/quiet/still (*jing*靜)." (National Center University, n.d.)

When you are seriously attentive there will be no mind wandering. Your mind will be calm, quiet, still, and empty. You will be single-minded in focus. For the Neo-Confucians, you will be able to learn without any barriers.

> Master Cheng Hao said, "One who practices being calm, quiet and still (jing 靜), will be able to learn." (Guoxue, n.d.)
>
> To cultivate and nourish oneself, you must employ attentiveness (jing 敬). To progress in learning, you need to gather and extend your knowledge (zhizhi致知). (Guoxue, n.d.)
>
> Master Cheng Yi, talking to his students, said, "Now everyone of you, when I say something and it is incompatible with what you think, you then no longer think about it. This is why, ultimately, you are different from the students of Confucius and Mencius. You should not then no longer think about it. Even more so should you think about it. This is how to gather and extend knowledge (zhizhi 致知). (Guoxue, n.d.)

Over 800 years ago, the Neo-Confucians were raising the same problem with mind wandering compromising learning and psychological well-being and being intimately involved with chronic stress as the researcher today in neuroscience. In addition, both turned to meditation as a way of addressing it. Given the mind of the sage is still, calm, quiet, and empty, it is clear that the sage is not chronically stressed physically or psychologically—again, the benefits of meditation that researchers today have discovered.

SPIRITUALITY

Spirituality can be defined in many ways such as a relationship with something greater than oneself; inner awareness; peak experiences; encounters with the sacred; absorption or loss of a separate sense of self; non-duality, interpersonal selfless love; release from restrictions and limitations; authentic and humanistic relationships with others; being one with nature; prayer, religious worship, attending and participating in a church, synagogue, mosque, temple, etc.; and faith/belief in a deity or deities, etc. It can be individual/personal and/or structured, organized, and as a member of a group. Meditation is a practice that has, for thousands of years, been utilized as a modality for spiritual experience. Given the selections on Buddhism, Daoism, and Confucianism that you just read, do they fall in the realm of spirituality? If so, why? If not, why not? How is spirituality connected to managing chronic stress?

Moving and Standing Meditation

The American College of Sport Medicine (ACSM, 2010) lists exercise under four categories of fitness: stretching, aerobic, anaerobic, and neuromuscular. Neuromuscular exercises are concerned with such areas as agility, balance, coordination, and proprioceptive awareness (ACSM, 2010; Roy, 2104). As moving and standing meditation such as taijiquan, qigong, and yoga also fall under this category, they will be examined for both their exercise and meditative benefits in **chapter 6, "Exercise."**

PRACTICAL APPLICATIONS

Meditation: Safe-Space Visualization

The meditative process of visualization incorporates, both still and moving, various objects/processes such as images, scenes, colors, deities, spirits, the body and its organs, meridians, and energies (Kohn, 2008). It may be self-generated or be by guided imagery. It is an integral aspect of both Daoism and certain types of

Buddhism such as Tibetan/Tantric Buddhism (Kohn, 2008). It can be utilized for such areas as spiritual cultivation, relaxation, self-healing, physical and psychological transformation, performance enhancement, and managing chronic stress.

Safe-space visualization is a visualization exercise that allows you to mentally disengage from your everyday stress and relax both your mind and body. Safe-space visualizations can be self-generated and/or be a guided process utilizing a CD, DVD, an app, a script, the Internet, etc.

Essentially, safe-space visualization is creating a safe space in your mind where you feel secure, safe, grounded, and not stressed. It can be place from your past, in the present, or some place in the future. It can be on a mountain, in a park, in a garden, on the beach, in a house, or room you felt or feel safe in, and so on. It can be a real place or one entirely created out of your imagination. You can bring whoever and whatever you want to your safe space. The important point is that it and you are free from stress. You are not, however, fantasizing about your future, engaging in wish fulfilment, or day dreaming. It is not mind wandering! You are in control and the sole purpose is to have a place in your mind that you can consciously disengage from stress, allowing your body and mind to relax, rest, and heal.

You can visualize for a set time, setting an alarm or your phone for 5 or 10 minutes or just letting it happen until you feel like returning. Once you begin do not change your safe space while you are engaged in the exercise unless you find yourself stressing out. It may be a challenge but see if you can stick with it. Do not be judgmental in any shape or form as you go through the process. If you find yourself mind wandering (it occurs with all types of meditation), simply return to your safe space. If you are going to use an alarm, set it now. Begin:

- Take three deep breaths, inhaling and exhaling evenly, slowly, and quietly.
- After the third breath, create in your mind your safe space.
- Bring whoever and whatever you want to your safe space.

- Fully engage your experience by looking at, smelling, listening, feeling, and, if available, tasting the various aspects of your safe space.
- Off you go; enjoy your journey!

So, how did it go? How do you feel? Were you able to stay focused and create a safe space? What did you notice while you were journeying through your safe space? Did your mind wander? Were you able to easily return? Did you find yourself judging the entire process?

Zhanzhuang: Position Four

As this is the fourth position in the practice of *Zhan Zhuang*, you can continue the sequence that was developed in the previous chapter, moving from the first, to the second, and to the third posture, holding each position for 1 minute (you can, of course, hold it longer). Breathing naturally through your nose, simply observe, without making any judgments, what you feel in your body. You are observing *via guan* throughout the entire sequence.

From the third position, your arms are holding/encircling the large beach ball in front of your chest; simply lower your arms, still holding/encircling the large beach ball, until your hands, palms facing each other, are at hip level, which is about 3 or so inches below your bellybutton. You have returned to the second position. Stay in this position for a minute or so. Upon completion of the fourth position, let your hands arc down to your sides and return to the *wuji* position. Hold this position for 1 minute. After 1 minute take a deep breath and simply do a short walk.

Upon completion, how do you feel? What did you notice? Was there a difference between doing the positions/postures individually as opposed to doing them in a sequence? Did your mind wander? If so, were you able to easily refocus? Was one position easier for you? If so, why?

Yoga: Warrior Two Pose (*Virabhadrasana*)

From the mountain, step into the warrior one pose with your left leg forward, knee bent at a 90-degree angle, with the knee directly above your ankle. Do both sides. From the warrior one pose with your right leg forward, breathing naturally, inhaling and exhaling through your nose, simply lower and extend both arms to your sides, shoulder level, with palms facing down. Do not lock your elbows. With your legs and feet maintaining the same position from the warrior one pose, turn your waist/pelvis to the left so that your chest is facing to the left side. Your head does not turn and remains looking forward.

Hold for 30 seconds. Step up with your rear leg, lower your arms to your sides, and return to the mountain pose. Pause for a moment, take a breath, let it out, and then perform the warrior two pose on the other side, stepping straight forward with your left leg, knee bent at a 90-degree angle, with the knee directly above your ankle, raising both arms to shoulder level while extending them to sides with palms down. Turn your waist/pelvis to the right so that your chest is facing to the right side. Your head does not turn and remains looking forward. Hold for 30 seconds. Step up with your rear leg, lower your arms to your sides, and return to the mountain pose. Pause for a moment, take a breath, and let it out.

How do you feel upon completion of the warrior two pose? What did you notice while you were in the pose? Was one side easier than the other side? Does your body feel relaxed and stretched out? How does your mind feel? Did you get distracted while performing it? If so, were you able to easily return to your focus on it? How did you feel transitioning from the mountain pose to the warrior one pose and then to the warrior two pose? What do you feel and notice about the two warrior poses? How are they different? How are they the same?

KEY TERMS

autobiographical self
social self
psychosocial past
psychosocial future
meditation
still meditation
moving meditation
vipassana/vipasyana
mindfulness (*Sati*)
one-point concentration (*Samadhi*)
mind/heart fasting (*Xinzhai*)
sitting in forgetfulness/

Oblivion (*Zuowang*)
quiet/tranquil sitting (*Jingzuo*)
default network
mind wandering
the negativity bias
chronic stress
neuroplasticity
correct effort
correct mindfulness
correct concentration
four dwellings of mindfulness
mindfulness of the body

mindfulness of breathing
zhenren
qi
neiguan
serious attentiveness (*Jing*)
gathering and extending knowledge
single mindedness
naturally (*Ziran*)
without desire (*Wuyu*)

EXERCISES

1. What is meditation? How can it be performed?

2. Why and how is meditation beneficial for addressing and eliminating chronic stress?

3. From the perspective of neuroscience, in the context of chronic stress, why is the autobiographical self problematic?

4. Describe the relationship between the default network, mind wandering, the negativity bias, the autobiographical self, chronic stress, neuroplasticity, meditation, and stress management.

5. Why is it important to have an understanding of neuroplasticity when addressing the benefits of meditation?

6. Compare mindfulness (*sati*), one-point concentration (*samadhi*), mind/heart fasting (*xinzhai*), sitting in forgetfulness/oblivion (*zuowang*), and quiet/tranquil sitting (*jingzuo*).

7. Compare the Buddhist, Daoist, and Confucian incorporation of meditation into their adaptive solutions for their adaptive problems.

8. Indicate how mind wandering is an adaptive problem for the Buddhist, Daoist, and Confucian traditions. How do they address and resolve it?

REFERENCES

Agama. (2019). *Numerical Discourses.* Translated from http://agama.buddhason.org/AN/AN0489.htm

Agama. (2019a). *Middle length sayings.* Translated from http://agama.buddhason.org/MN/MN141.htm

Agama. (1019b). *Middle length sayings.* Translated from http://agama.buddhason.org/MN/MN026.htm

Agama. (2019c). *Middle length sayings.* Translated from http://agama.buddhason.org/MN/MN140.htm

Agama. (2019d e). *Middle length sayings.* Translated from http://agama.buddhason.org/MN/MN010.htm

American College of Sports Medicine (ACSM). (2010). *ACSM's guidelines for exercise testing and prescription* (8th ed.). Baltimore, MD: Lippincott, & Williams.

Ames, R. T. & Hall, D. L. (2003). *Daodejing: Making this life significant. A philosophical translation.* New York, NY: Ballentine.

Andrews-Hanna, J. R. (2012). The brain's default network and its adaptive role in internal mentation. *Neuroscientist, 18*(3), 251–270.

Benson, H. (2000). *The relaxation response.* New York, NY: Harper.

Brandmeyer, T., & Delorme, A. (2016). Reduced mind wandering in experienced meditators and associated EEG correlates. *Experimental Brain Research, 263*(9), 2519–2528.

Brewer, J. A., Worhunsky, P. D., Gray, J. R., Tang, Y. Y., Weber, J., & Kober, H. (2011). Meditation experience is associated with differences in default mode network activity and connectivity. *Proceedings of the National Academy of Sciences, 108*(50), 20254–20259.

Buckner, R. L., & Carroll, D. C. (2012). Self-projection and the brain. *Trends in Cognitive Sciences, 11*(2), 49–57.

Chang, B., Casey A., Dusek, J. A., & Benson, H. (2010). Relaxation response and spirituality: Pathways to improve psychological outcomes in cardiac rehabilitation. *Journal of Psychosomatic Research, 69*(2), 93–100.

Chang, B., Dusek, J. A., & Benson, H. (2011). Psychobiological changes from relaxation response elicitation: Long-term practitioners vs. novices. *Psychosomatics, 52*(6), 550–559.

Chen, K. W., Berger, C. C., Manheimer, E., Forde, D., Magidson, J., Dachman, L., & Lejuez, C. W. (2012). Meditative therapies for reducing anxiety: A systematic review and meta-analysis of randomized controlled trials. *Depression and Anxiety, 29*(7), 545–562.

Cheng, C. Y. (2003). Philosophy of change. In A. S. Sua (Ed.), *Encyclopedia of Chinese philosophy* (pp. 517–524). New York, NY: Routledge.

Damasio, A. (2010). *Self comes to mind: Constructing the conscious brain.* New York, NY: Pantheon.

Davidson, R. J., & Kaszniak, A. W. (2015). Conceptual and methodological issues in research on mindfulness and meditation. *American Psychologist, 70*(7), 581–592.

Dakwar, E., & Levin, F. (2009). The emerging role of meditation in addressing psychiatric illness, with a focus on substance use disorders. *Harvard Review of Psychiatry, 17*(4), 254–267.

Davis, D. M., & Hayes, J. A. (2011). What are the benefits of mindfulness? A practice review of psychotherapy-related research. *Psychotherapy, 48*(2), 198–208.

Dimidjian, S., & Segal, Z. V. (2015). Prospects for a clinical science of mindfulness-based intervention. *American Psychologist, 70*(7), 593–620.

Dusek, J., & Benson, H. (2009). Mind-body medicine: A model of the comparative clinical impact of the acute stress and relaxation responses. *Minnesota Medicine 92*(5), 47–50.

Esch, T., Fricchione, G. L., & Stefano, G. B. (2003). The therapeutic use of the relaxation response in stress-related diseases. *Medical Science Monitor, 9*(2), RA23–34.

Farb, N. A., Anderson, A. K., Mayberg, H., Bean, J., McKeon, D., & Segal, Z. V. (2010). Minding one's emotions: Mindfulness training alters the neural expression of sadness. *Emotion, 10*(1), 25–33.

Goyal, M., Singh, S., Sibinga, E. M. S., Gould, N. F., Rowland-Seymour, A., Sharma, R., ... & Haythornthwaite, J. A. (2014). Meditation programs for psychological stress and well-being: A systematic review and meta-analysis. *JAMA Internal Medicine, 174*(7), 357–368.

Grossman, P., Niemann, L., Schmidt, S., & Walach, H. (2004). Mindfulness based stress reduction and health benefits. *Journal of Psychosomatic Research, 57*(1), 35–43.

Guo, Q. F. (1956). *A concordance to Chuang Tzu.* Cambridge, MA: Harvard University Press.

Guo, Q. F. (1974). *Zhuangzi jishi* 莊子集釋, Vols. 1 and 2. Taipei, Taiwan: Chung Hwa.

Guoxue. (n.d.). *Collection of similar thinking.* Translated from http://www.guoxue123.com/zhibu/0101/01jsl/005.htm

Gusnard, D. A., Akbudak, E., Shulman, G. L., & Raichle, M. E. (2001). Medial prefrontal cortex and self-referential mental activity: Relation to a default mode of brain function. *Proceedings of the National Academy of Sciences, 98*(7), 4259–4264.

Harrington, A., & Dunne, J. D. (2015). When mindfulness is therapy: Ethical qualms, historical perspectives. *American Psychologist, 70*(7), 621–631.

Ito, T. A., Larsen, J. T., Smith, N. K., & Cacioppo, J. T. (1998). Negative information weighs more heavily on the brain: The negativity bias in evaluative categorization. *Journal of Personality and Social Psychology, 75*(4), 887–900.

Jazaieri, H., Lee, I. A., McGonigal, K., Jinpa, T., Doty, J. R., Gross, J. J., & Goldin, P. R. (2015). A wandering mind is a less caring mind: Daily experience sampling during compassion meditation training. *Journal of Positive Psychology, 11*(1), 37–50.

Kabat-Zinn, J. (2005). *Full catastrophe living: Using the wisdom of Your body and mind to face stress, pain, and illness.* New York, NY: Random House.

Killingsworth, M. A (2011). *Want to be happier? Stay in the moment* [TED Talk]. Retrieved from http://www.ted.com/talks/matt_killingsworth_want_to_be_happier_stay_in_the_moment

Killingsworth, M. A., & Gilbert, D. (2010). A wandering mind is an unhappy mind. *Science, 330*(6006), 932.

Kohn, L. (1989). *Taoist meditation and longevity techniques.* Ann Arbor, MI: University of Michigan.

Kohn, L. (2008). *Meditation works: In the Hindu, Buddhist and Daoist traditions*. Magdalena, NM: Three Pines Press.

Kohn, L. (2010). *Sitting in oblivion: The heart of Daoist meditation*. Dunedin, FL: Three Pines Press.

Kohn, L. (2011). *Chuang-Tzu: the Tao of perfect happiness. Selections annotated and explained*. Nashville, TN: Skylights Paths Publishing.

Kristeller, J. L. (2007). Mindfulness meditation. In P. M. Leher, R. L. Woolfolk, & W. E. Sime (Eds.), *Principles and practice of stress management* (pp. 393–427). New York, NY: Guilford.

Lutz A., Jha, A. P., Dunne, J. D., & Saron, C. D. (2015). Investigating the phenomenological matrix of mindfulness-related practices from a neurocognitive perspective. *American Psychologist, 70*(7), 632–658.

Lutz, A., Slagter H. A., Dunne, J. D., & Davidson, R. J. (2008). Attention regulation and monitoring in meditation. *Trends in Cognitive Sciences, 12*(4), 163–169.

Mooneyham, B. W., & Schooler, J. W. (2013). The costs and benefits of mind-wandering: A review. *Canadian Journal of Experimental Psychology, 67*(1), 11–18.

Mrazek, M. D., Smallwood, J., & Schooler, J. W. (2012). Mindfulness and mind-wandering: Finding convergence through opposing constructs. *Emotion, 12*(3), 442–448.

Mrazek, M. D., Franklin, M. S., Phillips, D. T., Baird, B., & Schooler, J. W. (2013). Mindfulness training improves working memory capacity and GRE performance while reducing mind wandering. *Psychological Science, 24*(5), 776–781.

Mrazek, M. D., Mooneyham, B. W., & Schooler, J. W. (2014). Insights from quiet minds: The converging fields of mindfulness and mind-wandering. In S. Schmidt & H. Walach (Eds.), *Meditation-neuroscientific approaches and philosophical implications: Studies in neuroscience, consciousness and spirituality, vol. 2*, (pp. 227–241). Frankfurt, Germany: Springer.

Mrazek, M. D, Broadway, J. M., Phillips, D. T., Franklin, M. S., Mooneyham, B. W., & Schooler, J. W. (2014). Mindfulness: An antidote for wandering mind. In A. Le, C.T. Ngnoumen, & E. J. Langer (Eds.), *The Wiley Blackwell handbook of mindfulness, vol. 1* (pp. 153–167). Hoboken, NJ: Wiley.

National Center University. (n.d.). *The sayings of Master Zhu on various topics. Retrieved from* https://in.ncu.edu.tw/~phi/confucian/docs/resource/05_5/11-20.htm

Northoff, G., Heinzel, A., de Greck, M., Bermpohl, F., Dobrowolny, H., & Panksepp, J., (2006). Self-referential processing in our brain—a meta-analysis of imaging studies on the self. *NeuroImage, 31*(1), 440–457.

Rahula, W. (1959). *What the Buddha taught*. New York, NY: Grove.

Roy, B. (2014). Functional exercise training. *ACSM's Health & Fitness Journal, 18*(3), 3. Retrieved from http://journals.lww.com/acsm-healthfitness/Fulltext/2014/05000/FUNctional_Exercise_Training.3.aspx

Rozin, P., & Roysman E. B. (2001). Negativity bias, negativity dominance, and contagion. *Personality and Social Psychology Review, 5*(4), 296–320.

Santee, R. (2003). An inquiry into the Dao of the Dao de Jing. *World Hong Ming Philosophical Quarterly.*

Santee, R. (2004, July 22). *A Daoist and an existential psychotherapist: A comparative study*. Paper presented at the First World Hong Ming Philosophy Conference. Honolulu, HI.

Santee, R. (2005a, October 12–15). *Cultivating emptiness: The practice of xin zhai, an ancient Daoist solution to the problem of chronic stress*. Paper presented at the International Conference of Daoist Cultivation and its Modern Value. Chengdu, China.

Santee (2005b). An Exploration of an Early Source: Nourishing Life, Cultivating Qi and Qi Gong. *Qi: the Journal of Traditional Eastern Health and Fitness*. Summer 2005, Volume 15, No. 2.

Santee, R. (2005c, May 20–23). *Carl Rogers and the Dao de Jing: A comparative study*. Paper presented at the International Conference on Daoism Mt. Tiantai And Zhejiang. Zhejiang, China.

Santee, R. (2007). *An Integrative Approach to Counseling: Bridging Chinese Thought, Evolutionary Theory, and Stress Management*. Copyright © 2007 by SAGE Publications. Reprinted with permission.

Santee, R. (2010, June 2–6). *Sitting in forgetfulness and the relaxation response: An inquiry into managing the physical and psychological symptoms of chronic stress*. Paper presented at the Sixth International Daoist Studies Conference, Daoism Today: Science, Health and Ecology. Los Angeles, CA.

Santee, R. (2011). "The Zhuangzi: A Holistic Approach to Health Care," *Living Authentically: Daoist Contributions to Modern Psychology*, ed. Livia Kohn, pp. 45. Copyright © 2011 by Three Pines Press. Reprinted with permission.

Saohua. (n.d.). *Sitting in oblivion/forgetfulness.* Retrieved from http://www.saohua.com/shuku/zongjiao/daojiao/011.htm

Schacter, D. L., Addis, D. R., Hassabis, D., Martin, V. C., Spreng, R. N., & Szpunar, K. K. (2012). The future of memory: Remembering, imagining, and the brain. *Neuron, 76*(4), 677–794.

Schooler, J. W., Mrazek, M. D., Franklin, M. S., Baird, B., Mooneyham, B. W., Zedelius, C., & Broadway, J. M. (2014). The middle way: Finding the balance between mindfulness and mind-wandering. In B. H. Ross (Ed.), *The psychology of learning and motivation*, vol. 60 (pp. 1–33). Urbana, IL: Academic Press.

Schooler, J. W., Smallwood, J., Christoff, K., Handy, T. C., Reichle, E. D., & Sayette, M. A. (2011). Meta-awareness, perceptual decoupling and the wandering mind. *Trends in Cognitive Sciences, 15*(7), 319–326.

Sedlmeier, P., Eberth, J., Schwarz, M., Zimmermann, D., Haarig, F., Jaeger, S., & Kunze, S. (2012). The psychological effects of meditation: A meta-analysis. *Psychological Bulletin, 138*(6), 1139–1171.

Smallwood, J., Fishman, J. D., & Schooler, J. W. (2007). Counting the cost of an absent mind: Mind wandering as an underrecognized influence on educational performance. *Psychonomic Bulletin & Review, 14*(2), 230–236.

Smallwood, J., Fitzgerald, A., Miles, L. K., & Phillips, L. H. (2009). Shifting moods, wandering minds: Negative moods lead the mind to wander. *Emotion, 9*(2), 271–276.

Smallwood, J., & O'Connor, R. C. (2011). Imprisoned by the past: Unhappy moods lead to a retrospective bias to mind wandering. *Cognition & Emotion, 25*(8), 1481–1490.

Smallwood, J., & Schooler, J. W. (2009). Mind-wandering. In T. Bayne, A. Cleermans & P. Wilken (Eds.), *The Oxford companion to consciousness* (pp. 443–445). Oxford, UK: Oxford University Press.

Sood, A. S., & Jones, D. T. (2013). On mind wandering, attention, brain networks, and meditation. *Explore, 9*(3), 136–141.

Spreng, R. N., & Andrews-Hanna, J. R. (2015). The default network and social cognition. In A. W. Toga (Ed.), *Brain mapping: An encyclopedic reference* (pp. 165–169). London, UK: Academic Press.

Stawarczyk, D., Cassol, H., & D'Argembeau, A. (2013). Phenomenology of future-oriented mind-wandering episodes. *Frontiers in Psychology, 4*, 1–12.

Szpunar, K. K. (2017). Directing the wandering mind. *Current Directions in Psychological Science, 26*(1), 40–44.

Tang, Y., Posner, M. I., & Rothbart, M. K. (2014). Meditation improves self-regulation over the life span. *Annals of New York Academy of Sciences, 1307*(1), 104–111.

Tang, Y., Ma, Y., Wang, J., Fan, Y., Feng, S., Lu, Q., … & Posner, M. I. (2007). Short-term meditation training improves attention and self-regulation. *PNAS, 104*(43), 17152–17156.

Tripitaka. (2016). *The sutra of one night of the good and wise person.* Retrieved from http://tripitaka.cbeta.org/mobile/index.php?index=N12n0005_015

Wallace, B. A., & Shapiro, S. L. (2006). Mental balance and well-being: Building bridges between Buddhism and Western psychology. *American Psychologist, 61*(7), 690–701.

Walsh, R. (2000). Asian psychotherapies. In R. J. Corsini & D. Wedding (Eds.), *Current psychotherapies* (pp. 407–444). Ithaca, NY: F.E. Peacock.

Walsh, R. (2011). Lifestyle and mental health. *American Psychologist, 66* (7), 579–592.

Walsh, R., & Shapiro, S. L. (2006). The meeting of meditative disciplines and Western psychology: A mutually enriching dialogue. *American Psychologist, 61*(3), 227–239.

Wang, K. (1993). *Laozi daodejing he shanggong zhang zhu.* Beijing, China: Zhong Hua Shu Ju.

Yang, J. L. (zhu bian) (1972). *Laozi ben yi, Laozi xin kao shu lue.* Taipei, Taiwan: Shi Jie Shu Ju.

Zanesco, A.P., King, B. G., MacLean, K. A., Jacobs, T. L., Aichele, S. R., Wallace, B. A., … & Saron C. D. (2016). Meditation training influences mind wandering and mindless reading. *Psychology of Consciousness: Theory, Research, and Practice, 3*(1), 12–33.

Zedelius, C. M., Broadway, J. M., & Schooler, J. W. (2015). Motivating meta-awareness of mind wandering: A way to catch the mind in flight? *Consciousness and Cognition, 36*, 44–53.

Zeidan, F., Johnson, S. K., Diamond, B. J., David, Z., & Goolkasian, P. (2010). Mindfulness meditation improves cognition: Evidence of brief mental training. *Consciousness and Cognition, 19*(2), 597–605.

CREDITS

- Fig. 4.1: Copyright © 2015 Depositphotos/AndreyPopov.
- Fig. 4.2: Copyright © 2016 Depositphotos/Wavebreakmedia.
- Fig. 4.3: Copyright © 2014 Depositphotos/vensk.
- Fig. 4.4: Copyright © 2013 Depositphotos/Fieryphoenix.
- Fig. 4.5: Copyright © 2012 Depositphotos/ tomwang.
- Fig. 4.6: Copyright © 2013 Depositphotos/realinemedia.
- Fig. 4.7 : Copyright © 2012 Depositphotos/Maugli.
- Fig. 4.8: Copyright © 2010 Depositphotos/muha04.
- Fig. 4.9: from Robert Santee, "The Yijinjing," *Qi: The Journal of Traditional Eastern Health and Fitness,* vol. 21, no. 2. Qi, 2011.
- Fig. 4.10: Copyright © 2014 Depositphotos/AnnaTamila.
- Fig. 4.11: Copyright © 2017 Depositphotos/Xalanx.

Cognitive Restructuring

After finishing this chapter, you will be able to do the following:

- Describe the evolutionary basis of threat-based thinking and indicate how threat-based thinking can be a problem today
- Explain how the default network, mind wandering, and the negativity bias are linked to threat-based psychosocial thinking and how they can contribute to maladaptive, dysfunctional thinking and chronic stress
- Describe negative automatic thoughts and indicate how they are linked to chronic stress and psychological disorders
- Define cognitive distortions and link them to chronic stress and psychological disorders
- Compare cognitive restructuring and cognitive reframing relative to addressing chronic stress
- Explain how the approach of cognitive therapy can be utilized to address chronic stress and psychological disorders
- Indicate how meditation can be viewed as being with dysfunctional, maladaptive, psychosocial beliefs and thoughts while cognitive therapy can be viewed as changing them

- Compare Buddhism, Daoism, and Confucianism relative to their integrating meditation with cognitive restructuring and cognitive reframing
- Indicate how positive psychology can be integrated with cognitive restructuring and cognitive reframing relative to addressing chronic stress

As noted in previous chapters, the primary source of chronic stress is our ongoing negative, absolute, inflexible, and judgmental, **psychosocial threat-based thinking**. Whether it is oriented to the past, future, or present, this type of chronic **dysfunctional thinking** is detrimental to our physical and psychological health/well-being. According to cognitive therapists (Beck, Rush, Shaw, & Emery, 1979; Ellis, 2001) underlying this type of thinking are problematic, absolute, and unrealistic beliefs, demands, values, and schemas regarding the world around us, other people, and ourselves. These problematic absolute beliefs, demands, values, and schemas guide and tell us how to behave in various environmental contexts. They are believed and not questioned. It is not so much the situation or context in and of itself that is the problem, as it is what the situation or context means to us. Given these beliefs are problematic, unrealistic, and dysfunctional, they give rise to our problematic, unrealistic, judgmental psychosocial thinking, which in turn results in dysfunctional emotions and behavior. Thus, our problematic, unrealistic, and dysfunctional beliefs and thinking about the world around us, other people, and ourselves, give rise to chronic stress and the subsequent physical and psychological problems associated with it.

From the perspective of **cognitive therapy** (Beck 1979, 1999/2010; Beck & Weishaar 2005; Burns 1999; Ellis 1998, 2004, 2005; Ellis & MacLaren 2003), by changing an individual's problematic, unrealistic, and dysfunctional beliefs and thinking to being functional, realistic, and beneficial, the subsequent emotions and behaviors will also change and no longer be problematic and dysfunctional. This change in beliefs, thinking, emotions and behavior also contributes to the removal of chronic stress.

EVOLUTION AND THOUGHT PROCESSES

In addition to the physical changes that occur during the activation of the fight/freeze/flight or stress response, there are series of psychological changes, such as increased levels of attention, concentration, arousal, watchfulness, anxiety, and vigilance, that occur for the purpose of keeping the individual aware of the perceived acute threat and enhancing his or her chances of survival. A specific type of thinking, also part of our evolutionary survival toolkit, occurs to keep the individual free from distractions and focused on the perceived acute threat for the purpose of resolving it either by fleeing, freezing, or fighting.

This type of thinking is a sort of tunnel vision that is self-centered, judgmental, absolute, black and white, dichotomous (win/lose; die/survive; right/wrong; good/bad; etc.), and inflexible. Insofar as it is oriented toward danger to oneself, it has a clear negativity bias. It occurs automatically and suddenly, without any conscious reflection. For our distant ancestors, given their precarious environment, if they were to consciously and ponderously reflect on the perceived physical danger before reacting, in all likelihood they would have ended up dead. This type of thinking is called **threat-based thinking**. Cognitive therapists Beck and Weishaar (2005) essentially refer to this as "primitive thinking."

Threat-based thinking served our distant ancestors well in responding to acute physical threats. It was realistic, functional, and adaptive. Once the physical problem was resolved, threat-based thinking, along with the other components of the stress response, were turned off. The problem for us today is that our environment is radically different from that of our distant ancestors. Our threats are primarily psychosocial in nature. Our brain, however, does not make a distinction between a perceived real, acute physical threat and a perceived psychosocial, threat. In either case, the stress response will be activated.

If the perceived psychosocial threat is unrealistic, the activation of the stress response and its threat-based thinking is of no benefit. Its activation is inappropriate as it does not assist the individual in resolving the perceived unrealistic psychosocial threat. In fact, it often makes the situation worse. In addition, as long as you continue to think about this self-generated, imagined, and unrealistic psychosocial threat, your stress response along with the threat-based thinking associated with it will be continually activated. This results in chronic stress.

Default Network

As noted in previous chapters, research in neuroscience has indicated that the default network is essentially the home of the autobiographical or social self. It is toward this self that one's unrealistic **psychosocial beliefs, judgments**, and **thoughts** about one's self-worth are directed. It is toward this self that one's unrealistic psychosocial beliefs and judgments regarding their demands and expectations of how others and the world around them should behave are directed. It is toward this self that one's unrealistic psychosocial beliefs and judgments concerning how one should feel and/or not feel relative to his or her expectations and demands about the world around him or her, other people, and his or her own self are directed. In all three cases, the perceived violation of these unrealistic beliefs and judgments is viewed as a threat and results in a perceived attack on the autobiographical or social self, resulting in chronic stress and the associated physical and psychological dysfunction.

Threat-based thinking

Mind Wandering/Simulation

It is within the framework of the default network, as noted in previous chapters, that the autobiographical or social self engages in mind wandering. While it has been noted that mind wandering in and replaying the **psychosocial past** and imagining the **psychosocial future** may have beneficial aspects such as, via simulation, learning from one's past mistakes, reinforcing successful behaviors, planning for the future, and practicing potential successful behaviors, the research suggests that one's autobiographical or social self tends not to be happy when mind wandering. Within the context of cognitive therapy, this is due to the unrealistic and negative judgments individuals make as they obsess and ruminate about the past and excessively worry about and anticipate the worst from the future. All of these thinking processes are threat based and, if ongoing, lead to chronic stress.

Threat-based psychosocial thinking

Negativity Bias

As covered in previous chapters, the negativity bias is part of our evolutionary toolkit because it assisted our distant ancestors in surviving in a continually changing and physically threatening environment. Upon the perception of a threat to one's self, the fight/freeze/flight or stress response was activated, which allowed our distant ancestors to address the threats, which were physical in nature. For the most part, real physical threats to one's self were easily discernable, and, as such, the negativity bias worked quite well. This being the case, it was passed on to us. The negativity bias today is, however, quite problematic. It has, essentially, become a predisposition to be looking for potential psychosocial threats.

Negativity bias

Our formulation into societies and the inherent competition among us in those societies has generated an endless series of potential psychosocial threats and the subsequent chronic activation of the stress response. As indicated in previous chapters, the stress response is primarily being activated by threat-based, self-referential psychosocial thinking, which in many cases, is being guided by unrealistic, beliefs, demands, values, and schemas regarding the world around us, other people, and our autobiographical or social self. This type of self-referential threat-based thinking reflects an evolution-based negativity bias (Ito, Larsen, Smith, & Cacioppo, 1998; Rozin & Roysman 2001). Ongoing self-referential obsessing and rumination about threat-based psychosocial occurrences from the past and ongoing self-referential anticipation and worrying about threat-based psychosocial occurrences in the future, maintains the activation of the stress response and results in chronic stress (Sood & Jones, 2013).

Thus, from the perspective of cognitive therapy, in order to address these issues, there is a necessity for cognitive restructuring—in other words, changing our unrealistic and dysfunctional beliefs, schemas, judgments, demands, values, and thinking regarding the world around us, other people, and our autobiographical or social self.

Problematic Absolute Beliefs and Thoughts

Within the context of cognitive therapy and cognitive restructuring, problematic absolute beliefs and thoughts are dysfunctional, maladaptive, inflexible, and unrealistic. They are manifested in one's assumptions, judgments, values, expectations and demands about how the world around us should/must behave, how other people should/must behave and feel, and how one's autobiographical or social self must/should feel and behave (Ellis, 2001, 2005; Ellis & MacLaren, 2003). These absolute thoughts and their underlying absolute beliefs are considered to be irrational as they are unrealistic and counterproductive relative to the individual generating adaptive solutions for adaptive problems (Ellis, 1998; Ellis & MacLaren, 2003). Absolute thoughts include such words as "must," "should," "all," "everybody," "nobody," "never," and so on. When these absolute beliefs and thoughts are contradicted and/or opposed it is viewed as a threat to the individual, which in turn sets off and/or maintains the stress response.

Negative Automatic Thoughts

Given our negativity bias, we have a wired-in predisposition to look for threats. **Negative automatic thoughts** (think mind wandering) are the initial thoughts that gallop through our mind; appear rapidly and involuntarily; are not due to reflection or analysis; are self-referential, specific, and judgmental; and occur as a result of our perception of an occurrence or event that we believe to be a threat and before the arising of the subsequent emotion and/or behavior associated with the situation (Beck, 1979, 1999/2010; Beck, Rush, Shaw, & Emery, 1979). The negative automatic thoughts in response to the situation is what gives rises to dysfunctional emotions and/or behaviors. It is what gives rise to the activation of and the maintaining of the stress response and leads to chronic stress. If this negative automatic thought process is ongoing, it will literally become wired in the brain via neuroplasticity. In addition, it will reinforce and functionally strengthen our negativity bias, making it even more readily accessible.

Negative automatic thoughts

Cognitive Distortions

Cognitive distortions are categorical, unrealistic, rigid, maladaptive, extreme, negative-based, judgmental, usually self-referential patterns of errors in thinking that may lead, if ongoing, to emotional problems, behavioral problems, and chronic stress (Beck, 1999/2010; Burns, 1999). Cognitive distortions misrepresent and misinterpret events in our world.

TABLE 5.1 **Typical cognitive distortions**

COGNITIVE DISTORTIONS	EXAMPLES
Black-and-white thinking	Winner or loser, right or wrong, good or bad, friend or enemy, success or failure
Selective abstraction	Ten people evaluate you. Nine say you are great and one says you are terrible. You ignore the overall context and just focus on/abstract out the terrible evaluation
Awfulizing	The proverbial making a mountain out of a molehill. You notice a small bump on the back of your hand and then you awfulize about it until you get to the point that you have skin cancer, are going to die, and your family will be destroyed.
Jumping to conclusions	Because your boss didn't notice you when she walked by, you conclude, without any evidence, that she thinks you are performing your job unsatisfactorily.
Labeling	You do not do as well as you thought on an exam and label yourself as "dumb," "stupid," "ignorant." (Discussions and/or lists of cognitive distortions can be found in Beck, 1999/2010; Burns, 1999; Benson & Casey, 2013; Grohol, 2017; Hartney, 2016; Pretzer & Beck, 2007.)

THE APPROACH OF COGNITIVE THERAPY

The two most well-known approaches to cognitive therapy and cognitive restructuring are rational emotive behavioral therapy (REBT) of Albert Ellis and cognitive behavioral therapy (CBT) of Aaron Beck (Hyland & Boduszek, 2012). There is considerable research supporting the effectiveness of cognitive therapy across a wide range of areas such as anxiety, depression, anger, hostility, stress, bulimia, somatoform disorders, chronic low back pain, and chronic fatigue syndrome (Beck & Weishaar, 2005; Ellis, 2005; Driessen & Hollon 2010; Hofmann, Asnaani, Vonk, Sawyer, & Fang, 2012; Hoseini, Vaziri, & Kashani, 2014: Olatunji, Cisler, & Deacon, 2010; Roth & Fonagy, 2005; Rupke, Blecke, & Renfrow, 2006; Tolin, 2010; Wiles et al., 2016; Zhaleh, Zarbakhsh, & Faramarzi, 2014).

Given that, from the perspective of cognitive therapy, the cause of chronic stress, emotional problems, and behavioral problems is absolute, rigid, unrealistic, maladaptive, and dysfunctional beliefs and thinking, which the client or individual believes to be true and thus does not question; the therapeutic focus of cognitive therapy is changing those absolute, problematic, maladaptive beliefs and thoughts by disputing, questioning, contradicting, and challenging them (Beck, 1999/2010; Beck & Dozois, 2011; Beck, Rush, Shaw, & Emery, 1979; Burns, 1999; Ellis, 2001, Ellis & MacLaren, 2003). In other words, it is **cognitive restructuring**. This disputing, questioning, and challenging approach takes the form of "where is it written that," "show me the evidence that," "can this be explained or interpreted in another way" (often referred to as **cognitive reframing**), and so on (Beck, 1999/2010; Beck, Rush, Shaw, & Emery, 1979; Burns, 1999; Ellis, 2001; Ellis & MacLaren, 2003).

> **Cognitive restructuring**
> **Replacing unrealistic, maladaptive,** and dysfunctional beliefs, judgments, and thoughts with realistic, adaptive, and functional ones

There are two basic approaches to cognitive therapy and **cognitive restructuring**: the didactic and the Socratic. They can often be integrated with the didactic used early on and then followed by the Socratic (Ellis & MacLaren, 2003). The **didactic approach** can be viewed as the therapist/counselor teaching the client about the fundamentals of cognitive therapy (Ellis, 1998, 2001, 2004; Ellis & MacLaren, 2003). It is often seen as more therapist/counselor driven, more direct, and less collaborative with a strong focus on vigorously disputing the unrealistic, maladaptive, and dysfunctional absolute beliefs and thoughts of the client (Ellis, 1988, 2001, Ellis & MacLaren, 2003). These thoughts and beliefs are changed into more rational, realistic, adaptive, evidence-based, and functional beliefs, thoughts, or preferences.

> **Cognitive reframing**
> **Looking at the** situation from a different perspective

The **Socratic approach** is a guided, interactive rational/logical process of inquiry, analysis, and teaching derived from the philosophical approach of the ancient Greek philosopher Socrates (470–399 BCE) who is believed to be

> **Socratic approach**
> **A collaborative, questioning,** guided process of analysis that leads to self-discovery regarding the truth or falsity of one's beliefs, judgments, and thoughts

one of the founders of Western philosophy. In cognitive therapy, the Socratic approach, where the client is much more active and engaged, is often seen as a more collaborative, questioning, guiding process that leads to self-discovery of thoughts and beliefs that are often out of the client's awareness (Beck & Dozois, 2011; Beck, Rush, Shaw, & Emery, 1979; Braun, Strunk, Sasso, & Cooper, 2015; Carey & Mullan, 2004; Clark & Egan, 2015; Ellis & MacLaren, 2003; Fenn & Burne, 2013; Padesky, 1993; Padesky & Beck, 2003). The therapist guides or leads the client with such questions "What do you mean by x?" "What does feeling x do for you?" "How does believing x help you?" "What does believing x allow you to avoid?" "What makes you believe that x is the case?" "How would you verify x is the case?" "If you didn't believe x, what would happen?" "Can x be explained or interpreted in another way (cognitive reframing)?" "What would happen if your new interpretation was the case?" and so on.

As a result of the **guided questioning**, the client is able to discover, question, examine and clarify whether there is any evidence supporting the truth or falsity of his or her beliefs, thoughts, assumptions, demands, and expectations. It is an exercise in critical thinking. The unrealistic, maladaptive, and dysfunctional absolute beliefs and thoughts are replaced with ones that are more rational, realistic, evidence based, adaptive and functional relative to the social context.

When individuals or clients understand the errors in their thinking, and the problems associated with maladaptive absolute beliefs and thoughts, they then can change, restructure, or reframe their absolute, maladaptive beliefs and thoughts. In many cases, it would be changing from an absolute belief/thought to a preference.

The cognitive approach is essentially a **psychoeducational approach** to counseling and/or managing stress. Individuals learn the process so they will have the skills and competencies to address and resolve their maladaptive thinking on their own. Fundamental to this approach is homework where you put into practice the new belief and thoughts. A common example of homework would be a log where you kept track and monitored the situation:

- When and where you started to feel uncomfortable/stressed?
- What beliefs/thoughts went through/popped into your head prior to feeling stressed?
- Link the beliefs/thoughts to some specific feeling/feelings such as anxious, angry, afraid, and so on.
- Examine/question and/or dispute the beliefs/thoughts. Is there any evidence to support the beliefs/thoughts? Are they maladaptive? Unrealistic? Absolute? Distortions?

- If so, replace them with rational, realistic, evidence-based thoughts and/or preferences.
- After replacing them, note how you feel. What exactly are you feeling? Are you less stressed?
- What about your behavior? Are you more engaged?

In other words, a successful outcome is contingent on ongoing, continual monitoring (think practice) outside of the original therapeutic environment.

The homework or continual practice will wire in a new neural network for the adaptive alternative belief and thoughts, making them more readily accessible. At the same time, you are making the neural network for the maladaptive belief and thoughts, because you are spending less and less time replaying them, less readily accessible. The following example regarding George, although greatly simplified, will give you a general idea how this process works. Assume that a positive therapeutic environment has been established, George has learned about cognitive restructuring, put it into practice, and did his homework.

George is quite stressed because his girlfriend Sally dumped him. The **first step** is to get George to remember what thoughts automatically popped into his head immediately when Sally said she was breaking up with him. George indicates, "Sally must love me forever. We were perfect together. If she leaves me, I will always be alone. If I am alone, I will always be stressed and unhappy. I am a total loser."

The **second step** is to get George to link these thoughts to his specific feelings. He notes being tense, afraid, depressed, and angry.

The **third step** is for George to dispute his absolute, maladaptive, and unrealistic thoughts and challenge his cognitive distortions such as black-and-white thinking, awfulizing, jumping to conclusions, and labeling. Offer an alternate explanation for the situation. This is accomplished by asking George, "Where is it written/show me the evidence that Sally must love you forever, that you were perfect together, that you will always be alone if she leaves you, if you are alone that you will always be stressed and unhappy, and that you are a total loser."

The **fourth step**, after George disputes his thoughts and realizes that his thoughts are absolute, unrealistic, and maladaptive, is to have him replace them with preferences that are realistic, relative, and adaptive. George comes up with the following: "I would have preferred Sally loved me forever, but I know that is unrealistic and there really are no absolutes such as forever. Clearly, we were not perfect together as perfect is an absolute and Sally did leave me. I will not always be alone as I have friends and family. I will find a new girlfriend. There are instances, in fact, when I actually like to spend some time alone and enjoy myself when I do. I am not a total loser. We had a relationship for about a year or so, and as I think back on it we had our ups and downs. The relationship didn't work out in the end. That does not mean I am a total loser. These things are simply part of life. Change happens."

The **fifth step** is for George to link his new thoughts to his feelings. George notes, "I do not feel as stressed, afraid, and angry as I did before; nonetheless I am still not happy. I do not feel depressed, but I am still a little sad about the whole situation. This is normal. Life goes on. I have a new tool to help me deal with life and I am going to practice it regularly. It may take a little time to reengage with all the things I did before, but I will be back."

While this process addressed and helped George resolve his situation with Sally, there may still be more fundamental absolute, unrealistic, rigid, inflexible, maladaptive beliefs underlying his thinking, such as "I should never feel uncomfortable; I must always feel happy; I must always get my way; people must behave the way I want them to; I must never fail at anything or not get my way; if I fail or not get my way, then I will not be able to tolerate it, I will feel terrible, I won't be a good person," and so on.

If you find yourself feeling stressed, it is quite important that you examine and question your thoughts and expectations to determine if they are realistic. If they are not, they need to be changed. In some cases, they may be true. In these cases, appropriate coping devices need to be developed and applied relative to your specific situation. However, even though your thoughts and expectations may be true, it is extremely important, given that you are feeling stressed, that you examine any possible underlying maladaptive, unrealistic, and absolute beliefs that may be exacerbating your stress. If found, they need to be changed.

Cognitive Therapy and Mindfulness

Cognitive therapy is focused on changing one's thoughts while mindfulness is focused on observing, being aware, and being with one's thoughts nonjudgmentally in the present. Kabat-Zinn's (2003, 2005a, 2005b) **mindfulness-based stress-reduction program (MBSR)**, a holistic approach to health and well-being with a focus on practicing mindfulness and observing/being aware of one's thoughts and feelings while using one's breath

Mindfulness-based stress reduction

as an anchor for which to return, was initially developed to assist patients, which the medical profession was essentially unable to completely help, in managing their stress and the associated problems with it. Fundamental to the program is consistent, regular practice (think developing and reinforcing new neural networks of mindfulness (Kabat-Zinn, 2005a). MBSR is utilized, not only with managing stress, but with a wide range of physical and psychological disorders (Davis & Hayes, 2011; Marchand, 2012).

Using MBSR as a foundation, Segal, Williams, and Teasdale (2002) created **mindfulness-based cognitive therapy (MBCT)** as a way of preventing relapse in depression. While utilizing aspects of cognitive therapy, such as automatic thoughts, clients are taught how to be, nonjudgmentally, with/aware of their dysfunctional, unrealistic, absolute, and maladaptive thoughts (Segal, Williams, & Teasdale, 2002; Eisendrath et al., 2016; Piet & Hougaard, 2011; Williams, Teasdale, Segal, & Kabat-Zinn, 2007). Unlike CBT and REBT, there is no attempt to change their dysfunctional thinking. There is significant research regarding the effectiveness of mindfulness, MBSR, and MBCT across a wide variety of areas (Abbott et al., 2014; Britton, Shahar, Szepsenwol, & Jacobs, 2012; Cherkin et al., 2016; Lazar, 2004; McCracken & Vowles, 2014; Rimes & Wingrove, 2013). Mindfulness is also being incorporated into other approaches to psychotherapy, some with and some without CBT (Germer, Siegel, & Fulton, 2005; Hayes, Follette, & Linehan, 2004).

> **Mindfulness-based cognitive therapy**

POSITIVE PSYCHOLOGY

One of the major concerns about counseling/psychotherapy is the tendency to focus solely on addressing, alleviating, and preventing mental illness, weaknesses, problematic thinking, dysfunctionality, and maladaptive behavior (Linley, Joseph, Harrington, & Wood, 2006; Seligman & Csikszentmihalyi 2000). In other words, it is psychopathology. Stress management itself can also often be seen as mainly directing its attention toward addressing, reducing, removing, and preventing chronic stress. In both cases, clients/individuals may be given pharmaceuticals and/or taught coping skills regarding these issues relative to healing.

Positive psychology, while acknowledging the necessity of addressing and resolving these life challenges, is focused on optimizing human behavior by studying and analyzing individuals, groups, and institutions regarding positive qualities, positive thoughts, strengths, positive emotions, satisfaction, well-being, happiness, positive relationships, optimism, hope, self-actualization, growth, enjoyment of life, spirituality, and so on (Linley, Joseph, Harrington, & Wood,

2006; Magyar-Moe, Owens, & Conoley, 2015; Seligman & Csikszentmihalyi, 2000; Seligman, Steen, Park, & Peterson, 2005). Karwoski, Garratt, and Ilardi (2006), however, have worked on integrating CBT and positive psychology, while Hamilton, Kitzman, and Guyotte (2006) have looked at integrating CBT, mindfulness, and positive psychology.

Humor

Think of all the time you spend during the day worrying, complaining, whining, awfulizing, ruminating, negativizing, being upset and/or angry, frowning, mind wandering, walking around as if you were constipated, and so on. What does it do for you? How does it make you feel? Is it adaptive? As long as these types of behaviors continue, and thus are reinforced, you strengthen the respective neural networks in your brain and make these behaviors more readily accessible in your daily life.

Stop for a moment and simply smile. Come on, a big toothy smile that you can feel in your eyes. How do you feel? Did you know you cannot have a negative thought when you authentically smile? Go ahead, try!

Smile, laugh, and look for **humor** in life. Watch a comedy on TV, go see a comedy in the movies, ready a funny book, and so on. How do you feel? If you want an even bigger sense of enjoyment, go smile and laugh with friends and family. Even bigger? Think young children! Give yourself some time each day to strengthen these behaviors and their respective neural networks in your brain and make them more readily accessible in your daily life.

Positive Perspective on Life

This is really straight forward. It is your life and you have a limited time navigating through it. Wouldn't it be more beneficial, physically and psychologically, for you and your friends, family, classmates, coworkers, and people in general, to engage life from a more positive perspective—positive thinking, feeling, and behaving? I know, there are significant challenges in life that clearly are not pleasant. You need to address them. Nonetheless, don't let them color your entire engagement with life. Smile! Laugh! Enjoy life!

In the context of this text, the techniques, practices, and lifestyle changes of this holistic and integrative approach that have been and will be discussed are oriented toward assisting you in reducing/eliminating chronic stress, preventing chronic stress, and optimizing your strengths, growth, well-being, and enjoyment of life.

BUDDHISM

In the *Jian Jing* (箭經)/*Sallatha* Sutra or *Arrow Sutra*, Buddha indicates to his disciples that the uninstructed masses experience pleasant, unpleasant, and neither pleasant nor unpleasant sensations. His disciples who have received instruction also experience pleasant, unpleasant, and neither pleasant nor unpleasant sensations. He then points out that this being the case, how do we distinguish and differentiate between the masses who have not received instruction and his disciples who have received instruction? The disciples defer to Buddha. He states:

> Monks! For the masses who have not received instruction, when they experience unpleasantness, they become sad, sorrowful, lethargic, grief stricken, confused, beat their chest and wail, as they become confused and bewildered. They have two experiences of unpleasantness: physical (body) and then psychological (mental).
>
> Monks. It is just like they shot an arrow at a man and then immediately shot a second arrow at the man with both hitting him. Monks, this person has the unpleasant sensation of being hit by arrows twice. Similarly, people in general, when they have unpleasant sensations, they become sad, sorrowful, lethargic, grief stricken, confused, beat their chest and wail, as they become confused and bewildered. They experience two sensations of unpleasantness: physical (body) and then psychological (mental).
>
> ... Furthermore Monks! When the wise disciples who have received instruction experience unpleasant sensations, they do not become sad, sorrowful, lethargic, grief stricken, confused, beat their chest and wail or become confused and bewildered. They experience one sensation of unpleasantness: physical (body). There is no psychological (mental) sensation/reaction. Monks. It is just like they shot an arrow at a man and then immediately shot a second arrow at the man with only the first arrow hitting him.
>
> ... The learned, discerning individuals do not have a secondary (mental) experience/reaction to pleasure or pain. This is the difference between the skillfulness of those truly aware and the masses. For the learned ones who have awakened to the teachings,

nonjudgmentally observing the present and the future, desirable things do not cause the mind to be disturbed. Undesirable things are not detested or loathed. (Agama, 2012)

Essentially, what this sutra is saying is that unpleasantness in life is inevitable. Getting chronically stressed about it is a choice. Fundamental to not having a secondary reaction to pleasant, unpleasant, and neither pleasant nor unpleasant sensations is the practice of mindfulness. It is through the consistent and regular practice of mindfulness that you reduce the probability of being hit by a second arrow or dart (Hanson, & Siegel, 2009; Kingsland, 2016). In other words, the practice of mindfulness is extremely beneficial for the removal and prevention of chronic stress.

Mindfulness

In the *Dwelling of Mindfulness* sutra Buddha explains how to encounter one's thoughts or mental objects when meditating. It is learning how to be with one's thoughts or mental objects without becoming entangled with them. The practitioner nonjudgmentally observes as one's thoughts or mental objects arise and pass away. There is no attempt to change them. The goal is simply to be with/observe them in the present. The individual, by following the Four Noble Truths and consistently practicing, gradually becomes aware that like everything else thoughts or mental objects are impermanent, non-substantial, and interdependent. As such, ignorance and craving stop, karma is no longer produced, there is no attachment or dependence, and the individual is released from *dukkha*. When you stop and hold on to your thoughts or mental objects, believing they, and yourself, are permanent, substantial, independent, absolute, it results in craving. You become dependent and attached to them. This gives rise to, reinforces, and maintains karma, chronic stress or dukkha. In order to address this problem, Buddha prescribes mindfully observing thoughts or mental objects:

> Thus, following along non-judgmentally observing mental objects internally as mental objects, following along non-judgmentally observing mental objects externally as mental objects, following along non-judgmentally observing mental objects internally and externally as mental objects, following along non-judgmentally observing mental objects originating as mental objects, following along non-judgmentally observing mental objects ceasing as mental objects, following along non-judgmentally observing mental objects originating and ceasing as mental objects. In the present, mindfully,

he says, "The mental objects are this." Thus, is the establishment of his wisdom and his remembrance. Wherever he goes in the world there is no dependence or attachment. This is a monk following along non-judgmentally observing the mental object of the five hindrances as a mental object. (Santee, 2007, p. 114; for Chinese text see Agama, 2019.)

Mindfulness

Correct Thinking, Speech, Action, and Livelihood

Buddha's Eight-Fold Path or treatment plan/intervention not only incorporates meditation, with mindfulness as the core of the path, as a way to address problems associated with thinking, it also incorporates cognitive and behavioral components. While Buddha did not use the same terminology as is used today such as negative thinking is essentially perceived threats, perceived threats activate the fight/freeze/flight or stress response, ongoing threat-based thinking maintains the stress response, continual activation of the stress response results in chronic stress, and chronic stress is detrimental to one's physical and psychological health, he was clearly aware, although using different terminology, of the process. This being the case, negative thinking needed to be eliminated.

Buddha clearly realized that a holistic approach was necessary to become free from *dukkha* or chronic stress. There must be commitment, enthusiasm, and consistent regular practice (think **correct effort**) across all aspects of one's being. In addition to practicing mindfulness in a meditative context, the practitioner knowingly and mindfully focuses on removing negative thinking and behavior by consciously attending to and monitoring one's thinking, speech, and behavior. The following selections, regarding components of the Eight-Fold Path, from the *Analysis of Truths* sutra makes this quite clear:

> Friends, now what is **Correct Thinking**? It is thinking of the cessation of suffering, thinking of not being hateful and angry, thinking of not doing harm. Friends this is the meaning of Correct Thinking.
>
> Friends, now what is **Correct Speech**? It is not speaking falsehoods, not speaking in a manner that causes dissension, not speaking in a slanderous manner, not speaking in an obscene manner. Friend this is the meaning of Correct Speech.
>
> Friends, now what is **Correct Action**? Not killing, not stealing, and not behaving wrongly in circumstances associated with the sense pleasures. Friends, this is the meaning of Correct Action. (Santee, 2007, p. 101; for Chinese text see Agama, 2019a)

Friends, now what is a **Correct Livelihood**? Friends, disciples of the sages abandon unhealthy behavior and select Correct Action for their lives. This is the meaning of Correct Livelihood. (Santee, 2007, p. 102)

It is important to understand that although mindfulness was viewed by Buddha as the key to the removal of *dukkha* or chronic stress, he saw it within the context of the entire interdependent, integrated, holistic treatment plan or Eight-Fold Path. There are clear, deliberate, guidelines regarding thinking, speaking, and behaving, which are, for Buddha, interdependent, non-substantial, and impermanent. In one sense, Buddha saw the necessity of not only meditation, but of also what we refer to as cognitive restructuring, removal of negative threat-based thinking, and cognitive reframing, thinking about the world as impermanent, non-substantial, and interdependent.

DAOISM

Zhuangzi (4th–3rd century BCE) clearly recognized the damage that absolute dichotomous (black-and-white, either/or) threat-based thinking or words could do to one's body and mind. For Zhuangzi, this type of thinking was artificial and compromised one's natural state of being. It resulted in what we today refer to as chronic stress. In chapter 5 of the *Zhuangzi* there is a conversation between Zhuangzi and his friend Huizi regarding human emotions. Like cognitive therapy and stress management, the *Zhuangzi* links what it views as problematic thinking, words, and judgments to physical and psychological harm.

Laozi is the traditional author of the Daodejing. Wudangshan Museum, Wudangshan City, Hubei.

Huizi asked Zhuangzi, "Are humans originally without emotions (*qing*情)?

Zhuangzi replied, "Yes."

Huizi said, "If humans are without emotions, how can they be called humans?

Zhuangzi replied, "*Dao* (道) allows for appearance. Nature (*tian*天) allows for form.

Why is it not proper to call them humans?

Huizi said, "If they are already called human, how could they be without emotion?

Zhuangzi replied, "Right and wrong is what I mean when I refer to emotions. That which I refer to as being without emotions are humans not taking the words good and bad to internally injure their body (*shen*身). On this basis, they are always natural (*ziran*自然) and don't add on to their life.

Huizi said, "If they don't add on to their life, how can their body exist?

Zhuangzi replied, "Dao allows for appearance. Nature (*tian*天) allows for form. The words good and bad, likes and dislikes, and so on do not internally injure one's body. (Santee, 2004; Guo, 1974, pp. 119–121)

For the *Zhuangzi*, there is a clear distinction between emotions evoked naturally and emotions evoked artificially by problematic thinking and judgments. With artificial emotions, the feelings are real and are evoked by absolute abstract concepts and dichotomies such as right/wrong, like/dislike, good/bad—in other words, by absolute, black-and-white judgments. Anything that contradicts your absolute judgments are perceived as threats. As such, for Zhuangzi, they compromise, add on to, one's life and well-being. Zhuangzi is not denying that one has natural emotions; think back to the story in chapter 1 of the death of his wife and his initial reaction during her funeral. By removing the artificial sources of evoking emotions, absolute dichotomous, threat-based thinking, judgments, and words, one's life will be less stressful and more enjoyable. In this sense, he appears to be engaging in what we today call cognitive restructuring. The commentary of Cheng Xuanying (631–652 CE) to this section from the *Zhuangzi* reinforces Zhuangzi's perspective regarding the necessity of the removal of absolute, threat-based thinking, judgments, and words:

> That which evokes emotions is right and wrong, yours and mine, good and bad, abhorrence and adoration, and so on. If he is without an absolute sense of right and wrong, good and bad and so on, although he has form and appearance, he truly is a person whose emotions will not be evoked. (Santee, 2011, p. 49; Guo, 1974, p. 120)

Simplifying Thinking and Behavior

For Zhuangzi, the second way of addressing issues with threat-based thinking and behavior is to develop a new outlook regarding how you think about and engage the world around you, essentially, what we today call cognitive reframing. This is accomplished, for Zhuangzi, by consciously **simplifying one's thinking and behavior**. In other words, removing complexity from one's life! This reduces/

eliminates the tendency to get entangled with absolute judgments and the chronic stress associated with them. Essentially, this means realizing there are problems that you cannot solve and situations you cannot control. This being the case, stop wasting energy, physically and psychologically, trying to solve problems that you cannot solve and wasting energy trying to control what you cannot control. Stop interfering with yourself! Stop stressing yourself out! Zhuangzi also points out there are, as a result of your choices, obligations you have and situations you cannot avoid, so stop wasting energy, physically and psychologically, whining, complaining, and moaning about them. Just do them and stop avoiding them. Stop interfering with yourself! Stop stressing yourself out! The benefits of removing complexity or simplifying your life is made quite clear in the following selections from the *Zhuangzi*:

> Take responsibility for your own mind/heart so that sorrow and joy do not easily affect you. Knowing what you cannot resolve, and being at peace with it by adapting to destiny, is the perfection of inner power (*de*德). As a subject and a son, there is that which you cannot avoid. Forget about your ego and deal with the situation. (Santee, 2011, p. 50; Guo, 1974, p. 86)
>
> Reside in the world by letting your mind/heart flow without any obstructions. Accepting what you cannot avoid as well as nourishing what is within is perfection. What more can be said? (Santee, 2011, p. 50; Guo, 1974, p. 89)
>
> To know what you cannot resolve and to be at peace with it by adapting to destiny, only the person of inner power (*de*德) can do this. (Santee, 2011, p. 49; Guo, 1974, p. 108)

Wuwei or Non-Interference

Wuwei (無為), previously touched on in chapter 3, is a fundamental practice in Daoism. It means to not to interfere with yourself psychologically and/or physically. Do not let your thinking, judgments, and words compromise your well-being. Do not let your behavior compromise your well-being. It means to not to interfere with others by trying to force or coerce them to do something for your own benefit. It is directly applicable to not trying to solve problems that you cannot solve and control situations you cannot control. Understanding that there are occurrences/events/people for which you have no control over and not attempting to interfere with these occurrences/events/people is *wuwei*. Not attempting to force, coerce, control, manipulate, or seek self-gain with those occurrences/events/people that cannot be avoided is *wuwei*. The application of *wuwei* to that which cannot be avoided and the psychological impact of practicing *wuwei* on the sage or Daoist role model are clearly presented in the following passage (Santee, 2011, adapted):

> If the sage is unable to avoid attending to the world, it is best if he practices non-interference (*wuwei* 無為). If he does not interfere, then he will be at peace with his nature and destiny. (Santee, 2011, p. 50; Guo, 1974, p. 201)

In chapter 18 of the *Zhuangzi* it is stated, "I take *wuwei* to be true happiness" (Santee, 2011, p. 51; Guo, 1974, p. 318). The commentary of Guo Xiang (252–312 CE) to this statement links *wuwei*, happiness and freedom from chronic stress, all together. He notes, "The happiness of *wuwei* is to simply be without chronic stress (*you*憂), that is all" (Santee, 2011, p. 51; Guo, 1974, p. 318). The practice of meditation allows one to naturally, not utilizing reason, develop *wuwei*. Nonetheless, similar to Buddha's Eight-Fold Path, an intentional, conscious monitoring and changing of one's thinking and behavior is also required for the development of *wuwei*. Although the core is in meditation, both psychological and physical approaches are necessary. The key is regular, consistent, and ongoing practice of both methods.

Wuwei: Non-interference

Beliefs

In the *Liezi* (2nd century CE), there is a concern, much like cognitive therapy, with how one's beliefs have a direct impact on one's emotions and behaviors. There is also a focus on how one's beliefs color how you see and behave regarding your various environmental contexts and the people who populate it. If you believe something to be the case, you will see and act as if it is the case. In the following selection, it is quite clear that the man's belief about the boy colored or framed what he saw and the judgment he made about the boy

> There was a man who lost his ax. He suspected the neighbor boy. Looking at the way he walked, he was the one who stole the ax. Given his facial expressions, he was the one who stole the ax. Observing the manner in which he talked, he was the one who stole the ax. The manner in which he moved about, it could not be that he did not steal the ax. Later on, while excavating his grain, he found his ax. When he returned one day he saw the neighbor boy. The manner in which he moved about did not resemble someone who stole his ax. (Santee, 2010, p. 10; Yang, 1972, p. 100)

The man's absolute, rigid beliefs and judgments about the boy colored or framed his seeing the boy's behavior as a thief who stole his ax. When the man found his ax, his beliefs and judgments changed regarding the boy. He was responding to concrete evidence as opposed to abstract, absolute beliefs and subsequent judgments. He no longer saw the boy's behavior as indicating the boy stole the ax. The man no longer confused his beliefs, judgments, or abstract labels/names (*ming*名) with concrete reality (*shi*實) (Santee, 2010, adapted).

Daoism very much operates on the principle that the greatest danger we face in navigating our way through life is what is within our self, our beliefs, judgments and thoughts and how we look at and interact with the world around us. The following selection from the *Liezi* makes this point quite forcefully:

> Lie, Yukou (Liezi) was demonstrating his skills in archery to Bohun Wuren. He drew the bow to its fullest extent. A measured cup of water was on his elbow. The arrow was released. This was repeated two more times. When he was doing this, it was if he was a wooden statue. Bohun Wuren said: "This is the shooting of shooting. It is not the shooting of not shooting. We should ascend the mountain, step on a precipitous rock, overlooking an abyss of about 800 feet. Will you be able to shoot?" Thereupon, they took a look around, and ascended the mountain. They stepped on a precipitous rock, overlooking an abyss of about 800 feet. Bohun Wuren began walking backwards. The back of his feet hung over the edge. He bowed to Liezi and beckoned him forward. Liezi dropped to the ground in a prostrate position. Sweat flowed to his heels. Bohun Wuren said: "The complete person (zhiren至人) can go up to the blue sky, dive down to the nether worlds, and wander freely in the eight directions (universe). His spirit (*shen*神) and breath (*qi*氣) are unmoved. Now you are frightened and have an agitated focus. The danger is within you!" (Santee, 2010, p. 11; Yang, 1972, pp. 16–17)

Don't confuse the label for reality

This selection from the *Liezi* demonstrates how an individual's beliefs can compromise his or her performance. While on the ground, the mind/heart of Liezi was still and focused. He did not believe or think that the external environment presented any threats. Thus, he shot quite well. Bohun Wuren, however, did not view the archery skills of Liezi as representing the shooting of the not shooting of the complete person or role model of Daoism. When Liezi's belief, judgment, and thinking were oriented toward falling off the cliff, he felt threatened. As a result, his stress response was activated and maintained. He became quite agitated and threatened. His spirit (*shen*神) and breath (*qi*氣) were compromised. He sweat profusely. The psychological, emotional, and behavioral reactions of Liezi were directly related to his beliefs. The danger, his absolute, rigid and judgmental beliefs, was, as Bohun Wuren noted, within Liezi (Santee, 2010, adapted).

The holistic approach of Daoism integrates meditation with a reframing of how one thinks about and behaves in the world and a restructuring of one's beliefs, judgments, and thinking. This addresses and resolves the danger within and leads to the removal of chronic stress. All of this requires continual, consistent, and regular practice.

CONFUCIANISM

The Confucian approach to cognitive restructuring specifically focuses on teaching the individual the right way to think, feel, and behave in a morally appropriate manner. It is all about continual, internal and external, self-monitoring to make you think, feel, and behave in a manner that is conducive to establishing and maintaining authentic, empathic, and respectful relationships with others relative to establishing and maintaining social harmony. From the Confucian perspective, self-centeredness, self-gain at the expense of others, greed, the need to be recognized by others for your own accomplishments, and self-focused desires for your own benefit are the source of interpersonal and social disharmony. All beliefs, judgments, and thinking associated with these need to be removed. They are the source of chronic stress. Confucianism focuses on the practical not theoretical perspective. You do not really learn until you can put what you have learned into practice. Learning is to be enjoyable. The first section of chapter 1 makes this quite clear:

> The Master (Confucius) said, "To learn and have the opportunity to put what you have learned into practice, is this not joyful? To have friends come from afar, is this not a delight? Not being acknowledged by others, yet not getting angry about it, is this not the morally integrated person (*junzi*君子)?" (Chinese Classic, n.d.)

Continual Self-Examination

As Confucianism is about learning how to properly think, feel, and behave in an appropriate moral manner, it is quite important that individuals daily monitor themselves regarding what they have learned. That which is appropriate will be continually practiced and thus reinforced. While that which is inappropriate, such as thinking only about yourself, self-centeredness, greed, and personal gain, is considered to be dysfunctional and needs to be changed and removed. Thus, the individual, essentially, engages in what we today call cognitive restructuring and cognitive reframing. The reframing occurs by making, via thinking and behavior, social harmony and the group the focal point, not individuality and one's own self-gain. The cognitive restructuring occurs by changing those specific beliefs, judgments, and thoughts that have been maintaining the dysfunctional thinking and behavior. If this practice is followed, the individual will not be chronically stressed.

> Cengzi (a disciple of Confucius) said, "I daily examine myself in three areas. In working for other people, have I not done my best/been authentic (*zhong* 忠)? In interacting with my friends have I not been trustworthy (*xin* 信)? Have I not practiced what has been passed on to me?" (Santee, 2007, p. 194; Chinese Classic, n.d.)

> The Master said, "When traveling with 3 people, I will certainly have teachers. I will select that which is good and follow it. That which is not good, I will change it in myself." (Santee, 2007, p. 194)

> What you do not desire, do not impose on others." (Santee, 2007, p. 202; Chinese Classic, n.d.)

> Fan Chi (a disciple of Confucius) asked about interpersonal selfless relationships (*ren* 仁). The Master said, "In your home be respectful (*gong* 恭), in managing your affairs be attentive (*jing* 敬), and when interacting with others do your best/be authentic (*zhong* 忠). Even if you were amongst the barbarian tribes, it is not possible to abandon these." (Santee, 2007, p. 203; Chinese Classic, n.d.)

> Confucius said, "Zeng (a disciple of Confucius)! My *Dao* uses a single thread." Zengzi said, "So it does." The Master left. The disciples asked, "What did he mean?" Zengzi said, "The way of the Master is doing your best, being authentic (*zhong* 忠) and being empathic *shu* 恕). That's it!" (Santee, 2007, p. 201; Chinese Classic, n.d.)

As with Buddhism and Daoism, later Confucianism or Neo-Confucianism recognized the importance of the meditative and cognitive approach to removing what we today call chronic stress. The practitioners of Neo-Confucianism integrated meditation into the early Confucian cognitive approach.

PRACTICAL APPLICATION

If you find yourself forgetting what any of the previous postures look like and wondering what chapters they are in, simply look in the appendix as the entire sequence for Zhan Zhuang, yoga, and the Baduanjin can be found there.

Zhanzhuang: Position Five

The fifth and final position of this *Zhan Zhuang* form is essentially the first position of the form. You return to *wuji*. After completing the fourth position, simply let your arms return to your sides. Hold this position for 1 minute, breathing naturally through your nose, simply observing, without making any judgments, what you feel in your body. After 1 minute has passed, take a deep breath and simply do a short walk.

You now have a complete sequence for practicing *Zhan Zhuang*. Begin by spending 1 minute in each posture moving from the first to the second, then the third, the fourth, and finally the fifth where you return to *wuji* or the starting posture. Through the entire process, breathe naturally through your nose, just observing what happens to you. If you get distracted or mind wander, this is normal; don't make any judgments, just refocus on being in the present simply standing. You are simply observing yourself, *via guan*, throughout the entire sequence. Observe and reflect on what you feel and notice. Initially, set aside 5 minutes a day to practice this sequence and simply monitor what happens. You may find it helpful to keep a journal describing your physical and psychological experiences. This will allow you to track any changes that occur and monitor your progression. As you feel more comfortable you can increase the time for each posture.

Yoga: Tree Pose (*Vrksasana*)

This pose is very focused on balance. As such you do not want to be performing it if you are light-headed, have issues with blood pressure, dizziness, problems sleeping, headaches, and so on. From the mountain pose,

shift your weight onto your left foot, bend your right knee, and slowly start sliding your foot up your left leg. When you can easily reach your right ankle, grab it and pull your foot up, resting it above your knee on your thigh. Do not place it on your knee. If this is problematic, you can slide your foot up to your calf, but below and not pressing on your knee or your ankle. The toes of your right foot point down. Your right knee points to the side. Breathe naturally through your nose.

Pick a point to focus on in the distance. Make sure your jaw is parallel to the ground and you are looking forward. Bring your hands together in front of your sternum in what looks like prayer hands. To help stabilize yourself, push your right foot into your left thigh, calf, or ankle while pushing your left leg into your right foot. Essentially you are pushing both inward. Gently push your head upward, letting your shoulder sink, while gently pulling your tailbone down. This will open up and stretch your spine. Hold the pose for about five slow, deep breaths. You can increase the number of breaths as you feel more comfortable in this pose. Then let your right foot gently return to the ground while letting your hands return to your sides. Repeat on the other side.

You may want to stand next to a wall or table so you can catch yourself if this posture presents a challenge. Your safety is of utmost concern with this pose, as it is with all the other poses. Upon finishing the pose note what you observed and how you feel. What did you learn about yourself? Remember, stay positive.

Baduanjin: Preparation Form 1 and 2

The preparation form 1 of the *Baduanjin* form, or eight pieces of brocade, is essentially the *wuji* posture of the *Zhan Zhuang* form. To perform this qigong exercise, it is best to find a quiet place where you will not be disturbed or distracted. Breathe naturally. Begin by standing with your feet parallel, pointing forward, and touching. The weight is evenly distributed on both feet. Your feet are flat and there is no leaning or rolling of them to the sides, forward, or backward. Bend your knees slightly. Your arms hang naturally on your sides with your palms facing your thighs. Relax. Your eyes are looking straight forward. To align your body, gently push both feet down and gently push your head up. Imagine you

were a puppet being suspended by a string, centered on the top of your head, from above. Your shoulders will naturally sink. Your spine will align. Your jaw is parallel to the ground, and your tongue gently touches the roof of your mouth behind your upper teeth. Gently shut your eyes. Breathe naturally through your nose. Relax. At this point, simply observe, nonjudgmentally, what you feel for 1 minute throughout your body.

The preparation form 2 is essentially position two of the *Zhan Zhuang* form. Your eyes continue to look straight forward. Shift your weight onto your right foot and step to the side with your left foot. Your weight is evenly distributed. Your feet are shoulder-width apart with both feet pointing forward. Your knees are slightly bent. Let your arms arc slightly forward, staying thigh-width apart, until your hands, palms facing each other, are about 3 or so inches below your hips. Visualize you are holding a large beach ball with your hands, arms, and lower abdomen/pelvic area gently holding it in place. Staying in this position, slowly and gently inhaling and exhaling through your nose, nonjudgmentally observe what you are feeling for 1 minute. After 1 minute, let your arms return to your sides and take a deep breath. Let it out slowly and slowly walk away. Reflect on what occurred during these two preparation postures.

KEY TERMS

psychosocial threat-based thinking

dysfunctional thinking

cognitive therapy

threat-based thinking

psychosocial beliefs and judgments

negative automatic thoughts

cognitive distortions

cognitive restructuring

cognitive reframing

didactic approach

Socratic approach

guided questioning

psychoeducational approach

mindfulness-based stress-reduction program (MBSR)

mindfulness-based cognitive therapy (MBCT)

positive psychology

humor

correct effort

correct thinking

correct speech

correct action

correct livelihood

simplifying one's thinking and behavior

Wuwei

EXERCISES

1. Compare the didactic approach with the Socratic approach of cognitive therapy. How can they work together to address chronic stress?

2. Compare cognitive restructuring with cognitive reframing relative to addressing chronic stress.

3. Google "cognitive distortions" and find out how many you actually have. How are they linked to chronic stress? What do you need to do to eliminate them?

4. The next time you feel stressed (angry, anxious, depressed, and so on) uncover the negative automatic thoughts that preceded you feeling stressed. Address them via cognitive restructuring and cognitive reframing. Address them via mindfulness or *guan*. What do you notice?

5. Spend a day looking at the world around you from the perspective of positive psychology, in other words, no negativity. What do you notice? How do you feel?

6. Compare the Buddhist, Daoist, and Confucian approach to addressing and resolving chronic stress.

7. Describe the evolutionary basis of threat-based thinking and indicate how and why threat-based thinking can be a problem today.

REFERENCES

Abbott, R. A., Whear, R., Rodgers, L. R., Bethel, A., Thompson Coon, J., Kuyken, W., *Stein, K., &* Dickens, C. *(2014)*. Effectiveness of mindfulness-based stress reduction and mindfulness based cognitive therapy in vascular disease: A systematic review and meta-analysis of randomised controlled trials. *Journal of Psychosomatic Research, 76*(5), 341–351.

Agama. (2019). *Middle length sayings.* Translated from http://agama.buddhason.org/MN/MN010.htm

Agama. (2019a). *Middle length sayings.* Translated from http://agama.buddhason.org/MN/MN141.htm

Agama (2012). Kindred sayings. Translated from http://agama.buddhason.org/SN/SN1058.htm

Beck, A. T. (1979). *Cognitive therapy and the emotional disorders.* New York, NY: Penguin.

Beck, A. T. (1999/2010). *Prisoners of hate: The cognitive basis of anger, hostility, and violence.* New York, NY: HarperCollins.

Beck, A. T., & Dozois, D. J. (2011). Cognitive therapy: Current status and future directions. *Annual Review of Medicine, 62,* 397–409.

Beck, A. T., Rush, A. J., Shaw, B. F., & Emery, G. (1979). *Cognitive therapy of depression.* New York, NY: Guilford Press.

Beck, A. T., & Weishaar, M. E. (2005). Cognitive therapy. In R. J. Corsini & D. Wedding (Eds.) *Current psychotherapies* (pp. 238–268). Belmont, CA: Brooks/Cole.

Benson, H., & Casey, A. (2013). *A Harvard Medical School special health report. Stress management: Approaches for preventing and reducing stress.* Boston, MA: Harvard Health Publications.

Braun, J. D., Strunk, D. R., Sasso, K. E., & Cooper, A. A. (2015). Therapist use of Socratic questioning predicts session-to-session symptom change in cognitive therapy for depression. *Behaviour Research and Therapy, 70,* 32‑37.

Britton, W. B., Shahar, B., Szepsenwol, O., & Jacobs, W. J. (2012). Mindfulness based cognitive therapy improves emotional reactivity to social stress: Results from a randomized controlled trial. *Behavior Therapy, 43*(2), 365–380.

Burns, D. D. (1999). *Feeling good: The new mood therapy.* New York, NY: Avon Books.

Carey, T. A., & Mullan, R. J. (2004). What is Socratic questioning? *Psychotherapy: Theory, Research, Practice, Training, 41*(3), 217–226.

Cherkin, D. C., Sherman, K. J., Balderson, B. H., Cook, A. J., Anderson, M. L., Hawkes, R. J., Hansen, K. E., & Turner, J. A. (2016). Effect of mindfulness-based stress reduction vs. cognitive behavioral therapy or usual care on back pain and functional limitations in adults with chronic low back pain: A randomized clinical trial. *JAMA, 315*(12), 1240-1249.

Chinese Classic. (n.d.). *Lunyu.* Retrieved from http://www.chineseclassic.com/13jing/LeungYu/LeungYu01.htm

Clark, G. I., & Egan, S. J. (2015). The Socratic method in cognitive behavioural therapy: A narrative review. *Cognitive Therapy and Research, 39*(6), 863–879.

Davis, D. M., & Hayes, J. A. (2011). What are the benefits of mindfulness? A practice review of psychotherapy-related research. *Psychotherapy, 48*(2), 198–208.

Driessen, E., & Hollon, S. D. (2010). Cognitive behavioral therapy for mood disorders: Efficacy, moderators, and mediators. *Psychiatric Clinician North America, 33*(3), 537-555.

Eisendrath, S. J., Gillung, E., Delucchi, K. L, Segal, Z. V, Nelson, J. C, McInnes, L. A., Mathalon, D. H., & Feldman, M. D. (2016). A randomized controlled trial of mindfulness-based cognitive therapy for treatment-resistant depression. *Psychotherapy and Psychometrics, 85*(2), 99–110.

Ellis, A. (1988). *How to stubbornly refuse to make yourself miserable about anything: Yes anything.* New York, NY: Kensington.

Ellis, A. (1998). *How to control your anxiety before it controls you.* New York, NY: Citadel.

Ellis, A. (2001). *New directions for rational emotive behavior therapy: Overcoming destructive beliefs, feelings and behaviors.* New York, NY: Prometheus.

Ellis, A. (2004). *Rational emotive behavioral therapy: It works for me-it can work for you.* Amherst, MA: Prometheus.

Ellis, A. (2005). Rational emotive behavioral therapy. In R. J. Corsini & D. Wedding (Eds.) *Current Psychotherapies* (pp. 166–201). Belmont, CA: Brooks/Cole.

Ellis, A., & MacLaren, C. (2003). *Rational emotive behavioral therapy: A therapist's guide.* Atascadero, CA: Impact.

Fenn, K., & Burne, M. (2013). The key principles of cognitive behavioural therapy. *InnovAiT: Education and Inspiration for General Practice, 6*(9), 579–585.

Germer, C. K., Siegel, R. D., & Fulton, P. R. (Eds.). (2005). *Mindfulness and psychotherapy.* New York, NY: Guilford.

Grohol, J. M. (2017). 15 common cognitive distortions. *Psych Central.* Retrieved from https://psychcentral.com/lib/15-common-cognitive-distortions/

Guo, Q. F. (1974). *Zhuangzi jishi,* Vols 1 and 2. Taipei, China: Chung Hwa.

Hanson, R., & Mendius, D. J. (2009). *Buddha's brain: The practical neuroscience of happiness, love & wisdom.* Oakland, CA: New Harbinger Publications, Inc.

Hamilton, N. A., Kitzman, H., & Guyotte, S. (2006). Enhancing health and emotion: Mindfulness as a missing link between cognitive therapy and positive psychology. *Journal of Cognitive Psychotherapy, 20*(2), 123–134.

Hartney, E. (2016). Ten cognitive distortions identified in CBT. *Very Well Mind.* Retrieved from https://www.verywell.com/ten-cognitive-distortions-identified-in-cbt-22412

Hayes, S. C., Follette, V. M., & Linehan, M. M. (Eds.). (2004). *Mindfulness and acceptance: Expanding the cognitive-behavioral tradition.* New York, NY: Guilford.

Hofmann, S. G., Asnaani, A., Vonk, I. J. J., Sawyer, A. T., & Fang, A. (2012). The efficacy of cognitive behavioral therapy: A review of meta-analyses. *Cognitive Therapy Research, 36*(5), 427–440.

Hoseini, T. H. M., Vaziri, S., & Kashani, F. L. (2014). The effect of REBT on reducing the depression and anxiety of women in Qom. *Journal of Educational and Management Studies, 4,* 232–234.

Hyland, P., & Boduszek, D. (2012). Resolving a difference between cognitive therapy and rational emotive behavior therapy: Towards the development of an integrated CBT model of psychopathology. *Mental Health Review Journal, 17*(2), 104–116.

Ito, T. A., Larsen, J. T., Smith, N. K., & Cacioppo. J. T. (1998). Negative information weighs more heavily on the brain: The negativity bias in evaluative categorization. *Journal of Personality and Social Psychology, 75*(4), 887–900.

Kabat-Zinn, J. (2003). Mindfulness-based interventions in context: Past, present and future. *Clinical Psychology: Science and Practice, 10*(2), 144–156.

Kabat-Zinn, J. (2005a). *Full catastrophe living: Using the wisdom of your body and mind to face stress, pain, and illness.* New York, NY: Random House.

Kabat-Zinn, J. (2005b). *Coming to our senses: Healing ourselves and the world through mindfulness.* New York, NY: Hyperion.

Karwoski L., Garratt G. M., & Ilardi S. S. (2006). On the integration of cognitive-behavioral therapy for depression and positive psychology. *Journal of Cognitive Psychotherapy, 20*(2), 159–170.

Kingsland, J. (2016). *Siddhartha's brain: Unlocking the ancient science of enlightenment.* New York, NY: HarperCollins Publisher, Inc.

Lazar, S. W. (2004). Mindfulness research. In C. K. Germer, R. D. Siegel, & P. R. Fulton (Eds.), *Mindfulness and psychotherapy* (pp. 220–238). New York, NY: Guilford.

Linley, P. A., Joseph, S., Harrington, S., & Wood, A. M. (2006). Positive psychology: Past, present, and (possible) future. *Journal of Positive Psychology, 1*(1), 3–16.

Magyar-Moe, J. L., Owens, R. L., & Conoley, C. W. (2015). Positive psychological interventions in counseling: What every counseling psychologist should know. *The Counseling Psychologist, 43*(4), 508–557.

Marchand, W. R. (2012). Mindfulness-based stress reduction, mindfulness-based cognitive therapy, and Zen meditation for depression, anxiety, pain, and psychological distress. *Journal of Psychiatric Practice, 18*(4), 233–252.

McCracken, L. M., & Vowles, K. E. (2014). Acceptance and commitment therapy and mindfulness for chronic pain: Model, process, and progress. *American Psychologist, 69*(2), 178–187.

Olatunji, B. O., Cisler, J. M., & Deacon, B. J. (2010). Efficacy of cognitive behavioral therapy for anxiety disorders: A review of meta-analytic findings. *Psychiatric Clinician North America, 33*(3), 557–577.

Padesky, C. (1993, September 24). *Socratic questioning: Changing minds or guided discovery?* Retrieved from http://padesky.com/newpad/wp-content/uploads/2012/11/socquest.pdf

Padesky, C. A., & Beck, A. T. (2003). Science and philosophy: Comparison of cognitive therapy (CT) and rational emotive behavior therapy (REBT). *Journal of Cognitive Psychotherapy: An International Quarterly, 17*(3), 211–224.

Piet, J., & Hougaard, E. (2011). The effect of mindfulness-based cognitive therapy for prevention of relapse in recurrent major depressive disorder: A systematic review and meta-analysis. *Clinical Psychology Review, 31*(6), 1032–1040.

Pretzer, J. L., & Beck, A. T. (2007). Cognitive approaches to stress and stress management. In P. M. Lehrer, R. L. Woolfolk, & W. E. Sime (Eds.), *Principles and practice of stress management* (pp. 465–496). New York, NY: Guilford.

Rimes, K. A., & Wingrove, J. (2013). Mindfulness-based cognitive therapy for people with chronic fatigue syndrome still experiencing excessive fatigue after cognitive behaviour therapy: A pilot randomized study. *Clinical Psychology & Psychotherapy, 20*(2), 107–117.

Roth, A., & Fonagy. P. (2005). *What works for whom? A critical review of psychotherapy research.* New York, NY: Guilford.

Rozin, P., & Roysman, E. B. (2001). Negativity bias, negativity dominance, and contagion. *Personality and Social Psychology Review, 5*(4), 296–320.

Rupke, S. J., Blecke, D., & Renfrow, M. (2006). Cognitive therapy for depression. *American Family Physician, 73*(1), 83–86.

Santee, R. (2004, July 22). *A Daoist and an existential psychotherapist: A comparative study.* Paper presented at the First World Hong Ming Philosophy Conference. Honolulu, HI.

Santee, R. (2007). *An Integrative Approach to Counseling: Bridging Chinese Thought, Evolutionary Theory, and Stress Management.* Copyright © 2007 by SAGE Publications. Reprinted with permission.

Santee, R. (2010). The *Liezi*: The forgotten Daoist text? *The Empty Vessel, 17,* 9–13.

Santee, R. (2011). "The Zhuangzi: A Holistic Approach to Health Care," *Living Authentically: Daoist Contributions to Modern Psychology*, ed. Livia Kohn, pp. 49-51. Copyright © 2011 by Three Pines Press. Reprinted with permission.

Segal, Z. V., Williams, J. M. G., & Teasdale J. D. (2002). *Mindfulness-based cognitive therapy for depression: A new approach to preventing relapse.* New York, NY: Guilford.

Seligman, M. E. P., & Csikszentmihalyi, M. (2000). Positive psychology: An introduction. *American Psychologist, 55*(1), 5–14.

Seligman, M., Steen, T., Park, N., & Peterson, C. (2005). Positive psychology progress: Empirical validation of interventions, *American Psychologist, 60*(5), 410–421.

Sood, A. S., & Jones D. T. (2013). On mind wandering, attention, brain networks, and meditation. *Explore, 9*(3), 136–141.

Tolin, D. T. (2010). Is cognitive-behavioral therapy more effective than other therapies? A meta-analytic review. *Clinical Psychology Review 30*(6), 710–720.

Wiles, N. J., Thomas, L., Turner, N., Garfield, K., Kounali, D., Campbell, J., ... & Hollinghurst, S. (2016). Long-term effectiveness and cost-effectiveness of cognitive behavioural therapy as an adjunct to pharmacotherapy for treatment-resistant depression in primary care: Follow-up of the CoBalT randomised controlled trial. *Lancet Psychiatry, 3*(2), 137–144

Williams, J. M. G., Teasdale, J. D., Segal, Z. V., & Kabat-Zinn, J. (2007). *The mindful way through depression: Freeing yourself from chronic unhappiness.* New York, NY: Guilford.

Yang, J. L. (Zhu Bian) (1972). *Zhuangzi jijie*, Liezi zhu. Taipei, China: Shijie Shuju Yinxing.

Zhaleh, N., Zarbakhsh, M., & Faramarzi, M. (2014). Effectiveness of rational-emotive behavior therapy on the level of depression among female adolescents. *Journal of Applied Environmental and Biological Sciences, 4*(4), 102–107.

CREDITS

Exercise

After finishing this chapter, you will be able to do the following:

- Indicate why physical exercise is an important component of stress management, health, and well-being
- Demonstrate how we have evolved from being quite active as a species to having significant health risks as a result of our sedentary behavior
- Compare aerobic exercise with resistance training and indicate why they are both necessary to address chronic stress and the health-related issues associated with it
- Explain why, within the context of evolutionary theory, our tendency is toward being physically inactive and sedentary
- Indicate how obesity is linked to both lack of physical exercise, sedentary behavior, and chronic stress
- Compare proprioception, interoception, and exteroception within the context of applying mindfulness or *guan* to various exercises, especially neuromotor exercises
- Indicate why that even though you may meet the recommended weekly requirements for aerobic and resistance training you must still address your sedentary behavior as a separate and distinct issue

- Describe the American College of Sports Medicine's (ACSM) four components of a well-rounded exercise program
- Explain how threat-based psychosocial thinking, sedentary behavior, and the lack of physical exercise are three distinct sources of chronic stress
- Describe the link between physical and psychological disorders, chronic stress, and exercise
- Indicate what *Yangsheng* entails and how it is fundamental to addressing and managing chronic stress
- Specify, from the perspective of ACSM's four components of a well-rebounded exercise program, where such physical activities/exercises as taijiquan, qigong, and yoga would be placed and why.

We have been told, at least most of us, that exercise is good for us. Our parents have told us that just sitting around in the house is not good for us. Go out and play they would say as they chased us out of the house or apartment. I suspect this probably served two purposes: Physical activity is good for us and our parents may have wanted some peace and quiet. Why is physical activity good for us?

EVOLUTIONARY THEORY

For our distant, **hunter-gatherer ancestors**, in order to survive and adapt they needed to physically move on a regular basis. Depending on the adaptive problem, they needed to run and/or walk for food, water, safety, shelter, interacting with others, finding a mate, raising and protecting their offspring, and finding material for clothes and basic utensils/weapons. They needed to climb, balance, lift, reach, and/or jump as they traveled across various terrains and migrated in their search for food, water, safety, and shelter. The bottom line is physical movement was essential to adapting, across all areas, to an ever-changing environment. This is how we evolved (Bramble & Lieberman, 2004; Hallal et al. 2012; Malina, & Little, 2008; Mattson, 2012; O'Keefe, Vogel, Lavie, & Cordain, 2010; Raichlen & Polk, 2012; Ratey & Hagerman, 2008).

For our distant ancestors, physical movement, specifically what we call **aerobic exercise**, was fundamental to their survival in and adapting to various environmental contexts. This aerobic type of movement developed **cardiovascular fitness**, **endurance**, and stamina. In fact, it is our cardiovascular endurance capabilities over long distances that distinguish us, as far as physical survival skills are concerned, from other primates and most other animals where their skills are to be found in sprinting, power/strength, or a combination of the two (Bramble & Lieberman, 2004; Mattson, 2012; Noakes & Spedding, 2012; Raichlen & Polk, 2012).

Cardiovascular fitness is not only beneficial for our physical health and well-being, it is also beneficial for our psychological health and well-being. It has been found to be especially important for attention, concentration, memory, learning, and higher-order reasoning abilities and skills (Berryman, 2010; Lieberman, 2015; Mattson, 2012; Minter-Jordan, Davis, & Arany, 2014; Ratey, 2008). In addition, physical movement was essential to developing muscular fitness, strength, endurance, balance, coordination, agility, and gait. We need to move on a regular and consistent basis to stay healthy, physically and psychologically. It is essential to our adapting to our environment.

THE MOVEMENT TOWARD SEDENTARY BEHAVIOR

Over the course of time, the behavior of human beings gradually became more and more sedentary as our society and cultures evolved through various stages of technological advancement, farming, industrial revolution, electricity, and digital technology, such that there was no longer the same demand for physical movement that was required for our hunter-gather ancestors to survive (Malina & Little, 2008; O'Keefe, Vogel, Lavie, & Cordain, 2010; Owen, Sparling, Healy, Dunstan, & Matthews 2010; Ratey & Hagerman, 2008).

Humans began moving, somewhere around 8,000 to 10,000 or so years ago, to establish fixed villages and communities through an agricultural/domestication of animal's period where there was still a lot of physical activity, at least for those who were engaged in farming, required to survive. As society and cultural continued to evolve and the population grew, more new inventions/technology were created, making life somewhat easier and less physically demanding. In the 18th century, the industrial revolution began with the creation of the stream engine, which gave human beings the access to more power, strength, and speed. Machines were now able to work for humans. This of course meant many humans needed less physical activity, at least compared to our hunter-gatherer ancestors and the farmers of the agricultural period, to survive.

Technology has continued to evolve at such a breath-taking pace that humans have needed to engage in less and less physical activity to survive. Electricity, automobiles, airplanes, telephones, refrigeration, TV, air conditioners, and so on have made contributions to increasing our leisure time and reducing our need for physical activity. With the advent of computers, mobile phones, tablets, the internet, and the rapidly increasing use of technology in this digital age, one could say we have, in one sense, compared to those have come before us, become faster, stronger, and smarter. On the other hand, we have, at least most of us in this country, become extremely sedentary as a result.

The problem is that our bodies and brains evolved to adapt to an environment that required regular physical movement to survive and reproduce. This mismatch between what our brains and bodies require and our extremely sedentary behavior creates significant chronic stress on our brain and body, which compromises our physical and psychological health and well-being. So, not only do we need to address, as we have discussed in previous chapters, chronic stress and the damage it does as the result of problematic psychosocial thinking, but we also need to address chronic stress and the damage it does as the result of being sedentary, which leads to being overweight and **obesity.**

OBESITY

Obesity can be defined as a BMI of 30 or greater. The body mass index or BMI is the ratio of weight to height where an underweight BMI is less than 18.5, 18.5–24.9 is a normal BMI, being overweight is a BMI of 25–29.9, and obesity is a BMI of 30 or greater (American Cancer Society (ACS), 2016). Utilizing the BMI as an assessment tool, researchers examined data between 1990–2015 across 195 countries and came to the conclusion that the occurrence of high BMIs are escalating worldwide, with the disorders associated with high BMIs being of significant concern (Global Burden of Disease 2015 Obesity Collaborators (GBD), 2017; Gregg & Shaw, 2017). It should be noted that although BMI is the standard tool for assessing being overweight and obesity, it is actually measuring excess weight not fat. The Centers for Disease Control and Prevention (2017) does note it is correlated with measures that specifically assess fat levels and it is an acceptable measure regarding being overweight, obesity, and the associated disorders. If you are interested in your own BMI, there are numerous sites on the Internet that offer calculators to discover your BMI. Simply use your search engine of choice, put in BMI calculator, and you will be presented with various BMI calculator sites.

Given individual differences, chronic stress is clearly linked to both obesity and significant, problematic weight loss as a probable cause (Barrington, Ceballos, Bishop, McGregor, & Beresford, 2012; Razzoli & Bartolomucci, 2016; Scott, Melhorn, & Sakai, 2012; Sominsky & Spence, 2014). The **Centers for Disease Control and Prevention** (CDC, 2015c) notes such health-related problems associated with obesity as mortality; hypertension; diabetes; cholesterol; heart disease; joint functioning; strokes; gallbladder disease; breast, kidney, gallbladder, colon, and liver cancer; anxiety; depression; sleep disorders; physical functioning; and pain.

The Centers for Disease Control and Prevention (CDC, 2010) noted that in 1960–1962, 44.8% of the adult population 20 years and older were overweight or obese. By 2005–2008 this number had increased to 67.7%. Of this percentage, 13% were classified as obese in 1960–1962 with 34.7% being classified as obese in 2005–2008. This is an alarming trend to say the least!

This trend, unfortunately, has continued. The **National Institute of Diabetes and Digestive and Kidney Diseases** (NIDDK) publication regarding a 2009–2010 analysis of being overweight and obesity noted more than two-thirds of the adult population were overweight or obese with more than one-third considered to be obese (NIDDK, 2012). The Centers for Disease Control and Prevention (2016) noted that the 2013–2014 analysis of obesity and being overweight indicated 70.7% of the adult population 20 years and older were overweight or obese and 37.9% of this group were obese.

Research by Ladabaum, Mannalithara, Myer, and Singh, (2014) tracked the increase in the prevalence of obesity between 1988–2010, noting that their findings were not supportive of a corresponding daily increase in caloric intake as the primary explanation for the increasing levels of obesity. What they found, instead, was a relationship between obesity and reported amounts of time engaged in physical activity during leisure time.

PHYSICAL EXERCISE, HEALTH, AND CHRONIC STRESS

It is estimated that 60–90% of all office visits to medical doctors are associated with, exacerbated by, and/or caused by chronic stress (Benson, 1998; Boone & Anthony, 2003; Jackson, 2013; WebMD, 2016). As noted in chapter 2, **chronic stress**

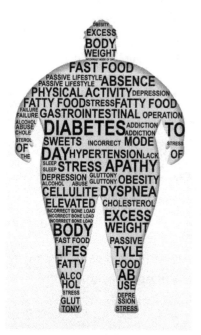

is linked to a wide range of physical and psychological disorders such cardiovascular disease, cancer, diabetes, gastrointestinal disorders, obesity, shrinkage in parts of the brain, memory problems, cognitive problems, learning problems, anxiety, depression, suppression of the immune system, and hypertension.

Research has demonstrated that physical exercise, with the primary focus being on aerobic exercise, is beneficial in preventing and alleviating chronic stress (American Heart Association (AHA), 2015b; Aziz, Wuensch, & Duffrin, 2015; Bushman, 2017; Coulter, Dickman, & Maradiegue, 2009; Jackson, 2013; Deslandes et al., 2009; Mayo Clinic, 2015; Milani & Lavie, 2009; Mitchell, Church, & Zucker, 2008; Otto & Smits, 2011; Puterman, Lin, Blackburn, O'Donovan, Adler, & Epe, 2010; Ratey & Hagerman, 2008).

Given the relationship between chronic stress and disease, and the fact that exercise is beneficial in preventing and alleviating chronic stress, it would seem to follow that physical exercise, with the primary focus on aerobic exercise, should be beneficial in addressing, preventing, and healing chronic physical and psychological diseases and disorders. The research is quite clear that this is the case across a wide range of diseases and disorders such as those noted (AHA, 2015a; Asmundson et al., 2013; Bushman, 2017; Bherer, Erickson, & Liu-Ambrose, 2013; Broman-Fulks, Berman, Rabian, & Webster, 2004; CDC, 2015a; Garber et al., 2011; Haennel & Lemire, 2002; Haskell et al., 2007; Hillman, Erikson, & Kramer, 2008; Leavitt, 2008; Milani & Lavie, 2009; Minter-Jordan, Davis, & Arany, 2014; Mitchell, Church, & Zucker, 2008; Otto & Smits, 2011; Pate et al., 1995; Pedersen & Saltin, 2006; Powers, Asmundson, & Smits 2015; Puterman et al., 2010; Ratey & Hagerman, 2008; Riebe, 2017; Roever, 2015; Wilkinson, Shur, & Smith, 2016).

The benefits of exercise have gotten to the point that it is being suggested that exercise be prescribed, by medical doctors and mental therapists, as part of a more holistic approach for addressing physical disorders, psychological disorders, and chronic stress (Anxiety and Depression Association of America (ADAA), 2014; Berryman, 2010; Otto & Smits, 2011; Ratey & Hagerman, 2008; Weir, 2011;

Wilkinson, Shur, & Smith, 2016). In some studies, research has shown that aerobic exercise is as effective as medication and, in some cases, more effective in the long run than medication in treating depression (Blumenthal et al., 1999, 2007). Naci and Ioannidis (2013) indicate that exercise may be as effective as medication, regarding mortality outcomes and across heart disease, strokes, and diabetes.

EXERCISE GUIDELINES

Given the alarming concerns with the increasing sedentary lifestyle of children, adolescents, adults, and the elderly, the linking of the sedentary lifestyle to the growing prevalence of being overweight and obese, the significant physical and psychological health concerns associated with being overweight and obese, the impact it is having on individuals and the public, and the previous research, collaboration, and generation of guidelines regarding the benefits of exercise by the **American College of Sports Medicine (ACSM)**, the **Centers for Disease Control and Prevention (CDC)**, and the **American Heart Association (AHA)**, the federal government addressed these concerns, via the U.S. Department of Health and Human Services (HHS), by publishing the "**2008 Physical Activity Guidelines for Americans**" (Haskell et al., 2007; HHS, 2008; Pate et al., 1995). These guidelines offer a comprehensive approach to physical activity across each of the age groupings including special concerns such as pregnancy and disabilities. The guidelines focus primarily on recommendations for aerobic and muscular strength exercises with warm-up and cool-down periods and address dosage, which consists of frequency, duration, and intensity. These exercise guidelines are in addition to one's normal light physical activity associated with daily living.

The recommendations for adults, for example, for aerobic activities or endurance exercises, such as running, biking, swimming, and brisk walking which stress, the good kind, your cardiovascular system, are a minimum of 150 minutes a week, which can be 30 minutes a day, over 5 days, of moderate intensity (for example, brisk walking at 3–4 miles an hour) at a minimum of 10 minutes a session, or a minimum of 75 minutes a week, which can be 25 minutes a day over 3 days of vigorous intensity (for example, very brisk walking at 4.5–5 miles an hour) at a minimum of 10 minutes a session, or a combination of the two (HHS 2008). (Intensity levels for various exercises and how to assess them can be found online by simply Googling "exercise moderate and vigorous intensity levels." You can add anyone of the major organizations such as CDC, AHA, Mayo Clinic, ACSM, etc. to your search for a stronger focus. Intensity levels are also discussed and described in the "2008 Physical Activity Guidelines for Americans," which is available for free online.)

The recommendations for adults for muscular strength/**anaerobic** exercises or resistance training, such as weight training, using your body weight (think pushups) and resistance bands, all of which stress, the good kind, your muscles and bone density, is a complete body workout incorporating the major muscle groups at a minimum of 2 days a week with a minimum of one set, 8–12 repetitions, per muscle group (HHS, 2008). Flexibility exercises, such as stretching, are encouraged as part of an overall physical fitness program but no guidelines are provided nor are there any reported, researched-based benefits (HHS, 2008).

The general guidelines for type of exercise and dosage (frequency, duration, intensity: moderate/vigorous) and the necessity of integrating well-balanced nutrition with exercise are supported and recommended by the American College of Sports Medicine, the Centers for Disease Control and Prevention, and the American Heart Association and can be found at their websites (ACSM, 2011; AHA, 2014a; CDC, 2009).

American College of Sports Medicine's Guidelines for Physical Activity

The American College of Sports Medicine has indicated that a comprehensive exercise program should include aerobic or endurance exercise, muscular fitness/resistance training, flexibility, and neuromotor or functional fitness exercises with an in-depth analysis of the research, type, dosage (frequency, duration, intensity), and recommendations to be found in ACSM (2011), Bushman (2017),

Garber and colleagues (2011), and Riebe (2017). In addition to the focus on aerobic exercise and incorporating muscular strength exercises and flexibility exercises, the ACSM has added neuromotor or functional fitness exercises to address concerns, especially for the elderly, with balance, coordination, integration, agility, **proprioception,** and gait (ACSM, 2011; Bushman, 2017; Garber et al., 2011; Riebe, 2017).

Aerobic or Endurance Exercise
Aerobic exercise refers to a type of energy conversion that utilizes oxygen to give the muscles energy during extended periods of time, minimal being estimated at 10 minutes, during the course of completing a specific type of exercise such as running, brisk walking, biking, swimming, or rowing with the heart rate and

respiration significantly elevated. This elevation requires your body, vascular system, and lungs to adapt and thus maintains and improves your overall cardiorespiratory functioning, health, and well-being.

In addition to improving cardiorespiratory fitness, aerobic exercise is beneficial for burning fat and along with nutrition is an important component of weight-management programs and, as it increases the production of **brain-derived neurotropic factor** or **BDNF**, which enhances neurogenesis and neuroplasticity, it is beneficial for brain health in such areas as memory, learning, and cognitive processing (Bushman, 2017; Heijnen, Hommel, Kibele, & Colzato, 2016; Piepmeier & Etnier, 2015; Ratey & Hagerman, 2008).

Muscular Fitness/Resistance Training

Musculoskeletal exercises/resistance training is essentially about establishing and improving **muscular fitness**, bone strength, and bone mineral density. Unlike aerobic training, resistance training or weight training occurs in brief spurts and is not dependent on oxygen for energy conversion, thus it is **anaerobic**, as it taps into energy already available in the body.

Research has found resistance or weight training to be beneficial as an important component of overall physical and psychological health by addressing, reducing and preventing such concerns as hypertension, diabetes, heart disease, anxiety, depression, chronic stress, pain, fatigue, cognitive functioning, risk of falling, weakening muscles due to aging, the risk of all-cause mortality, and weight management (Bushman, 2017; Garber et al., 2011; Riebe, 2017).

Stretching/Flexibility Exercises

The basic function of stretching, which is a natural, evolutionary-based process, is to increase **flexibility**, improve range of motion, warm up the body, increase blood flow, relax tendons and muscles, and reduce tension and tightness in the body and mind. Its fundamental purpose was to assist our distant ancestors in functionally adapting to the various challenges in their environmental contexts. While stretching is important across all ages, it is especially important for addressing the loss of range of motion and flexibility and thus our ability to functionally adapt as we age.

Within the framework of exercise, stretching, while being recommended, is embroiled in a controversy regarding what types of exercises it should or should not be used for, if it is or is not beneficial, if it should be used as part of a warm-up and/or cool-down or separate from each, if cold stretching before a warm up or stretching after warming up does do more harm than good, and, in some cases, if it is even necessary (Bushman, 2017; Garber et al., 2011; Riebe, 2017).

Within the context of stress management, stretching relieves and reduces the chronic tension in the body that has occurred as a result the tightening of muscles and tendons as part of the preparation process that happens because of the chronic and inappropriate activation of the stress response due to the rumination and/or obsessing over perceived threat-based psychosocial threats. Given the insidious nature of chronic stress, most people are not aware of the ongoing physical tightness and tension they carry in their body. This tension and physical tightness is often the basis of their symptoms of aching muscles, fatigue, lack of energy, compromised mobility, headaches, pain, inability to be focused and concentrate, irritability, and so on. Given its evolutionary basis, stretching is fundamental for our overall physical and psychological health and well-being (Elson & Gardiner, 2014).

Neuromotor/Functional Fitness Exercise

Neuromotor/functional fitness exercise refers to multidimensional exercises that may integrate agility, balance, gait, coordination, integration, flexibility, and resistance while they are being performed (Bushman et al., 2017; Garber et al., 2011; Riebe, 2017). Fundamental to neuromotor exercises is **proprioception** or self-awareness of your body, its position, and its movement in space. This self-awareness is especially important for the elderly as one their greatest fears and dangers is falling.

Taijiquan/tai chi ch'uan, qigong/c'hi kung, and **yoga** are prime examples of neuromotor exercises (Bushman et al., 2017; Garber et al., 2011; Riebe, 2017). Of the three, taijiquan is the most studied neuromotor exercise (Garber et al., 2011).

Research, primarily with the elderly although it is recommended for all ages, indicates the neuromotor benefits from practicing taijiquan are reducing/preventing and fearing falls; improving balance, flexibility, alignment, and posture; enhancing proprioception; improving agility and motor control; improving muscular strength; and controlling/reducing rate of bone density loss, and as such reducing fractures (Bushman et al., 2017; Garber et al., 2011; Jahnke, Larkey, Rogers, Etnier, & Lin, 2010; Lan, Chen, Lai, & Wong, 2013; Liu, 2010; Liu & Frank, 2010; Wayne & Furst, 2013). In addition to its neuromotor benefits, the research suggests the practice of taijiquan is beneficial for improving quality of life, physical and psychological well-being/health, and cognitive performance and for addressing, preventing, managing, and reducing such disorders as hypertension, osteoarthritis, chronic obstructive pulmonary disease (COPD), pain, anxiety, depression, anger, chronic stress, heart disease, hypertension, and sleep problems (Bushman et al., 2017; Dalusung-Angosta, 2011; Jahnke et al., 2010; Lan, Chen, Lai, & Wong, 2013; Wang, Bannuru, Ramel, Kupelnick, Scott, & Schmid, 2010; Wayne & Furst, 2013; Zhang,

Layne, Lowder, & Liu, 2012). Jahnke and colleagues (2010) suggest the benefits obtained from qigong are similar to the ones obtained from the practice of taiji-quan. Specific research on qigong has suggested benefits for hypertension, improving the immune system, lowering total cholesterol, reducing depression, and reducing stress (Lee, Pittler, Guo, & Edzard, 2007; Liu, 2010; Ng & Tsang, 2009).

The neuromotor benefits obtained from practicing yoga, specifically the asanas or postures of Hatha yoga, are strength, flexibility, alignment, posture, balance,

coordination, proprioception, agility, and motor control (Bushman et al., 2017; Khalsa & Elson, 2016). In addition to the neuromotor benefits, research indicates yoga is beneficial for improving quality of life, physical and psychological well-being/health, and cognitive performance and for addressing, preventing, managing and reducing such disorders as chronic stress, depression, anxiety, diabetes, pain, and sleep (Bushman et al., 2017; Gothe & McAuley, 2015; Khalsa & Elson, 2016; Li & Goldsmith, 2012).

The added benefit of practicing taiji-quan, qigong, and/or yoga is that all three approaches additionally incorporate meditative practices, moving and/or still, and flexibility/stretching practices while they are being performed.

THE PROBLEM

Even though the benefits of exercise are touted and easy-to-follow general guide-lines for both aerobic and resistance training have been made public, only 20% of the adult population report meeting the recommended amounts of both aerobic and resistance exercises, with approximately 50% reporting only performing aerobic exercise and about 30% report engaging only in resistance training (CDC, 2013, 2015b; HHS, 2008).

Research has indicated that adults spend an excessive amount of awake time during the day, including work, being sedentary/expending minimal energy, and primarily sitting, with various studies noting more than 50% of the day is spent being sedentary, with average sedentary time, depending on the study, ranging from 5–10 hours a day. (Biswas et al., 2015; Gardner, Smith, Lorencattod, Hamere, & Biddle, 2016; Proper, Singh, van Mechelen, & Chinapaw, 2011; Swartz et al., 2015). Increasing sedentary behavior has been associated with health risks such as anxiety, depression, metabolic syndrome, cardiovascular disease, obesity, diabetes, certain types of cancer, and all-cause mortality (Biswas et al., 2015; Chau et al., 2014; Halloway & Buchholz, 2016; Owen et al., 2010; Raynor, Bond, Freedson, & Sisson, 2012; Teychenne, Ball, & Salmon, 2010; Teychenne, Costigan, & Parker, 2015).

A rather unsettling discovery regarding research into sedentary behavior, physical exercise, and health risks is that even though the weekly guidelines for physical exercise may be met, if the rest of the day is primarily spent engaging in sedentary behavior, the individual is still at risk for the health-related disorders noted (Biswas et al., 2015; Chau et al., 2014; Halloway & Buchholz, 2016; Owen, Healy, Matthews, & Dunstan, 2010; Owen et al., 2010; Proper et al., 2011; Raynor, Bond, Freedson, & Sisson, 2012). In other words, lack of physical exercise (moderate/vigorous) and sedentary behavior are distinct. They both need to be addressed individually.

To address the health risks associated with sedentary behavior, the research suggests that sedentary behavior such as sitting time should be broken up during the day with such recommendations as becoming aware of the consequences of too much sedentary time; monitoring your sedentary time at home, at work, and while driving; and spending less time sitting watching TV, playing on the computer, tablet, mobile phone, and so on as (Chau et al., 2014; Biswas et al., 2015; Gardner et al., 2016; Owen, Healy, Matthews, & Dunstan, 2010; Owen et al., 2010). In other words, get up, move about, and/or stretch throughout the day.

WHY DON'T WE EXERCISE AND WHY ARE WE SO SEDENTARY?

The evolution of our cultures and society has basically eliminated the necessity to move very much from our life to survive (Malina & Little, 2008; O'Keefe, Vogel, Lavie, & Cordain, 2010; Owen et al., 2010; Ratey & Hagerman, 2008). We don't have to move very much, unlike our distant ancestors, to get food and drink, interact with others, get help if we need it, learn, make a living, find shelter and safety, and travel from one place to another.

A second reason is that not only is there an evolutionary instinct to move for survival, there also appears to be an instinct to not move. Not moving conserves energy and in a certain sense this was a necessity for our distant ancestors as sources for food were not as readily accessible as they are today (Lieberman, 2015; Nesse & Williams, 1996).

A third reason are all the excuses not to exercise: It is boring, it is too hard, I don't have enough time, I have no energy, I am too tired, I don't like exercising, none of my friends or family exercise, I have no motivation, I don't want to get hurt, I don't know how, I will feel embarrassed, I have kids to take care of, I don't have any equipment, even if I did I won't stay with it, and so on (AHA, 2014b; CDC, 2011; HHP, 2012; Springen, 2009).

Given neuroplasticity, as long as an individual engages in sedentary behavior, not exercising behavior, and making excuses behavior, all those behaviors are reinforced, and their corresponding neural networks become stronger and stronger such that this behavior becomes dominant. To overcome these chronic behaviors, individuals need to reduce sedentary behavior, exercise on a regular basis, and stop making excuses. This allows new neural networks to be created, which in turn results in the weakening of the old problematic networks, and the brain learning and maintaining new, health- and well-being-affirming behaviors. This of course requires regular and consistent implementation. Regarding the various excuses for not exercising, the references in the preceding paragraph offer solutions on how to address them.

Otto and Smits (2011) suggest that most of the reasons offered to people for why they should exercise focus on goals that are in the distant future, such as preventing illness, weight loss, getting more energy, and looking good. Because there appears to be no immediate benefit, starting and/or adhering to an exercise program becomes a challenge. They suggest to simply focus on the present and how much better you feel after you exercise and offer a series of solutions on how to get started (Otto & Smits, 2011).

DAOISM

When you think about engaging in physical exercise for the purposes of health and well-being, within the context of Buddhism, Daoism and Confucianism,

Daoism clearly stands alone as physical exercise and has become an integral aspect of its teachings (Kohn, 2008, 2012, 2017).

Yangsheng, Daoyin, and Qigong

Although the Daoist tradition did not invent what is known as *Yangsheng* (養性) or nourishing life, nor what is known as *Daoyin* (導引) or the circulating of vital energy/breath (*qi*氣) through the body by guiding/leading and stretching, they both have become fundamental aspects of its teachings.

Yangsheng is a general term that addresses and covers all aspects of a holistic, healthy lifestyle. The earliest written mentioning of this term appears to occur in chapter 3, titled *Yangsheng zhu* (養生主) or the "Fundamentals of Nourishing Life," of the 4th to 3rd century BCE Daoist text known as the *Zhuangzi* (Despeux, 2008a). Guo Xiang's commentary to the title of the chapter notes,

> Life is that which you preserve and nourish. This is the ultimate principle (li zhi ji 理之極) for those who nourish life (Yangsheng 養生). What does it mean to exceed this ultimate principle? If your nourishing harms, damages, or threatens life, this is not the process of nourishing life (Yangsheng 養生). (Santee & Zhang 2015, p. 25)

Ongoing, threat-based psychosocial thinking, sedentary behavior, and not exercising harms, damages, and threatens, in other words chronically stresses, one's mind and body, which is clearly not an example of *Yangsheng*.

Yangsheng is further expanded in chapter 2 of the "Simple Questions" (*Suwen* 素問) section of the over 2,000-year-old medical text *Huangdi Neijing* (黃帝內經) or the *Yellow Emperor's Discourse on Internal Medicine*. It addresses behavior within each of the four seasons. Regarding the spring it states,

> The three months of Spring are called issue forth and display. The sky and the earth produce life together. All things are thriving. At night lie down and go to sleep. Rise up early in the morning, stretch out and take a brisk walk in the courtyard. By issuing energy the body recuperates. This is applying your will (zhi 志) to live and grow. Living and growing you will not weaken. Enjoy life and do not punishing yourself. This is responding to the *qi* (氣) of spring. This is the Tao of nourishing life (*Yangsheng* 養生). (Santee & Zhang, 2015, p. 26)

Don't punish yourself! Engage in physical exercise! Enjoy Life! Be in harmony! In other words, don't chronically stress yourself!

What is entailed by Yangsheng is even further expanded in the *Yangxing yanming lu* (養性延命录) or *Records of Nourishing Your Nature and Extending Your*

Life, which many believe to be the most important compendium of selections on Yangsheng and longevity practices (Kohn, 2012). It appears to have been actually constructed during mid- to late-Tang dynasty (618–907 CE) and its authorship is unclear. Its preface, attributed to the Chinese physician and apparent Daoist Sun Simiao (581–682 CE), provides a succinct summary of the practice of Yangsheng or nourishing life (Despeux, 2008b; Kohn, 2012). He notes,

> If you are able to let the mind/heart (心 *xin*) flow in emptiness and stillness, stop worrying and thinking excessively, not interfere (*wuwei* 無為) with yourself and others, ingest original breath/vital energy (*yuan qi* 元氣) after the hour of the rat (子 earthly branch [11:00 p.m.-1:00 a.m.]), regularly practice *qi* circulation, breathing exercises, and the physical exercises of daoyin (導引) in a stress free environment, conserve and nourish your health consistently, eat good food and herbs, then an energetic life of 100 years is most likely. Because of this I am able to still my mind/heart and nonjudgmentally observe my environment. (Santee & Zhang, 2015, p. 27)

The term *Daoyin,* which is noted in the previous quote, first appears in written form in chapter 15 of the *Zhuangzi* (Despeux, 2008c; Kohn, 2008). The author appears to view the practice as problematic because the practitioners are just focused on extending their life and are not concerned with meditation, the mind, or being in harmony with Dao.

> Blowing out (Chui 吹) and sucking in (xu 呴), exhaling and inhaling (huxi 呼吸). Spitting out the old, taking in the new. Bear climbing and hanging (xiong jing 熊經), and bird stretching (niao shen 鳥申). Desperately seeking long life (shou 壽). This is the Daoyin (道引) or guiding/leading and stretching of the scholar. The person who nourishes the body (yang xing 養形) seeks the long life of Peng Zu [believed to have lived over 800 years]. (Translation mine; for Chinese text see Guo, 1974, p. 280)

While the practice of *Daoyin* may have been problematic and fragmented for the author of this quote in the *Zhuangzi,* some 900-plus years later it did not appear to be a problem for Sun Simiao, as it has been clearly integrated into a holistic life style consistent with the principles of *Yangsheng.*

The preventive, healing, nourishing, and enhancing life practices associated with *Yangsheng* and *Daoyin* continue today under the name of *qigong* (氣功), which is a relatively recent term coined in 1948 (Kohn, 2017). Qigong literally means working (*gong* 功) with vital energy/breath (*qi* 氣). *Qi* is vital energy/breath, and from the classical Chinese medicine perspective if *qi* is able to flow through the meridians or channels in the body without any obstructions, it means you are centered, rooted, and in harmony with your environment (Liu, 2010). The unobstructed flow of qi through your body is indicative of physical and psychological health and well-being. If *qi* is obstructed, then the body and mind are chronically stressed, resulting in physical and/or psychological illness, disease, and disorders.

The practice of *Qigong* focuses on slow, rhythmic body movements coordinated with your breathing. Guided by your mind, *qi* can be gathered, cultivated, and circulated throughout the meridians in your body. The various postures of the *Qigong* forms stimulate different meridians.

Of special importance while practicing *Qigong* is a nonjudgmental awareness, or *guan*, of (a) your body moving in and through space, which is known proprioception; (b) of sensations generated by internal stimuli, such as muscle tension, in your body, which is known as **interoception**; and (c) of sensations generated by external stimuli outside of your body, such as a sound, which is known as **exteroception.**

Thus, qigong is clearly an integrated mind, body, and environment practice that keeps you holistically focused in the present. The practice of qigong is utilized for prevention, healing, enhancing life and, in the case of Daoism, once one's body and mind are appropriately nourished, for spiritual cultivation.

It must be noted that the concepts of *qi* and meridians or channels running throughout your body are not consistent with the Western medical and physiological sense of the geography of the body. Both are considered, for all intents and purposes, to not exist as they cannot, from a Western research perspective, be operationalized and hence cannot be measured.

Taiqiquan/Tai Chi Ch'uan

Although taijiquan (太極拳) is primarily practiced today for its health benefits and to address chronic stress, it was originally created as a self-defense sometime during the mid-17th century and is attributed to a Chen Wangting (circa 1580–1660) who was a former battle-experienced warrior (Kang, 1995; Henning, 2012; Shahar, 2008; Wayne & Fuerst, 2013). It was not, however, called taijiquan at the time (Henning, 2012; Shahar, 2008). This Chen style of taijquan is essentially the style from which all later variations of taijiquan are based. The remaining four major styles are Yang, which is the most popular, Wu, Wu Hao, and Sun, the most recent. Each style is connected to a family of the same name. Over the course of time, *daoyin*, breathing techniques (*tuna* (吐納, literally exhaling and inhaling), and various Daoist techniques, practices, and concepts, were integrated into the martial practice and theory of taijiquan, which also resulted in a focus of the practice of taijiquan on health, well-being, and, for some, spiritual cultivation (Shahar, 2008; Wayne & Fuerst, 2013). Taijiquan was not, however, created specifically within the Daoist tradition. Its practice, like qigong, requires a nonjudgmental self-awareness of (a) your body, its position and its movement in space (proprioception); (b) sensations generated from internal stimuli (interoception); and (c) sensations generated from external stimuli (exteroception)—all of which are fundamental for both its martial applications and for health and well-being.

The earliest written mentioning of the term *Taiji* appears to occur in the over 2000-year-old text known as the *Yijing* or *Book of Changes* (Lam, 2007). The concept Taiji or Great Ultimate (a) refers to the reciprocal, interdependent continually changing relationship between yin and yang; (b) is a fundamental explanation of movement and change in the universe; and (c) denotes the importance of being in harmony internally and externally with movement and change. Excessiveness and deficiency are associated with danger and harm. Moderation is the key. Within yin there is yang and within yang there is yin which is clearly seen in the Taiji symbol where black reflects yin and white reflects yang. Yin, for example, refers to night, earth, moon, female, softness, internal, yielding, still, empty, dark, and downward, while yang refers to the sky, sun, male, hardness, external, tenacious, active, full, light, and upward. All the pairings, such as soft and hard, are interdependent and do not exist without the other. The term *quan* (拳) refers to fist or boxing. It is often used to refer to a particular style or method of martial arts such as the martial style or martial method of the Great Ultimate (taijiquan).

This notion of being in harmony internally and externally with change and movement, not being excessive or deficient, and practicing moderation is fundamental not only for the practice of Daoism, for the practice of taijiquan and qigong, but also for the behavior that is required for physical and psychological health and well-being. In other words, not exercising is being deficient! Being sedentary is being excessive! Both chronically stress the body and mind.

PRACTICAL APPLICATION

Baduanjin: Both Hands Supporting Heaven Regulates the Triple Burners (*sanjiao* 三焦)

Both hands supporting heaven regulates the triple burners is the first actual posture of the *Baduanjin* or eight pieces of brocade. The triple burner (*sanjiao*), as part of traditional Chinese medicine, is an integrative function as opposed to a body organ system that has a location in the body. It essentially has to do with all metabolism, hence the burners, associated with water and fluids in the body. In other words, the creation, transformation, and distribution of energy throughout the body (Chinese Health Qigong Association (CHQA), 2007; Kaptchuk, 1983). The three refers to respiration (upper burner), digestion (middle burner), and elimination (lower burner) which must work together to maintain health and well-being. In chapter 8 of the Suwen section of the *Huangdi Neijing* or the *Yellow Emperor's Discourse on Internal Medicine*, it notes

> The Triple Burner: That which manages the dredging of the drains and opening up/keeping clear the water pathways. (Translation mine; for Chinese text see Chines Text Project (CTP), n.d.)

In chapter 18 of the Lingshu section of the *Huangdi Neijing* or the *Yellow Emperor's Discourse on Internal Medicine*, it states

> The Yellow Emperor said, "Good. As I understand that which has been said, 'The upper burner is like mist, the middle burner is like foam, and the lower burner is like a drain.'" (see CTP, n.d.)

From the perspective of Western science, regarding the triple burner, insofar as it cannot be defined and thus not operationalized (located, mapped, etc.), it cannot be measured. This being the case, it does not exist, at this point in time, within the domain of Western science (Kaptchuk, 1983). Remember interoceptive, exteroceptive, and proprioceptive awareness is practiced throughout all eight repetitions.

From the second preparation position, where it appears you are holding a large beach ball, your feet are shoulder-width apart and your arms are circled forward and in front of you with your palms facing inward about 3 inches below your hips, shift your weight onto your right foot and step with your left foot, placing it next to your right foot as in the first preparation position. Your knees are slightly bent. Don't move your arms as you are stepping. Distribute your weight evenly across both feet.

Slowly inhaling through your nose, bring your hands together, palms up, and gently clasp your fingers together. Continuing your inhalation, slowly pull up your hands, palms still facing up, along the centerline of your body, about 2 or so inches from your body. When your hands reach your chest level, while still moving upward, slowly rotate them inward, downward, outward, and upward and while they continue to rise, tilt your head back and follow your hands with your eyes. Your arms are extended fully upward, elbows are not locked, with the back of your hands above and facing toward your head, and palms are facing and gently pushing upward. At the same time your hands begin to move upward, slowly and gently straighten your legs. Do not lock your knees. Coordinate your inhalation with the movement of your arms, hands, and legs. It is one slow inhalation from the time your hands start moving until your arms are fully extended, elbows are not locked, and your hands are above your head with palms facing and gently pushing upward. As you push upward you should notice that your feet are naturally pushing down while your legs are straightening out. This is both hands supporting heaven and regulating the triple burners.

Pause for a moment in this position, lower your chin and look forward, and then begin slowly exhaling while circling your arms outward, downward, and inward, returning to the position where your fingers are clasped together in front of your body about 3 inches below your hips. At the same time, your knees are slowly and gently bending slightly. This is one complete, one inhalation and one exhalation, repetition. Repeat seven more times. After the eighth repetition, let your hands gently return to your sides such that you have returned to the first preparation position. Take a few deep breaths and slowly walk away.

How do you feel? Physically? Psychologically? What do you notice? Is your mind still and empty? Do you notice a difference between how you felt before you started and how you felt after you started? Were you distracted internally? Externally? The next time you practice the *Baduanjin*, begin with the first two preparation stages followed by both hands supporting heaven regulates the triple burners. Remember, to receive the long-term benefits of the *Baduanjin*, it must be practiced on a regular and consistent basis. This allows neuroplasticity to occur, which in turns allows you to learn about and explore the depth and many benefits of this ancient Chinese approach to addressing, managing, and eliminating chronic stress.

Yoga: Corpse Pose (*Savasana*)

The *Savasana* pose, the final pose of the yoga sequence, is about being totally present and observing, in the here and now, whatever occurs in a nonjudgmental and detached manner. It is just about being, not doing. Just resting and rejuvenating. When your mind wanders (it will and it is normal) simply observe your thoughts in a detached and nonjudgmental manner. Then let them naturally fade away. The idea here is to simply observe the present moment without any judgments. Just be! Remember interoceptive, exteroceptive, and proprioceptive awareness throughout the entire duration of the pose.

Lie on your back on the floor or on a mat on the floor. Close your eyes. Your legs are spread about shoulder-width apart. Your arms are angled out to the sides with your palms up. Adjust your body so you feel comfortable. If you need to support for your head use a folded towel or blanket. You may also place a folded towel or blanket under your lower back or under your knees. The idea is to feel comfortable so you can relax, rest, and rejuvenate. Breathe naturally through your nose. Let your body sink, if you will, into the floor. Observing the present in a nonjudgmental and detached manner, let everything go. You are not trying to get or obtain anything. Allow your mind and body to simply relax, rest, and rejuvenate. Spend a few minutes, you can of course adjust the time frame, in the corpse pose. After completing the pose, open your eyes, stretch your fingers and toes, take a couple of deep breaths, roll to your side and slowly sit up. After adjusting to this position, slowly stand up. How do you feel? What did you notice?

It is important to note that when you are practicing the corpse pose as part of your personal stress-management program (PSMP), you do not want to fall asleep. If you do so, you are not practicing the corpse pose and are clearly not getting enough sleep or rest. The topic of sleep will be covered in the next chapter, and if you are having problems with sleep you will see how the corpse pose may be utilized to address sleep problems.

You now have a sequence of yoga poses that you can practice as part of your personal stress-management program (PSMP). Remember, for you to reduce/eliminate chronic stress and receive the long-term physical and psychological health benefits of yoga, you need to practice it on a regular and consistent basis. This ongoing practice literally wires (neuroplasticity) new neural networks in your brain, allowing you to learn about and explore the depths of your yoga practice and how to manage stress.

KEY TERMS

evolutionary theory
hunter-gatherer
ancestors
aerobic
cardiovascular fitness
endurance exercise
sedentary
obesity
Centers for Disease
Control and Prevention
National Institute of
Diabetes and Digestive
and Kidney Diseases
chronic stress
American College of
Sports Medicine
(ACSM)

American Heart
Association (AHA)
2008 Physical Activity Guidelines for
Americans
U.S. Department of
Health and Human Services (HHS)
proprioception
aerobic/endurance
muscular fitness
musculoskeletal
exercises
resistance training
anaerobic
flexibility
stretching

neuromotor or functional fitness
brain-derived neurotropic factor (BDNF)
high-intensity interval
training or HIIT
yawning
interoception
exteroception
dosage
Taijiquan/Tai Chi
Ch'uan,
qigong/C'hi Kung,
yoga
Yangsheng
Daoyin
yin and yang

EXERCISES

1. For a few days, monitor your awake sedentary time both at work and at home (watching TV, working on a computer, standing around talking, driving in a car, using a smart phone or tablet, and so on) both at work and at home time. On average, how much of your awake time is sedentary? What do you notice when you engage in sedentary behavior? Does your mind wander? How do you feel?

2. Over the course of a week, monitor your physical exercise. What type of exercises do you do? How often (frequency), how long (duration), and how hard (intensity) are your exercise sessions? Does your mind wander during the exercises? How do you feel after you exercise? Why?

3. Select one of the neuromotor postures from the yoga sequence, Zhan Zhuang sequence, or Baduanjin sequence and, utilizing mindfulness/guan, with your eyes closed, observe, say for 5 minutes, the sensations generated from within your body (interoception). What do you notice? Feel? Did your mind wander? If so, why?

4. Select one of the neuromotor postures from the yoga sequence or Zhan Zhuang sequence and, utilizing mindfulness/guan, observe, say for 5 minutes, the sensations (sound, sight, smell) generated by stimuli outside of your body. What do you notice? Feel? Did your mind wander? If so, why?

5. Find an area where you can safely walk, say for 5 minutes, in a brisk manner and, utilizing mindfulness/guan, observe how your body moves through space (proprioception). What do you notice? Feel? Did your mind wander? If so, why?

6. Select either the entire Zhan Zhuang sequence or the entire yoga sequence. Utilizing mindfulness/guan while moving through the various postures of the entire sequence, observe both internally generated sensations (interoception) and externally generated sensations (exteroception). What do you notice? Feel? Did your mind wander? If so, why?

7. During the course of the day, monitor how often you stretch. Why are you stretching? How do you feel while you are stretching? After you stretch?

8. What do *Yangsheng, Daoyin,* and *qigong* mean? How are the relevant to stress management, health, and well-being?

REFERENCES

American Cancer Society (ACS). (2016). *Normal weight ranges: Body mass index (BMI)*. Retrieved from https://www.cancer.org/cancer/cancer-causes/diet-physical-activity/body-weight-and-cancer-risk/adult-bmi.html

American College of Sports Medicine (ACSM). (2011). *ACSM issues new recommendations on quantity and quality of exercise.* Retrieved from https://www.prweb.com/releases/2011/6/prweb8606343.htm

American Heart Association (AHA). (2014). *Breaking down barriers to fitness.* Retrieved from https://www.heart.org/HEARTORG/HealthyLiving/PhysicalActivity/StayingMotivatedforFitness/Breaking-Down-Barriers-to-Fitness_UCM_462208_Article.jsp

American Heart Association (AHA). (2015a). *Physical activity improves quality of life.* Retrieved from http://www.heart.org/HEARTORG/HealthyLiving/PhysicalActivity/FitnessBasics/Physical-activity-improves-quality-of-life_UCM_307977_Article.jsp#.WSCyRbpFyUl

American Heart Association. (AHA). (2015b). *Fight stress with healthy habits.* Retrieved from http://www.heart.org/HEARTORG/HealthyLiving/StressManagement/FightStressWithHealthyHabits/Fight-Stress-with-Healthy-Habits_UCM_307992_Article.jsp#.WSCz-LpFyUk

American Heart Association (AHA). (2017). *American Heart Association recommendations for physical activity in adults.* Retrieved from http://www.heart.org/HEARTORG/HealthyLiving/PhysicalActivity/StartWalking/American-Heart-Association-Guidelines_UCM_307976_Article.jsp#.WSpU07pFyUk

Anxiety and Depression Association of America (ADAA). (2014). *Exercise for stress and anxiety.* Retrieved from https://www.adaa.org/living-with-anxiety/managing-anxiety/exercise-stress-and-anxiety

Asmundson, G. J. G., Fetzner, M. G., DeBoer, L. B., Powers, M. B., Otto, M. W., & Smits, J. A. J. (2013). Let's get physical: A contemporary review of the anxiolytic effects of exercise for anxiety and its disorders. *Depression & Anxiety, 30*(4), 362–373.

Aziz, S., Wuensch, K. L., & Duffrin, C. (2015). Workaholism, exercise, and stress-related illness. *Journal of Workplace Behavioral Health, 30*(4), 93–406.

Barrington, W. E., Ceballos, R. M., Bishop, S. K., McGregor, B. A., & Beresford, S. A. A. (2012). Perceived stress, behavior, and body mass index among adults participating in a worksite obesity prevention program, Seattle, 2005–2007. *Preventing Chronic Disease.* Retrieved from https://www.cdc.gov/pcd/issues/2012/12_0001.htm

Benson, H. (1998, September 22). Testimony of Herbert Benson regarding mind/body interventions, healthcare and mind/body medical centers before the United States Senate Appropriations Subcommittee on Labor, HHS & Education, Senator Arlen Specter, Chair. Washington DC.

Berryman, J. W. (2010). Exercise is medicine: A historical perspective. *Current Sports Medicine Reports, 9*(4), 195–201.

Bherer, L., Erickson, K. I., &Liu-Ambrose, T. (2013). A review of the effects of physical activity and exercise on cognitive and brain functions in older adults. *Journal of aging research, 2013.* Retrieved from https://www.ncbi.nlm.nih.gov/pmc/articles/PMC3786463/pdf/JAR2013-657508.pdf

Biswas A., Oh, P. I., Faulkner, G. E., Bajaj, R. R., Silver, M. A., Mitchell, M. S., &Alter, D. A. (2015). Sedentary time and its association with risk for disease incidence, mortality, and hospitalization in adults: A systematic review and meta-analysis. *Annals of Internal Medicine, 162*(2), 123–132.

Blumenthal, J. A., Babyak M. A., Doraiswamy, P. M., Watkins, L., Hoffman, B. M., Barbour, K. A., ... &Sherwood, A. (2007). Exercise and pharmacotherapy in the treatment of major depressive disorder. *Psychosomatic Medicine, 69*(7), 587–596.

Blumenthal J. A., Babyak M. A., Moore K. A., Craighead, W. E., Herman, S., Khatri, P., ... &Krishnan, K. R. (1999). Effects of exercise training on older patients with major depression. *Archives of Internal Medicine, 159*(19), 2349–2356.

Boone, J. L., &Anthony, J. P., (2003). Evaluating the impact of stress on systemic disease: The most protocol in primary care. *Journal of the American Osteopathic Association, 103*(5), 239–246.

Bramble, D. M., &Lieberman, D. E. (2004). Endurance running and the evolution of *Homo. Nature, 432*(7015), 345–352.

Broman-Fulks, J. J., Berman, M. E., Rabian, B., &Webster, M. J. (2004). Effects of aerobic exercise on anxiety sensitivity. *Behaviour Research and Therapy, 42*(2), 125–136.

Bushman, B. (Ed.) (2017). *American College of Sports Medicine complete guide to fitness and health.* Champaign, IL: Human Kinetics.

Chinese Text Project. (n.d.). *Yellow Emperor's discourse on internal medicine. Translated from* http://ctext.org/huangdi-neijing/suwen/zh

Centers for Disease Control and Prevention (CDC). (2009). *How much physical activity do adults need for health benefits?* Retrieved from https://www.cdc.gov/physicalactivity/downloads/pa_fact_sheet_adults.pdf

Centers for Disease Control and Prevention (CDC). (2010). *Overweight, obesity, and healthy weight among persons 20 years of age and over, by selected characteristics: United States, selected years 1960–1962 through 2005–2008.* Retrieved from https://www.cdc.gov/nchs/data/hus/2010/071.pdf

Centers for Disease Control and Prevention (CDC). (2011). *Overcoming barriers to physical activity.* Retrieved from https://www.cdc.gov/physicalactivity/basics/adding-pa/barriers.html

Centers for Disease Control and Prevention (CDC). (2013). *One in five adults meet overall physical activity guidelines.* Retrieved from https://www.cdc.gov/media/releases/2013/p0502-physical-activity.html

Centers for Disease Control and Prevention (CDC). (2015a). *Physical activity and health: The benefits of physical activity.* Retrieved from https://www.cdc.gov/physicalactivity/basics/pa-health/index.htm

Centers for Disease Control and Prevention (CDC). (2015b). *How much physical activity do adults need?* Retrieved from https://www.cdc.gov/physicalactivity/basics/adults/index.htm

Centers for Disease Control and Prevention (CDC). (2015c). *The health effects of overweight and obesity.* Retrieved from https://www.cdc.gov/healthyweight/effects/index.html

Centers for Disease Control and Prevention (CDC). (2016). *Obesity and overweight.* Retrieved from https://www.cdc.gov/nchs/fastats/obesity-overweight.htm

Centers for Disease Control and Prevention (CDC). (2017). *Body mass index: Considerations for practitioners.* Retrieved from https://www.cdc.gov/obesity/downloads/bmiforpractitioners.pdf

Chau, J., Grunseit, A., Midthjell, K., Holmen, J., Holmen, T., Bauman, A., &Van Der Ploeg, H. (2014). Cross-sectional associations of total sitting and leisure screen time with cardiometabolic risk in adults. Results from the HUNT Study, Norway. *Journal of Science and Medicine in Sport, 17*(1), 78–84.

Chinese Health Qigong Association (CHQA). (2007). *Ba Daun Jin.* Beijing, CN: Foreign Language Press.

Coulter, P. A., Dickman, K., &Maradiegue, A. (2009). The effects of exercise on stress in working women. *Journal of Nurse Practitioners, 5*(6), 408–413.

Dalusung-Angosta, A. (2011). The impact of tai chi exercise on coronary heart disease: A systematic review. *Journal of the American Academy of Nurse Practitioners, 23*(7), 376–381.

Deslandes, A., Moraes, H., Ferreira, C., Veiga, H., Silveria, H., Mouta, R., … &Laks, J. (2009). Exercise and mental health: Many reasons to move. *Neuropsychobiology, 59*(4), 191–198.

Despeux, C. (2008a). Yangsheng: Nourishing life. In F. Pregadio (Ed.), *The encyclopedia of Taoism* (pp. 1148–1150). New York, NY: Routledge.

Despeux, C. (2008b). Yangsheng yanming lu: On nourishing inner nature and extending Life. In P. Pregadio (Ed.), *The encyclopedia of Taoism* (pp. 1152–1153). New York, NY: Routledge.

Despeux, C. (2008c). Daoyin: Guiding and pulling, gymnastics. In F. Pregadio (Ed.), *The encyclopedia of Taoism* (pp. 334–337). New York, NY: Routledge.

Elson, L. E., &Gardiner, J. (2014). *A Harvard Medical School special report: Stretching.* Boston, MA: Harvard Medical School.

Garber, C. E., Blissmer, B., Deschenes, M. R., Franklin, B. A., Lamonte, M. J., Lee, I. M., Nieman, D. C., & Swain, D. P. (2011). Quantity and quality of exercise for developing and maintaining cardiorespiratory, musculoskeletal, and neuromotor fitness in apparently healthy adults: Guidance for prescribing exercise. *Medicine & Science in Sports & Exercise, 43*(7), 1334–1359.

Gardner, B., Smith, L., Lorencattod, F., Hamere &Biddle, S. J. H. (2016). How to reduce sitting time? A review of behaviour change strategies used in sedentary behaviour reduction interventions among adults. *Health Psychology Review, 10*(1), 89–112.

Global Burden of Disease 2015 Obesity Collaborators (GBD). (2017). Health effects of overweight and obesity in 195 countries over 25 years. *New England Journal of Medicine, 377*(1). Retrieved from http://www.nejm.org/doi/pdf/10.1056/NEJMoa1614362

Gothe, N. P., &McAuley, E. (2015). Yoga and cognition: A meta-analysis of chronic and acute effects. *Psychosomatic Medicine, 77*(7), 784–797.

Guo, Q. (1974). *Zhuangzi jishi.* Taipei, TW: Chung Hwa.

Gregg, E. W. &Shaw, J. E. (2017). Global health effects of overweight and obesity. *New England Journal of Medicine, 377, 80–81.* Retrieved from http://www.nejm.org/doi/full/10.1056/NEJMe1706095#t=article

Haennel, R. G., &Lemire, F. (2002). Physical activity to prevent cardiovascular disease. How much is enough?. *Canadian family physician Medecin de famille canadien, 48,* 65–71.

Hallal, P. C., Andersen L. B., Bull, F. C., Guthold, R., Haskell, W., &Ekelund, U. (2012). Global physical activity levels: Surveillance progress, pitfalls, and prospects. *The Lancet, 380*(9838), 247–257.

Halloway, S., &Buchholz, S. W. (2016). Sedentary behavior: Considerations for the nurse practitioner. *Journal of Nurse Practitioners, 13*(1), 59–63.

Harvard Health Publications (HHP). (2012). What are your *barriers to exercise?* Retrieved from http://www.health.harvard.edu/heart-health/what-are-your-barriers-to-exercise

Haskell, W. L., Lee, I. M., Pate, R. R., Powell, K. E., Blair, S.N., Franklin, B. A., …&Bauman, A. (2007). Physical activity and public health: Updated recommendation for adults from the American College of Sports Medicine and the American Heart Association. *Medical Science and Sports Exercise, 399*(8), 1423–1434.

Health and Human Services (HHS). (2008). *2008 physical activity guidelines for Americans.* Retrieved from https://health.gov/PAGuidelines/pdf/paguide.pdf

Heijnen, S., Hommel, B., Kibele, A., &Colzato, L. S. (2016). Neuromodulation of aerobic exercise—A review. *Frontiers in Psychology, 6.* Retrieved from https://www.researchgate.net/publication/289586875_Neuromodulation_of_Aerobic_Exercise-A_Review

Hempel, S., Taylor, S. L., Solloway, M., Miake-Lye, I. M., Beroes, J. M., Shanman, R., &Shekelle, P. G. (2014). *Evidence map of tai chi.* Retrieved from https://www.hsrd.research.va.gov/publications/esp/taichi-REPORT.pdf

Henning, S. E. (2012, September 22). *Thoughts on the origin and development of taijiquan.* Paper presented at the 3rd Shenjiang International Forum on Wushu. Shanghai, China.

Hillman, C. H., Erikson, K. I., &Kramer, A. F. (2008). Be smart, exercise your heart: Exercise effects on brain and cognition. *Nature Reviews Neuroscience, 9*(1), 58–65.

Jackson, E. M. (2013). The role of exercise in stress management. *ACSM's Health & Fitness Journal, 17*. Retrieved from http://journals.lww.com/acsm-healthfitness/Pages/articleviewer.aspx?year=2013&issue=05000&article=00006&type=Fulltext

Jahnke, R., Larkey, L., Rogers, C., Etnier, J., & Lin, F. (2010). A comprehensive review of health benefits of qigong and tai chi. *American Journal of Health Promotion, 24*, e1–e25.

Kang, G. W. (1995). *The spring and autumn of Chinese martial arts: 5000 years.* Santa Cruz, CA: Plum.

Kaptchuk, T. J. (1983). *The web that has no weaver: Understanding Chinese medicine.* Chicago, IL: Congdon, & Weed.

Khalsa, S. B. S., & Elson, L. E. (2016). *A Harvard Medical School special health report: An introduction to yoga.* Boston, MA: Harvard Medical School.

Kohn, L. (2008). *Chinese healing exercises: The tradition of Daoyin.* Honolulu, HI: University of Hawaii Press.

Kohn, L. (2012). *A source book in Chinese longevity.* St. Petersburg, FL: Three Pines Press.

Kohn, L. (2017). *Daoism and the origins of qigong.* Retrieved from http://abodetao.com/daoism-and-the-origins-of-qigong/

Ladabaum, U., Mannalithara, A., Myer, P. A. & Singh, G. (2014). Obesity, abdominal obesity, physical activity, and caloric intake in U.S. adults: 1988–2010. *American Journal of Medicine, 127*(8), 717–727.

Lam, P. (2007). *History of tai chi.* Retrieved from https://taichiforhealthinstitute.org/history-of-tai-chi-2/

Lan, C., Chen, S. Y., Lai, J. S., & Wong, A. M. K. (2013). Tai chi chuan in medicine and health promotion. *Evidence-Based Complementary and Alternative Medicine, 2013.* Retrieved from https://www.hindawi.com/journals/ecam/2013/502131/

Leavitt, M. O. (2008). *2008 physical activity guidelines for Americans.* Retrieved from https://health.gov/PAGuidelines/pdf/paguide.pdf

Lee, M. S., Pittler, M. H., Guo, R., & Ernst, E. (2007). Qigong for hypertension: A systematic review of randomized clinical trials. *Journal of Hypertension, 25*(8), 1525–1532.

Li, A. W., & Goldsmith, C. A. W. (2012). The effects of yoga on anxiety and stress. *Alternative Medicine Review, 17*(1), 221–235.

Lieberman, D. E. (2015). Is exercise really medicine? An evolutionary perspective. *Current Sports Medicine Reports, 14*(4), 313–319.

Liu, H., & Frank, A. (2010). Tai chi as a balance improvement exercise for older adults: A systematic review. *Journal of Geriatric Physical Therapy, 33*(3), 103–109.

Liu, T. (Ed.) (2010). *Chinese medical qigong.* London, UK: Singing Dragon.

Malina, R. B., & Little L B. (2008). Physical activity: The present in the context of the past. *American Journal of Human Biology, 20*(4), 373–391.

Mattson, M. P. (2012). Evolutionary aspects of human exercise—Born to run purposefully. *Ageing Research Reviews, 11*(3), 347–352.

Mayo Clinic. (2015). *Exercise and stress: Get moving to manage stress.* Retrieved from http://www.mayoclinic.org/healthy-lifestyle/stress-management/in-depth/exercise-and-stress/art-20044469

Milani, R. V., & Lavie, C. J. (2009). Reducing psychosocial stress: A novel mechanism of improving survival from exercise training. *American Journal of Medicine, 122*(10), 931–938.

Minter-Jordan, M., Davis, I. S., & Arany, Z. (2014). *Healthy mind, healthy body: Benefits of exercise.* Retrieved from https://hms.harvard.edu/sites/default/files/assets/Sites/Longwood_Seminars/Exercise3.14.pdf

Mitchell, T., Church, T., & Zucker, M. (2008). *Move yourself: The Cooper Clinic medical director's guide to all the healing benefits of exercise (even a little!).* Hoboken, NJ: Wiley.

Naci, H., & Ioannidis, J. P. A. (2013). Comparative effectiveness of exercise and drug interventions on mortality outcomes: Metaepidemiological study. *British Medical Journal, 347*, 1–14.

National Institute of Diabetes and Digestive and Kidney Diseases (NIDDK) (2012). *Overweight and obesity statistics.* Retrieved from https://www.niddk.nih.gov/health-information/health-statistics/overweight-obesity

Nesse, R. M., & Williams, G. C. (1996). *Why we get sick: The new science of Darwinian medicine.* New York, NY: Vintage.

Ng, B. H. P., & Tsang, H. W. H. (2009). Psychophysiological outcome of health qigong for chronic conditions: A systematic review. *Psychophysiology, 46*(2), 257–269.

Noakes, T. & Spedding, M. (2012). Run for your life. *Nature, 487*(7407), 295–296.

O'Keefe, J. H., Vogel, R., Lavie, C. J., & Cordain, L. (2010). Organic fitness: Physical activity consistent with our hunter-gatherer heritage. *The Physician and Sports Medicine, 38*(4), 11–18.

Otto, M., & Smits, J. A. J. (2011). *Exercise for mood and anxiety: Proven strategies for overcoming depression and enhancing well-being.* New York, NY: Oxford University Press.

Owen, N., Healy, G.N., Mathews, C. E. & Dunstan, D. W. (2010). Too much sitting: The population health science of sedentary behavior. *Exercise and Sports Sciences Reviews, 38*(3), 105–113.

Owen, N., Sparling, P. B., Healy, G. N., Dunstan, D. W., & Matthews, C. E. (2010). Sedentary behavior: Emerging evidence for a new health risk. *Mayo Clinic Proceedings, 85*(12), 1138–1141.

Pate, R. R., Pratt, M., Blair, S. N., Haskell, W. L., Macera, C. A., Bouchard, C., ... & Wilmore, J. H. (1995). Physical activity and public health: A recommendation from the Centers for Disease Control and Prevention and the American College of Sports Medicine. *Journal of the American Medical Association, 273*(5), 402–407.

Pedersen, B. K., & Saltin, B. (2006). Evidence for prescribing exercise as therapy in chronic disease. *Scandinavian Journal of Medicine & Science in Sports, 16*(3), 3–63.

Piepmeier, A. T., & Etnier, J. L. (2015). Brain-derived neurotrophic factor (BDNF) as a potential mechanism of the effects of acute exercise on cognitive performance. *Journal of Sport and Health Science, 4*(1), 14–23.

Powers, M. B., Asmundson, G. J. G., & Smits, J. A. J. (2015). Exercise for mood and anxiety disorders: The state-of-the science. *Cognitive Behaviour Therapy, 44*(4), 237–239.

Proper, K. I., Singh, A. S., van Mechelen, W., & Chinapaw, M. J. M. (2011). Sedentary behaviors and health outcomes among adults: A systematic review of prospective studies. *American Journal Preventive Medicine, 40*(2), 174–182.

Puterman, E., Lin, J., Blackburn, E., O'Donovan, A., Adler, N., & Epe, E. (2010). The power of exercise: Buffering the effect of chronic stress on telomere length. *PLoS ONE, 5*, 1–6. Retrieved from http://journals.plos.org/plosone/article?id=10.1371/journal.pone.0010837

Raichlen, D., & Polk, J. (2012). Linking brains and brawn: Exercise and the evolution of human neurobiology. *Proceedings of the Royal Society of Biological Sciences, 280*(1750), 1–9.

Ratey, J. J., & Hagerman, E. (2008). *Spark: The revolutionary new science of exercise and the brain.* New York, NY: Little, Brown and Company.

Raynor, H. A., Bond, D. S., Freedson, P. S., & Sisson, S. B. (2012). Sedentary behaviors, weight, and health and disease risks. *Journal of Obesity, 2012*, 1–3.

Razzoli, M., & Bartolomucci, A. (2016). The dichotomous effect of chronic stress on obesity. *Trends in Endocrinology and Metabolism, 27*(7), 504–515.

Riebe, D. (Ed.) (2017). *ACSM's guidelines for exercise testing and prescription.* Philadelphia, PA: Lippincott, Williams & Wilkins.

Roever, L. (2015). Exercise training versus drug interventions on mortality outcomes: The research evidence. *Epidemiology, 5*, 1.

Santee, R., & Zhang, X. (2015). Yangsheng 養生 and the yin style baguazhang of wang fu and wang shangzhi. *The Empty Vessel: The Journal of Taoist Philosophy and Practice, 22*, 24–30.

Scott, K. A., Melhorn, S. J., & Sakai, R. R. (2012). Effects of chronic social stress on obesity. *Current Obesity Reports, 1*(1), 16–25.

Shahar, M. (2008). *The Shaolin Monastery.* Honolulu, HI: University of Hawaii Press.

Sominsky, L., & Spence, S. J. (2014). Eating behavior and stress: A pathway to obesity. *Frontiers in Psychology.* Retrieved from http://journal.frontiersin.org/article/10.3389/fpsyg.2014.00434/full

Springen, K. (2009). Top 6 exercise excuses and how to beat them: How to stop making excuses and start getting fit. *WebMD.* Retrieved from http://www.webmd.com/fitness-exercise/features/the-top-6-exercise-excuses-and-how-to-beat-them#1

Swartz, A. M., Rote, A. E., Welch, W. A., Maeda, H., Hart, T. L., Cho, Y. I., & Strath, S. J. (2014). Prompts to disrupt sitting time and increase physical activity at work, 2011–2012. *Preventing Chronic Disease, 11.* Retrieved from https://www.cdc.gov/pcd/issues/2014/13_0318.htm

Teychenne, M., Ball, K., & Salmon, J. (2010). Sedentary behaviour and depression among adults: A review. *International Journal of Behavioral Medicine, 17*(4), 246–254.

Teychenne, M., Costigan, S. A., & Parker, K. (2015). The association between sedentary behaviour and risk of anxiety: A systematic review. *BMC Public Health, 15.* Retrieved from http://bmcpublichealth.biomedcentral.com/articles/10.1186/s12889-015-1843-x

Wang, C., Bannuru, R., Ramel, J., Kupelnick, B., Scott, T., & Schmid, C. H. (2010). Tai chi on psychological well-being: Systematic review and meta-analysis. *Complementary and Alternative Medicine, 10*(1), 1–16.

Wayne, P. M., & Furst, M. L. (2013). *The Harvard Medical School guide to tai chi: 12 weeks to a healthy body, strong heart & sharp mind.* Boston, MA: Shambala.

WebMD. (2016). *The effects of stress on your body.* Retrieved from http://www.webmd.com/balance/stress-management/effects-of-stress-on-your-body

Weir, K. (2011). The exercise effect: Evidence is mounting for the benefits of exercise, yet psychologists don't often use exercise as part of their treatment arsenal. Here's more research on why they should. *APA.* Retrieved from http://www.apa.org/monitor/2011/12/exercise.aspx

Wilkinson, T. J., Shur, N. F., & Smith, A. C. (2016). Exercise as medicine in chronic kidney disease. *Scandinavian Journal of Medicine & Science in Sports, 26*(8), 985–988.

Zhang, L., Layne, C., Lowder, T., & Liu, J. (2012). A review focused on the psychological effectiveness of tai chi on different populations. *Evidence-Based Complementary and Alternative Medicine, 2012,* 1–9. Retrieved from https://www.hindawi.com/journals/ecam/2012/678107/abs/

CREDITS

Sleep

After finishing this chapter, you will be able to do the following:

- Describe the vicious cycle associated with sleep and chronic stress
- Demonstrate the negative impact deficient/excessive sleep has on our physical, psychological, and interpersonal well-being
- Explain why sleep deprivation/deficiency is bordering on being a public health crisis
- Describe the relationship between circadian rhythm and homeostasis
- Indicate how the concept of yin and yang is important for understanding sleep health
- Describe the stages of sleep
- Explain what the *Zhuangzi* has to say about dreams
- Indicate how you can determine you obtained an adequate amount of restful sleep
- Explain how REM sleep is associated with psychological disorders
- Describe how Hui Hai's and the *Huangdi Neijing's* approach to sleep is related to circadian rhythm and homeostasis

Approximately one third of our life is spent asleep. Even though we are most vulnerable to harm and death when we are asleep, it was selected by evolution as part of our toolkit for survival. This being the case, it clearly must be important for our overall physical and psychological health and well-being. The concern is that many of us are not getting enough restful sleep each night. As a result, we are tired during the day, loaded up with caffeine and energy drinks, and have a major problem with **sleep debt**.

A basic problem is that sleep has not, in the past, been recognized or focused on as significant component of overall health and well-being.

OVERALL HEALTH AND WELL-BEING: EXERCISE, NUTRITION, AND SLEEP

Generally, when concerns regarding overall health and well-being are discussed, the focus is primarily on physical activity and nutrition. Sleep has not usually been part of the discussion. For example, in the Department of Health and Human Services' (HHS) "2008 Physical Activity Guidelines for Americans," sleep is mentioned only three times and only in the context of physical activity being likely to improve sleep (HHS, 2008). The link between physical activity and nutrition, however, is clearly established:

> The content of the Physical Activity Guidelines complements the Dietary Guidelines for Americans, a joint effort of HHS and the U.S. Department of Agriculture (USDA). Together, the two documents provide guidance on the importance of being physically active and eating a healthy diet to promote good health and reduce the risk of chronic diseases. (HHS, 2008, p. vi)
>
> In the "Dietary Guidelines for Americans, 2005" (HHS & USDA, 2005), to which the previous quote refers, an entire chapter is devoted to physical activity and it is mentioned often within the text linking it to nutrition. The importance of sleep to overall health and well-being is not indicated or mentioned at all. The importance of the

relationship between physical activity and nutrition/diet to overall health and well-being, and addressing and preventing chronic diseases, is established quite early in the text.

The Dietary Guidelines for Americans [Dietary Guidelines] provides science-based advice to promote health and to reduce risk for major chronic diseases through diet and physical activity. ... Combined with physical activity, following a diet that does not provide excess calories according to the recommendations in this document should enhance the health of most individuals. (HHS & USDA, 2005, p. v)

Ten years later, in the "2015–2020 Dietary Guidelines for Americans" (HHS & USDA, 2015), the beneficial prevention and overall health and well-being link between physical activity and nutrition is further reinforced and sleep is still not mentioned. The importance for one's health and well-being, in addition to nutrition, of following and meeting the "2008 Physical Activity Guidelines" is strongly emphasized:

|A| large body of evidence now shows that healthy eating patterns and regular physical activity can help people achieve and maintain good health and reduce the risk of chronic disease throughout all stages of the lifespan. (HHS & USDA, 2005, p. xi)

As you discovered in the last chapter, however, research has shown that sedentary behavior, independent of meeting the weekly exercise requirement recommended in these guidelines, significantly compromises one's health and well-being and is clearly linked to obesity. So, not only is meeting the weekly requirements for exercise necessary, so is monitoring and reducing one's sedentary behavior. Such is the case for sleep, as exercise and nutrition are simply not enough as sleep deficiency, quantity, and quality significantly compromises one's health, well-being, and overall performance and is also clearly linked to obesity. Let's take a further look as to why sleep needs to be a part of this discussion on overall health and well-being.

EVOLUTIONARY THEORY AND SLEEP

Research indicates that the necessity for sleep or sleep-like behavior appears to be the case for all species, which have been observed and examined thus far, from insects onward (Luyster, Strollo, Zee, & Walsh, 2012; Siegel, 2003; Tononi & Cirelli, 2014; Woo, 2011). Given that sleep has been selected via the evolutionary process, it must serve some major, important adaptive functions. For humans, approximately one-third of our 24-hour wake-sleep cycle is reserved for continuous, restful sleeping. When this wake-sleep schedule is compromised, there are significant, detrimental physical, psychological, and interpersonal consequences. This is quite clear. However, determining what exactly the major, important adaptive functions of sleep are has been a major challenge for researchers who study and analyze the process of sleep.

Why Do We Sleep?

While clearly agreeing that sleep is important and has restorative and preventive functions, sleep researchers are not quite exactly sure why we sleep. There is no question about the detrimental consequences of not getting adequate restful sleep. We all know how we feel and behave if we don't get enough sleep and how we feel and behave if we do get enough sleep. But this does not explain why and what exactly is going on, relative to our overall well-being and health, while we are sleeping. Although there is no agreed-on, definitive, evidence-based, consensus regarding the specific function or functions of sleep, (Assefa, Diaz-Abad, Wickwire, & Scharf, 2015; Barone, & Krieger, 2015; National Institute of Neurological Disorders and Stroke (NINDS), 2017; Siegel, 2003; Tononi & Cirelli, 2014; Walker, 2009), sleep research does have some evidence-based insights and theories.

The first is that normal restful sleep provides the **processing and regulation of emotions** (Goldstein & Walker, 2014; Gruber & Cassoff, 2014; van der Helm & Walker, 2009; Walker, 2009). The focus is on the rapid eye movement (REM) stage of sleep as being linked to the processing and regulation of emotions (Deliens, Gilson, & Peigneux, 2014; Kahn, Sheppes, & Sadeh, 2013; Palmer & Alfano, 2017; Vandekerckhove & Cluydts, 2010; Walker, 2009). It is suggested that during normal restful, **REM sleep,** the negative emotional content from the day's stressful experiences are unlinked from the event and allowed to fade away, thus preventing them from having a negative impact on the next day (Deliens, Gilson, & Peigneux, 2014; Goldstein & Walker, 2014; Vandekerckhove & Cluydts, 2010; Walker, 2009). Sleep deficiency, on the other hand, compromises the normal functioning of this process. Think about the last time you did not get sufficient, restful sleep. How did you feel?

The second is that sleep removes the toxic byproducts/waste material due to neural metabolism from the brain through a drainage system known as the **glymphatic system** (Barone & Krieger, 2015; Gallagher, 2013; National

Institutes of Health (NIH), 2013a, 2013b; Xie et al., 2013). The drainage appears to be approximately twice as fast during sleep as it is during the day (Barone & Krieger, 2015). It has been suggested that this finding may be important for addressing neurodegenerative disorders such as Alzheimer's, which appears to have a problematic waste drainage system (Barone & Krieger, 2015; Gallagher, 2013; NIH, 2013a, 2013b).

The third is that sleep increases, in facts doubles, the production of a type of glial cell, specifically **oligodendrocyte precursor cells**, which give rise to another glial cell known as **oligodendrocytes** (Bellesi, Pfister-Genskow, Maret, Keles Tononi, & Cirelli, 2013). **Oligodendrocytes** form the myelin sheath around the neuronal axons and enhance signaling function and impulse speed of neurons (Bellesi et al., 2013; Bradl & Lassmann, 2010).

The fourth is that sleep is important for **memory consolidation and learning** (Barone & Krieger, 2015; Maquet, 2000; National Heart, Lung, and Blood Institute (NHLBI), 2017b; Rasch & Born, 2013; Tononi & Cirelli, 2014; Walker, 2009). Sleep deprivation/deficiency may cause one's ability to learn to be reduced by 40%, as it affects the hippocampus, which is associated with memory and learning (NIH, 2013c; Walker, 2009).

The Process of Sleep

The sleep/wake cycle is regulated by two processes that work together, **circadian rhythm** and **homeostasis** (NINDS, 2017; National Sleep Foundation (NSF), 2006), which the *Huangdi Neijing* would describe as the interaction of yin and yang. Circadian rhythms (about a day) are mostly controlled by an internal biological clock located in the anterior hypothalamus called the **suprachiasmatic nucleus (SCN)**, occur over an approximately 24-hour period, and are essentially about controlling daily, internal changes/fluctuations such as body temperature, hunger, wakefulness, hormone secretion, timing of sleep, feeling sleepy at night, tendency to awake naturally, no alarm clock in the morning, and metabolism (NHLBI, 2017c; NINDS, 2017). These rhythms are synchronized with environmental cues such as light, dark, and temperature but still occur even if there are no environmental cues (NINDS, 2017). You may have experienced being out of sync with your circadian rhythms, on an acute level, if have ever suffered from jet lag or had to engage in shift work.

During the course of a day's energy consumption, the byproduct of this energy consumption **adenosine** continually increases every hour throughout the day, driving your need for sleep (NHLBI, 2017c; NINDS, 2017). This drive is known as **homeostasis** and is essentially monitoring and reminding you of your need for sleep (NINDS, 2017). If you are sleep deprived, its intensity results in longer and deeper sleep. In addition to adenosine, the **pineal gland**, via stimulation from the SCN, releases the hormone **melatonin** when it gets dark to assist you in going to sleep (NINDS, 2017). As you sleep, adenosine is broken down and its drive to sleep is lessened (NHLBI, 2017c). As the adenosine dissipates the melatonin drives the sleep.

The longer you are asleep, the drive to awake becomes stronger as the melatonin levels decrease and the **cortisol** levels for alertness increase to finally awake you (NHLBI, 2017b). Cortisol usually peaks in the morning, begins its descent, and then starts to rise again a few hours before you awake (NHLBI, 2017c; NSF, 2017b). Essentially this entire process of the wake sleep cycle is, from the perspective of Daoism and the *Huangdi Neijing,* nothing more than the natural, ongoing cyclic, reciprocal relationship between yin and yang. It is also clear from both the Western perspective and that of Daoism and the *Huangdi Neijing* that if this natural, interrelated, cyclic process is continually compromised, in other words you are chronically stressed, there will be a significant negative impact on one's overall physical and psychological health and well-being. Remember, chronic stress radically alters normal levels of cortisol, and this is detrimental as it significantly disrupts the normal functioning of your wake-sleep cycle.

Stages of Sleep

Essentially there are two stages of sleep: **rapid eye movement or REM sleep** and **non-REM sleep or NREM sleep** (NHLBI, 2006; NINDS, 2017). NREM sleep consists of two substages: light and deep. During the transition, which many define as a separate stage of NREM sleep, from being awake into NREM light sleep, your heart rate, breathing, and eye movement slow while your muscles relax. During **NREM light sleep** your eye movement stops, body temperature drops, your heart rate and breathing further slowdown, and your muscles relax even more. In addition, during this stage your brain waves begin to slow down although they are irregular. During **NREM deep sleep** your blood pressure drops, and your heart rate, breathing, and brain waves will be the slowest while you are asleep. Although there is a lot going on during

NREM sleep, the brain activity level is considerably less than when awake and your body can move.

During REM sleep your brain wave activity is almost the same as if you were awake, your sympathetic nervous system activity appears to be double of that when you are awake, your eyes are moving rapidly (hence the name of the stage), breathing is irregular and faster, heart rate and blood pressure are almost the same as if you were awake, body temperature increases, dreaming primarily occurs during this stage, there is some during NREM sleep, and your body is essentially paralyzed while you brain races. Why we dream is an issue of much debate (NHLBI, 2006; NINDS, 2017).

For the average adult, sleep cycles, each approximately 90–110 minutes in length, alternate between REM sleep and NREM sleep and occur four to six times during the night, with the amount of time in each stage during a specific cycle variable throughout the night (NHLBI, 2006; NINDS, 2017). Longer NREM deep sleep occurs during the first half of sleep and then lessens, while REM sleep, the first stage occurs approximately 90 minutes into sleep with longer REM sleep increasing toward morning (NHLBI, 2006; NINDS, 2017).

The total amount of average reported time asleep each night decreases across age groups from 7.5 hours for a 20-year-old to 5.6 hours for an 80-year-old, with 47% of the time spent in NREM light sleep for the 20-year-old increasing across age groups, to 57% spent in NREM light sleep for the 80-year-old, decreasing across age groups from 20% NREM deep sleep for the 20-year-old, to 7.5% NREM deep sleep for the 80-year-old, and decreasing across age groups from 22% REM sleep for the 20-year-old to 17% REM sleep for the 80-year-old (Epstein, 2013). The bottom line to remember across the circadian rhythms, homeostasis, and the stages of sleep is that chronic stress significantly compromises the functioning of all of them, which is thus detrimental to one's overall physical and psychological health.

Given this background, we can now turn to the problems, both physical and psychological, associated with compromised sleep in order to present a fuller understanding of why sleep is so important for our overall health and well-being.

INADEQUATE SLEEP DURATION IS A SIGNIFICANT PROBLEM

Research is also quite clear that chronic, inadequate sleep is such a problem for one's health and well-being that it borders on being a public health crisis (American Academy of Sleep Medicine (AASM), 2016; Barnes & Drake,

Sleep deprivation/deficiency borders on being a public health crisis.

2015; CDC, 2015; Barone & Krieger, 2015; Dement, 1997; Liu et al., 2016; Colten & Altevogt, 2006; Cramer & Espie, 2016; Czeisler, 2011; Hirshkowitz, 2014; Luyster et al., 2012; NHLBI, 2017a; NSF, 2014; Weinhouse, 2017). Research has also indicated that sleep problems are not restricted to just the United States and appear to have taken on a significant, global concern (Breus, 2012; Hafner, Stepanek, Taylor, Troxel, & Van Stolk, 2016; Walch, Cochran, & Forger, 2016; Wong & Fielding, 2011; Xu, 2016).

WHAT AMOUNT IS AN ADEQUATE/INADEQUATE SLEEP DURATION?

Attaining a consensus on what constitutes an inadequate amount of sleep or **sleep deprivation** has been somewhat problematic as various research studies are not consistent in how they define too little sleep and too much sleep. Even the concept of an adequate amount of sleep has variation. It appears that, for adults, around 7 hours of sleep a night is an optimal goal, although ranges are given, with some slight variation from 6–8, 7–8 hours, and 7–9 hours of sleep per night (Barnes & Drake, 2015; Cappuccio, D'Elia, Strazzullo, & Miller, 2010; Grandner, Chakravorty, Perlis, Oliver, & Gurubhagavatula, 2014; Lee, Ng, & Chin, 2017; Liu et al., 2016; Luyster et al., 2012; McCarthy & Brown, 2015; Ohkuma et al., 2013; St-Onge et al., 2016; Watson et al., 2015). What constitutes too little sleep and too much sleep is also subject to the researcher's definitions, with less than 6 hours being too little and greater than 9 hours being too much appearing to be a mid-point with ranges with slight variations, depending on the study, of less than 6 greater than 8, less than 6 greater than 9, less than 6 greater than 10, and less than 7 greater than 8 (Cappuccio, D'Elia, Strazzullo, & Miller, 2010; Grandner et al., 2014; Lee, Ng, & Chin, 2017; Liu et al., 2016; Luyster et al., 2012).

The recommended, by the Centers for Disease Control and Prevention (CDC, 2017) and the American Academy of Sleep Medicine (Paruthi et al., 2016) sleep duration per 24-hour period for infants, 4–12 months, is 12–16 hours including naps; for toddlers, 1–2 years old, is 11–14 hours including naps; for preschool, 3–5 years old, is 10–13 hours including naps; school age, 6–12 years old, is 9–12 hours; and teens, 13–18 years old, is 8–10 hours. The American Psychological Association's (APA, 2014) 2013 survey "Stress in America: Are Teens Adopting Adult's Stress Habits" noted that teens averaged 7.4 hours of sleep during school nights, with those with reported high stress levels sleeping an average of 6.9 hours per night and those with reported low stress levels

The vicious cycle: Stress significantly compromises sleep. Sleep deficiency/deprivation creates more stress.

sleeping an average of 7.8 hours per night. Given that the wake-sleep cycle changes during puberty resulting in teens going to sleep later and waking up later, it has been recommended that high schools start later, no earlier than 8:30, to ensure that teenagers are getting the adequate amount of sleep they need to perform optimally in school (NSF, 2017; Wahlstrom, 2016).

Aside from **quantity of sleep**, what is of fundamental importance is **quality of sleep**. In other words, although you may meet the required range of sleep hours, if it is not restful then this is a clear indicator of **sleep deficiency,** which includes sleep deprivation, **sleep disorders**, your natural **sleep stages** being compromised, and/or your **circadian rhythm** being out of sync (NHLBI, 2017a). The National Sleep Foundation's 2014 Sleep Health Index (NSF, 2014b) report indicates 35% of those adults surveyed reported the quality of their sleep as poor or fair, with African Americans more often than non-Hispanic whites indicating this to be the case. Hirshkowitz (NSF, 2014b) noted that 67% of these individuals rated their overall health as poor or fair.

The bottom line here is that you need to determine how much sleep, quantity and quality, you need and when you need it. Keep a sleep journal, for a few weeks to a month to monitor quantity, total hours, when you go to bed to sleep and when you wake up, and quality, how you feel when you wake up, using a scale of 1 (terrible) to 10 (fantastic). Also, monitor how you feel during the day regarding your energy, emotions, interpersonal, and cognitive functioning. Remember if you are sleep deficient/deprived your judgment is impaired, so be aware of how you rate yourself. If you feel tired around mid-afternoon that usually is normal as it appears we are wired with a need for a second sleep or short nap (Medina, 2014).

The problem is most of us just plough through it due to social/work/school demands.

SLEEP DISORDERS

While the general focus of sleep researchers and various organizations such as the Centers for Disease Control and Prevention, the National Sleep Foundation, the National Highway Traffic Safety Administration, and so on is on individuals not getting enough restful sleep, specific sleep disorders such as insomnia (although for some it is more akin to being a symptom), sleep apnea, restless legs syndrome, narcolepsy, bruxism, and parasomnias are of significant concern for the health profession (ADAA, 2016a; CDC, 2014; Epstein, 2013). These disorders are chronic in nature and usually require intervention by a medical professional (CDC, 2011, 2016; Colten & Altevogt, 2006). It is estimated that

If you feel drowsy, do not drive!

between 50–70 million adults in the United States have a sleep disorder (ASA, 2017; CDC, 2011, Colten & Altevogt, 2006).

DISEASES, DISORDERS, AND PROBLEMS ASSOCIATED WITH INADEQUATE SLEEP DURATION

Although the primary focus of research on sleep-related problems is not getting enough sleep, research also links significant problems with getting too much sleep to cardiovascular disease, strokes, diabetes, immune suppression, inflammatory disease, obesity, cancer, attention problems, mental disorders, memory problems, and increased risk of dying (AHA, 2016; Barone & Krieger, 2015; Cappuccio, D'Elia, Strazzullo, & Miller, 2010; Kondracki, 2012; Leger, Beck, Richard, Sauvet, & Faraut, 2014; LeWine, 2014; Liu et al., 2016; Ohkuma et al., 2013). Research has linked sleep deprivation/deficiency to cognitive, psychosocial, and emotional dysfunction; attention, concentration, memory, decision making, and judgment concerns; depression; anxiety; diabetes; reduced quality of life; cardiovascular disease; immune suppression; inflammatory disease; obesity; hypertension; cancer; kidney disease; stroke; metabolic disorders; hyperlipidemia; and increased all-cause mortality (APA, 2014; Barone & Krieger, 2015; Cappuccio, D'Elia, Strazzullo, & Miller, 2010; CDC, 2016; Cramer & Espie 2016; Epstein, 2013; Gobin, Banks, Fins, & Tartar, 2015; Grandner et al., 2014; HMS, 2008; Kondracki, 2012; Liu et al., 2016; Luyster et al., 2012; Ohkuma et al., 2013; Zohar, 2005). There is some suggestion that chronic lack of sleep may be indicative of declining health, while chronic excessive sleep may be indicative of an underlying comorbid disorder such as obesity and/or depression (Cappuccio, D'Elia, Strazzullo, & Miller, 2010; Liu et al., 2016; Kendzerska, & Shapiro, 2013). The ongoing problem with the research is there appears to be no consensus as to what exactly constitutes too little sleep and too much sleep.

HOW MUCH SLEEP ARE PEOPLE ACTUALLY GETTING?

According to research by the Gallup Poll (Jones, 2013), in 1942 the average amount of sleep per night reported by U.S. adults who were surveyed was 7.9 hours, with 11% reporting they got 6 hours or less of sleep per night, while in 2013, the average amount of sleep per night was 6.8, with 40% indicating they got less than 6 hours or less of sleep a night. In 1942, 14% reported they got 9 hours or more of sleep per night, while in 2013, 5% reported they got 9 hours or more sleep per night. The 2014 Gallup Poll (McCarthy & Brown, 2015) indicated that 42% of U.S. adults got 6 or less hours of sleep per night (41% of the 18–29 year-old group, 45% of the 30–44 year-old group, 45% of the 45–64 year-old group, 34% of the 65-plus year-old group), while 6% of adults got 9 or more hours of sleep per night (7% of the 18–29 year-old group, 4% of the 30–44 year-old group, 5% of the 45–64 year-old group, 10% of the 65-plus year-old group).

The National Sleep Foundation's 2014 Sleep Health Index (NSF 2014b) report indicates that the average amount of sleep for adults in the United States is 7 hours and 36 minutes, the average sleep time on nonworking days is 40 minutes more, the 18–29-year-old age group reported going to bed the latest, there was no difference between men and women regarding average duration of sleep, and if there was one more hour in the day, only 18% would use it to sleep.

SLEEP DEPRIVATION AND DEFICIENCY-RELATED PROBLEMS, ACCIDENTS, ERRORS, AND ECONOMIC COSTS

While the negative effects of not exercising, being excessively sedentary, or eating poorly are not immediately observable, the effects of lack/limited sleep for one night is most readily observable both physically and psychologically. Research has shown that performance on such tests as vigilance and attention, response/reaction time, hand-eye coordination, and spatial memory, while being

Lack of restful sleep and driving do not mix.

continuously awake between approximately 17–19 hours, was significantly compromised and was equivalent to a blood alcohol level of .05%, legally drunk in many countries, while being continuously awake between approximately 20–24 hours was considerably worse, being equivalent to a blood alcohol level

of .1% (Arnedt, Wilde, Munt, & MacLean, 2001; CDC, 2016; Dawson & Reid, 1997; Epstein, 2013; Lamond & Dawson, 1999; Williamson & Feyer, 2000). **Lack of restful sleep and driving do not mix.** Over the course of 2 straight weeks of sleeping 4–6 hours a night, cognitive performance on alertness, attention, vigilance, psychomotor reaction time, working memory, and mental arithmetic measurements was equivalent to approximately 2 nights of not sleeping at all (Van Dongen, Maislin, Mullington, & Dinges, 2003). This is extreme sleep debt! Judgment regarding one's performance and capabilities (I am ok I can drive/I am not tired) due to lack of sleep is significantly impaired (CDC, 2016; HMS, 2008; Van Dongen, Maislin, Mullington, & Dinges, 2003). **Lack of restful sleep and driving do not mix.**

We evolved and are thus wired to sleep on a regular daily basis. The longer we stay awake the stronger the body and brain push to go to sleep. We start to get drowsy! We are about to fall asleep. We cannot be driving while fatigued, tired, and drowsy. Just closing our eyes for a moment, losing focus, attention, and concentration, can result in an accident injuring or killing not only the driver but all in the same vicinity. Given that our judgment is impaired due to lack of sleep, use the fact you notice you are drowsy and nodding off as your cue not to drive (CDC, 2016; Dement, 1997). **Lack of restful sleep and driving do not mix.**

Think of any job were continuous vigilance, attention, concentration, memory, hand-eye coordination, psychomotor skills, and decision making are fundamental regarding safety of oneself and those around you. If you are sleep deprived, then you are putting yourself and others at risk. For example, consider the medical profession. If a physician or resident/intern is sleep deprived, then not only does he or she put his

Lack of sleep and job performance/productivity do not mix. It is estimated that economic costs/losses due to sleep deprivation/deficiency in the work force in the United States is $411 billion annually.

or her own health at risk, he or she puts your health at risk (Eddy, 2005; Landrigan et al., 2004; Lockley et al., 2004; Zohar, 2005). **Lack of restful sleep and optimum job performance do not mix.** For that matter, just think of any job or occupation; if you are sleep deficient/deprived your performance will suffer. Sleep deprivation/ deficiency stresses the brain and the body, and if it is continuous, the brain and body will be chronically stressed. In either case, your overall health, well-being, and safety is threatened (CDC 2015; NHLBI, 2017a).

Sleep Deprivation/Deficiency-Related Traffic Accidents

The National Highway Traffic Safety Administration (National Highway Traffic Safety Administration (NHTSA), 2017) estimated, based on traffic accident reports from police, that in 2015 there were 72,000 drowsy driver related crashes, 41,000 injuries, and over 800 deaths. The NHTSA report clearly acknowledges that community input suggests that the NHSTA figures are a gross underestimate, instead suggesting somewhere between 6,000–8,000 or more deaths a year can be associated with a drowsy driver (NHTSA, 2017). A study, using a more research- and representative-based approach, by the AAA Foundation for Traffic Accidents (Tefft, 2014) for the years 2009–2013 regarding a drowsy driver and traffic accidents found that a drowsy driver was involved in an estimated, of all crashes, 6% involving the towing of a car, 7% involving treatment for injuries, 13% involving a person being hospitalized, and 21% in which a person was killed. Tefft (2014) applied these percentages to all crashes over the course of years' time and estimated that a drowsy driver was involved in an average of 328,000 crashes, 109,000 injuries and 6,400 deaths annually.

Sleep Deprivation/Deficiency-Related Economic Costs

The Rand Corporation (Hafner et al., 2016) estimates economic costs/losses due to sleep deprivation/deficiency in the workforce, across productivity, not at work or lower performance while at work, and mortality, loss of skills, and productivity, was estimated annually to be $411 billion in the United States, $138 billion in Japan, $60 billion in Germany, $50 billion in the United Kingdom, and $21.4 billion in Canada. The NHSTA (2017) report estimated the cost, due to drowsy drivers, of harm to United States society being $109 billion annually.

It is estimated that a drowsy driver was involved in an average of 328,000 crashes, 109,000 injuries, and 6,400 deaths annually.

WHY ARE PEOPLE NOT GETTING ENOUGH RESTFUL SLEEP?

There are many reasons why you may not be getting enough restful sleep. The first one is that you are **choosing to stay up too late**. This may be due to spending excessive time, via technology such as mobile phones, tablets, and computers; on social media such as Instagram, Snapchat, Facebook, YouTube, and Twitter; texting; surfing the Web, talking on the phone, watching TV, studying, partying, working late, reading, and so on. The second reason is difficulty getting to sleep because of your **sleep environment** such as problems with your mattress, pillow, noise level, too much light, room temperature, snoring, a restless bed partner, a newborn baby, and so on. The third one is your **lifestyle habits** such as smoking, drinking alcohol, drinking coffee, eating certain foods or too much food, skipping dinner, exercising, drinking too much liquid of any sort, including water, and so on too close to the time you go to bed. The fourth one is an **irregular sleep schedule** such as shift work, jet lag, not going to sleep or getting up at around the same time, and so on. The fifth one is **physical and/or psychological medical conditions and the medications** that you may be taking to address the medical conditions. The sixth one is **specific sleep disorders and the medications** that you may be taking to address the medical conditions. The seventh one is **pain**. The eight reason is **overall poor health**. The ninth one is

chronic stress, which affects getting to sleep, obsessing/ruminating/making absolute judgments about the past and/or worrying and making absolute judgments about the future as you lay in bed, staying asleep, and quality of sleep. The truth of the matter is that all of the preceding reasons can significantly compromise and thus stress the normal functioning of both the body and the brain. Given these causes, if you have a problem sleeping, what do you need to do to address and resolve it?

SLEEP AND STRESS

There is a significant amount of research that indicates stress compromises the quantity and quality of sleep (APA, 2014; Blaxton, Bergeman, Whitehead, Braun, & Payne, 2015; Epstein, 2013; Jacobson & Monaghan, 2015; Kim & Dimsdale, 2007; NSF, 2015; Thomee, Härenstam, & Hagberg, 2011). This being the case, you may have difficulty getting to sleep and/or staying asleep because of the stress. When you do not get the adequate quantity and quality of sleep, this itself becomes a stressor. Thus, the original stress is now compounded by the stress from sleep deprivation/deficiency. In the case of the individuals who choose to go to sleep late and thus do not get the adequate quantity and quality of sleep, they are essentially stressing their body and brain. Thus, when they are awake, because of their sleep deprivation/deficiency, they start their day off stressed. This new stressor, **extended wakefulness,** not only compromises their normal daily functioning and safety, but has a direct impact on the quantity and quality of their next night of sleep. In both cases, there is a **vicious cycle of stress** induced by sleep disturbance, which itself wreaks havoc with the normal functioning of the HPA axis. The HPA axis is not only fundamental to the stress response, but also to the natural sleep-wake cycle (APA, 2014; Basta, Chrousos, Vela-Bueno, & Vgontzas 2007; Han, Kim, & Shim, 2012). The National Sleep Foundation (NSF, 2015) survey found that stress, poor health (which is stressful), and pain (which is also stressful), were the three major components linked to sleep deficiency/ deprivation. Sleep deficiency/deprivation, in turn, adds additional stress to the initial stress, poor health, and pain. Once again, we can see this vicious cycle between stress and sleep.

Research (Anderson & Platten, 2011; Barclay & Ellis, 2013; Gobin et al., 2015; Minkel et al., 2012; Motomura et al., 2013; Yoo, Gujar, Hu, Jolesz, & Walker 2007) has indicated that sleep deprivation/deficiency makes us more biased toward negative stimuli. For our brain, negative stimuli are perceived as threats. Perceived threats set off and maintain our fight/freeze/flight response. Remember we already have, courtesy of evolution, a negativity bias that served our distant hunter-gather ancestors well regarding real physical threats. The problem is that most of us do not live in a highly physically threatening environment as did our distant ancestors. As our brain does not make a distinction between a perceived, real physical threat and a perceived, psychosocial threat generated by our negative thinking, it will, in both cases, activate our stress response. While its activation in the case of a real, physical threat assisted our distant ancestors in addressing and resolving the threat, its activation in the case of the perceived psychosocial threat generated by our negative thinking is, quite often, of no benefit and often makes the situation worse. Just consider mind wandering.

Research (Yoo et al., 2007) has shown that missing one night's sleep, being continually awake for around 35 hours, increases amygdala activity (this is the part of the brain associated with sounding the alarm regarding potential threats) by 60%. In other words, our negativity bias is greatly enhanced as our attention focuses even more on perceived, psychosocial threats. Once again consider the research on mind wandering.

There appears to be a causal relationship/co-occurrence between sleep deficiency and emotional dysfunction/psychiatric disorders (Anwar, 2007; Epstein, 2013; Gobin et al., 2015; Goldstein & Walker, 2014; HMS, 2009; Krause et al., 2017; Krystal, 2013). It has been argued that the psychiatric disorders are the cause of the sleep deprivation/deficiency, but research suggests it may be the other way around or, more likely, bidirectional (ADAA, 2016b; Anwar, 2007; HMS, 2009; Krystal, 2013; Swaminathan, 2007; Yoo et al., 2007). Nonetheless, chronic stress is intimately intertwined with sleep deprivation, sleep deficiency, sleep disorders, emotional dysfunction, and psychiatric disorders.

DAOIST, CONFUCIAN, AND BUDDHIST APPROACHES

A major commonality between Buddhism, Daoism, and Confucianism is how our thoughts and desires can potentially compromise our health and well-being across all aspects of our existence. Our chronic, psychosocial, rigid, absolute, threat-based thinking, the subsequent moods and behaviors it generates, and the extent to which our excessive and deficient desires disrupt and control our behavior all result in chronic stress.

A common solution across all three traditions is to simplify one's thinking and behavior, which in turn results in being more natural and in harmony with the world around us. In one sense, all three traditions appear to be trying to return us, to a certain extent, to a functioning process that is more consistent with how we evolved to adapt to our surroundings, to being in harmony with our

Keep it simple. When you are hungry eat! When you feel tired, sleep!

internal rhythms and patterns and externally with the rhythms and patterns of the ever-changing world around us. The process of sleep is no exception.

Buddhism

Within the context of Buddhism, the sect or school that is most consistent with this focus on returning to our natural state and being in harmony with the world around us is Chan (禪) Buddhism, or, as probably most of you know it in Japanese, Zen (禪) Buddhism. The character Chan (禪) means meditation and represents the Sanskrit word for meditation, *dhyana*.

Although tradition traces Chan Buddhism's origination in China to a Buddhist monk from India named Bodhidharma (5th–6th century CE), the distinctly Chinese origination, creation, and development of Chan occurred in China during the Tang dynasty (618–907) and it is unlikely that Bodhidharma had much if anything to do with its creation (Shahar, 2008). Chan Buddhism is, essentially, Buddhism filtered through Daoism and Chinese culture.

The focus of Chan Buddhism is the ordinary, natural mind that has not been polluted by absolute restrictions, beliefs and ideas, and philosophical and logical speculation and is not dependent on the Buddhist sutras and scriptures for fully engaging life (Chang, 1969; Blofeld, 1972; Hershock, 2005). It is simply being natural, mindful, and in harmony with the here and now.

The most salient example of the practice of Chan Buddhism with a focus on sleep can be found in the dialogues regarding the teachings of the Chan Master Hui Hai (circa 8th century CE) known as *Records of Various Question-Based Dialogues* (zhu fang menren shen wen yulu 諸方門人參問語錄). Of particular importance in the following dialogue is the concept of *vinaya*. *Vinaya* refers to the often strict, required rules, regulations, codes, and discipline expected as a member of the Sangha or monastic Buddhist community in India (Hershock, 2005; Thera, 2017). Thus, the questioner is a master/teacher of these rules, regulations, and codes and requires discipline to be a member of the Sangha.

> On one occasion, a Master/Teacher of *Vinaya* asked Master Hui Hai (慧海), "Does your cultivating the Dao require effort and hard work?" Master Hui Hai said, "It requires effort and hard work." The *Vinaya* Master said, "What do you do?" Hui Hai said, "When hunger comes, I eat. When tiredness comes, I sleep." The *Vinaya* Master said, "Everybody behaves in that manner. Are they not acting the same as you?" Master Hui Hai said, "They are not the same." The *Vinaya* Master said, "How are they are not the same?" Master Hui Hai said, "When they eat, they are not willing to just eat. There are a hundred concerns that they feel they must ponder. When they go to sleep, they are not willing to simply go to sleep. There are a thousand apprehensions they feel they must evaluate. Thus, they are not the same." The *Vinaya* Master said no more. (Hui, 2017; all translations are mine)

For Hui Hai, hunger and sleep are something that come naturally, circadian rhythm, and should not be restricted by various rules, regulations, and codes. Hui Hai clearly makes the point that other people, including the *Vinaya* Master/ Teacher, compromise their very nature by essentially mind wandering when they eat and mind wandering as they try to go to sleep. In both cases, the inappropriate psychosocial concerns and apprehensions are threat based, interfere with the natural process of digestion and sleep, and lead to chronic stress.

The solution is quite straight forward. When you eat, just eat. No mind wandering. When you lay down to sleep, no mind wandering. Just go to sleep. In other words, practice mindfulness, listen to your body and harmonize with its natural rhythms and patterns throughout your day. Remember, for your brain to learn a new behavior (neuroplasticity) you must practice the new behavior on a consistent, daily basis. Sleep is a natural process. Don't mess it up with your chronic, inappropriate, threat-based psychosocial thinking.

Daoism

In this section, three Daoist perspectives regarding sleep will be presented and examined. The first is *Huangdi Neijing* or the *Yellow Emperor's Discourse on Internal Medicine*, followed by the *Zhuangzi*, and then the *Liezi*.

Stay in harmony with the ever-changing world around you.

Huangdi Neijing

The holistic approach of the *Huangdi Neijing*, regarding optimal health and well-being, emphasizes the importance of one's internal rhythms and patterns being in harmony with the rhythms and patterns, across the four seasons, of the ever-changing world around us. Basically, one's vital energy or *qi* is in harmony with vital energy or *qi* of the particular season. It is quite clear that not being in harmony, internally and externally, is detrimental to one's health. Being in disharmony, the individual is chronically stressed.

Essentially, when to go to sleep and when to arise in the morning is contingent on the specific season and the cyclic, rhythmic process of night and day. If one's circadian rhythms are compromised, one's sleep will be problematic and thus stressful. If this is ongoing, a vicious cycle of stress due to not going to sleep when you are supposed to and stress due to lack of sleep will ensue. Chapter 2 of the *Huangdi Neijing* states

The three months of spring are called issue forth and display (*fa chen* 發陳). The sky and the earth produce life together. All things are thriving. At night lie down and go to sleep. Rise up early in the morning, take an extended walk in the courtyard by which the body is revived. This is applying your will to live and grow. Living and growing you will not weaken. Enjoying life and not punishing yourself. This is responding to the vital energy or *qi* (氣) of the spring. This is the way or Dao (道) of cultivating life (*yangsheng* 養生). To act contrary to these guidelines injures the liver. During the summer, this will cause you to be transformed by cold as one's growth will be deficient. (Santee, 2015, p. 26)

The three months of the summer are called flourishing, abundance, and picturesque (fan you 蕃秀). The vital energy or *qi* (氣) of the sky and the earth are intertwined. All things flower and come to fruition. At night lie down and go to sleep. Awaken as the sun rises. Do not loath/detest the appearing of the sun. Allow your will to be without anger/rage, thus allowing this splendid and magnificent process to become complete. Allow *qi* (氣) to be released as if it cherished the world. This is the path (*Dao*) of how the summer *qi* should nourish (*yang*養) growth. If you act contrary to this you will injure your mind/heart and be subjected to malaria in the autumn. As little has been gathered, in the winter there will serious illness.

The three months of autumn are called being satiated (rong ping 容平). The *qi* of the sky moves quickly. The *qi* of the earth is bright and clear. Go to sleep when it is night and awake when the sun rises and the rooster crows. Allow your will to be peaceful and still by which you gradually adapt to autumn's changes. Gather and restrain your spirit and vital energy (*shenqi* 神氣) allowing autumn's vital energy (qi 氣) to be peaceful. Your will is not distracted allowing your lung *qi* (氣) to be clear. This is the path (Dao) of how the autumn *qi* should nourish (*yang*養) and be received. If you act contrary to this you will injure your lungs. As a result, In the winter, you will have diarrhea and have stored little.

The three months of winter are called closing and storing (bi cang 閉藏). Water freezes and the earth cracks. Do not disturb the *yang* process. Go to sleep early and get up late waiting for the sun to rise. Allow your will to appear as if it seems hidden. As if that which you desired is that which you have. Leave the cold and move toward warmth. Do not exert yourself/sweat profusely causing your *qi* to be drained. This is the way of how the winter *qi* nourishes that which is stored. If you act contrary to this you injure your kidneys. In the spring, your body and mind will be weakened. As a result, there will be little left for growth. (Chinese Text Project, 2017)

Across all four seasons, going to sleep at night and waking up in the morning is essentially following your circadian rhythm by allowing it to synchronize with the specific day/night rhythms of the various seasons. It is important to note that there is a strong focus, across all four seasons, on the cognitive and emotional processes as part of the holistic approach to health and well-being in the *Huangdi Neijing*. Thus, this approach addresses what we call chronic stress in a preventive manner and clearly offers an adaptive, natural solution to avoid stress and optimize one's health and well-being. Of course, for this to work it must be implemented/practiced on a daily basis, allowing neuroplasticity to occur as one learns how to optimize one's relationship with the world around us.

Fundamental to this holistic process of optimal health and well-being put forth in the *Huangdi Neijing* is understanding and following the natural, reciprocal, symbiotic, continually changing process known as yin and yang (Wang, 2012). Within the context of sleep, being awake or yang (陽) is gradually reduced through one's biological clock until eventually falling to sleep and sleep or yin (陰) begins to dominate. The influence of the cycle of yin is gradually reduced, once again through one's biological clock, until yang begins to dominate and the individual wakes up. In the same sense that our internal biological clock needs to be synchronized with the external day/night cycle, our internal yin and yang cycle needs to be in harmony with the external day/night cycle of yin and yang. Not being synchronized and not being in harmony on a continual basis results in chronic stress. Chronic stress often compromises one's sleep, which may result in sleep deprivation, sleep deficiency, sleep debt, and/or sleep disorders. These sleep problems in turn create additional stress and inadequate sleep, which gives rise to a vicious cycle of chronic stress—all of which leads to physical and psychological illnesses, diseases, and disorders. In the worst-case scenario, it leads to death.

The reciprocal, symbiotic, continually changing yin (陰) and yang (陽) process of the four seasons is the essence of all things. Thus, the sage nourishes and cultivates yang during the spring and summer and cultivates yin during the autumn and winter. This is being in accord with your root. This is the gate to the growth rhythms of life for the sage to be in harmony with all things.

The importance of being in harmony with yin and yang for all aspects of one's life, including sleep, is made quite clear at the end of chapter 2 of the *Huangdi Neijing* where it states,

> Therefore, the reciprocal, symbiotic, continually changing yin and yang process of the four seasons is the end and beginning of all things. Yin and yang are the root of death and life. Behavior that is contrary to yin and yang results in calamity and harm. Behavior that is in accord with yin and yang does not give rise to severe illness. This is called attaining Dao.

> This Dao is what the Sages put into practice. The fools merely admire it. Being in accord with yin and yang results in life. Being contrary to yin and yang results in death. Being in accord with yin and yang results in order. Acting contrary to yin and yang results in disorder. Not to follow the process of yin and yang is to act contrary to it. This is called internal resistance. Thus, the sage does not treat those who are already ill. The sage focuses on preventing illness. The sage does not manage that which is already in disorder. The sage focuses on preventing disorder. This being the case it is said, "To get medicine after you have already become ill or to manage something after it is already in disorder, is like digging a well after you are already thirsty or casting weapons after a fight has already broke out. Is it not too late?" (Chinese Text Project, 2017)

Zhuangzi

While the *Huangdi Neijing* focuses, in a holistic manner, on the importance of sleep within the context of one's internal, natural rhythms being in harmony with the external, natural rhythms of the world around us and the significant negative consequences if it is not, the focus of the *Zhuangzi* and the commentaries of Guo Xiang (fl. 252–312) and Cheng Xuanying (fl. 631–652), examines sleeping and dreaming within the context of chronic stress, the physical and psychological problems it generates, and the interdependent, reciprocal relationship between the mind/heart and the body. Chapter 2 of the *Zhuangzi* states,

> When a person is asleep, the mind/heart is entangled. When the person is conscious, the body is vulnerable. Interacting in the world creates entanglements. Daily their mind/hearts battle: plodding, concealing, and tentative. Their small fears/threats result

in anxiety and apprehensiveness. Their large fears/threats result in being depressed. In judging right and wrong, their words shoot out as if an arrow was released from a bow. They hold onto their judgments as if they were sacred oaths. Guarding what they call their victory, they are executed like autumn moving into winter. (Santee, 2004, p. 2)

What is immediately salient is the vicious cycle of chronic stress as it is manifested during the day with apprehensions, fears, anxiety, and depression, and at night with compromised, entangled, stressful sleep. Cheng's commentary to the first two lines of this passage is quite insightful as he links chronic stress to disturbed sleep, illnessm and disease. He notes,

> For the common person, when awake their minds range between racing around and being impulsive, to being sluggish, stagnant and slow to respond. As a result, the person dreams when asleep. Because their minds are agitated, they become entangled. Thus, when they are awake, their bodies are vulnerable to illness and disease. (Santee, 2011, p. 44)

Of particular importance, psychologically, is that dreaming appears to reflect disturbed sleep and is associated with an agitated and stressed mind. This relationship is made clearer when the *Zhuangzi* discusses the authentic person or *zhenren* (真人) in chapter 6.

> The authentic person of ancient times slept without dreaming, was not chronically stressed (*you* 憂) when awake, and ate without indulging. The authentic person breathes from the heels. All other people breathe from their throats. Being restricted, the words in their throats are like retching, their desires longstanding and deep, and their essential nature shallow. The authentic person of ancient times did not know life to be ecstatic or death to be dreaded. Emerging he was not joyful. Returning he was not resistant. He was carefree in his going and coming. He did not forget the place of his beginning nor seek the place of his end. Accepting life, he was happy. Forgetting life, he returned. This is called not using the mind/heart to abandon the Dao. Not using people to assist nature. This is called the authentic person. (Santee, 2011, p. 45)

The *zhenren* is the Daoist role model representing an individual who is free from self-imposed and society-imposed artificial restrictions. *The zhenren* does not compromise his health and well-being with ongoing, threat based, inappropriate psychosocial thinking. There is no obsessing and ruminating about the past or worrying about/fearing the future. The *zhenren* lives in the present. He is not entangled in mind wandering. As the mind of the *zhenren* is not agitated, anxious, or depressed, the *zhenren* is not chronically stressed. As such, his sleep is not disturbed and is restful. This being the case, the *zhenren* does not dream.

The commentary of Guo regarding the *zhenren* not dreaming is succinct and to the point, "The *zhenren* does not have expectations" (Santee, 2011, p. 45). There are no absolute musts regarding how people should behave, the world should behave, or how he should behave. Given there are no expectations, there is no agitation. This being the case, there is no chronic stress. Given there is no chronic stress, when the *zhenren* sleeps, there is no dreaming. The sleep for the *zhenren* is beneficial as the quantity and quality for restful sleep is met. When the *zhenren* awakes and moves about through the day, there is no vicious cycle of stress. For the *Zhuangzi* and the commentaries of Guo and Cheng, dreaming is symptomatic of being stressed. Cheng's subcommentary to this section links dreaming to both the past and the future.

> Those who dream have vain hopes and unsatisfied wishes. The authentic person is without emotions and has cut off wishful think-ing. Therefore, when he sleeps he is anchored in a quiet place and does not dream. (Santee, 2011, p. 45)

Given Cheng's analysis, it is clear those who dream are entangled in the process of mind wandering during the day and when they lay down to sleep. This being the case, as the research on mind wandering has shown, they are not happy. This is clearly suggested by Cheng's references to vain hopes (mind wandering in the future), unsatisfied wishes (mind wandering in the past), and wishful thinking. Their dreaming is indicative of being chronically stressed. The *zhenren*, on the other hand, does not engage in wishful thinking or have vain hopes or unsatis-fied wishes. When the *zhenren* lays down to sleep, there is no mind wandering or wishful thinking. The *zhenren* is simply going to go to sleep. There is no agitation or chronic stress. As such, the mind of the *zhenren* is quiet. This being so, there is no dreaming!

Liezi

The *Leizi* offers a simple solution to the elimination of the restless mind, essentially inappropriate, threat-based negativity bias, psychosocial thinking, which gives rise to chronic stress and dreaming: fully experience the ongoing, interdependent process of change and transformation. In other words, harmonize with yin and yang. Be in the present! There is nothing, including your sense of self (think default network), that is absolute and independent. In order to accomplish this, attend to, focus on, and concentrate on the here and now. By attending, focusing, and concentrating on the here and now, you will not be mind wandering. You will not be stressed. You will not dream. You will obtain the appropriate amount of restful sleep. Chapter 3 states,

> Liezi said, "The mind dreams because it is restless. The body gets entangled in the activities of the world because it is vulnerable/it makes contact." Thus, during the day your mind wanders. During the night, you dream. This is the restlessness/entanglement of the mind and body. When your mind is attentive, focused and concentrated, mind wandering and dreaming naturally disappear. What people don't understand regarding what they believe when they are awake, and don't fathom regarding what they believe when they are dreaming is that everything is a continual process of interdependent change and transformation. Thus, the *zhenren* when awake forgets the self. When asleep, does not dream. How could this be an empty saying? (Zhang, 1972, p. 35)

Confucianism

For Confucius (551–479 BCE), to fully engage life required reducing desires and keeping it simple. These two guidelines are best expressed in the following quote about hunger, thirst, and sleep from chapter 7 of the *Lunyu:*

> Confucius said, "If I have rice to eat, water to drink, and my bent arm as a pillow, within this there is joy. Wealth and status obtained immorally is for me like passing clouds." (Yang, 1972, p. 68)

PRACTICAL APPLICATION

Baduanjin: Pull the Bow Left and Right as if Shooting a Vulture (*zuoyou lagong ru she diao* 左右拉弓如射雕)

After performing the first and second preparation positions, perform the first posture. On the last repetition of the first posture, as you are circling your arms outward, downward, and inward, make a loose fist with your right hand. At the same time, point your left index finger straight out, your left thumb straight up, forming a right angle with your thumb and index finger, and gently curl the remaining three fingers into your palm. As your arms circle downward in front of your lower abdominal area, about 3 inches below your hips, let your wrists cross, with the back of your right wrist gently laying on the inside of your left wrist. You are looking forward. Make sure your back remains straight.

From this position, with your wrists still touching, inhale slowly through your nose while circling your arms forward, upward, and slightly inward at mid-chest level. As your arms move inward, shift your weight onto your right foot and step out with your left foot to the left side while keeping your feet parallel. The distance between your feet is as if you were riding on a horse.

From this position, imagine you are holding a bow with your left hand and the string of the bow with your right hand. While exhaling, nose or mouth, with the tip of your left index finger facing straight up, push the bow outward to the left side. Don't lock your elbow. As your left hand pushes to the side, follow your left index finger with your eyes by turning your head to the left. At the same time pull the string of the bow with your right hand to the right side in front of your shoulder. Your right arm is bent. Both arms are parallel to the ground. As you push and pull your arms, draw your shoulder blades together in your back. As you do this your chest will expand.

At the same time your arms are moving sideward, bend your knees and squat down. Make sure the tip of your knees does not protrude over your toes. While your upper body is stretching out horizontally, your lower body is dropping down on a vertical plane. This squatting-down posture is known in martials arts and qigong as a horse stance as it appears as if you could be riding a horse.

At this point, open your right hand as if releasing the string of the bow, causing the arrow to shoot outward, and begin inhaling slowly through your nose while letting your right hand circle upward and outward to the right side. Follow the movement of your right hand with your eyes and the turning of your head to the right. At the same time, your left hand opens up. Shifting your weight to your right foot, return your left foot to its original position next to the right foot. At the same time circle both your arms downward and inward to the front of your lower abdomen, about 3 inches below your hips.

As you are circling your arms downward and inward, this time make a loose fist with your left hand. At the same time, point your right index finger straight out, your right thumb straight up, thus forming a right angle with your thumb and index finger, and gently curl the remaining three fingers into your palm while letting your wrists cross, with the back of your left wrist gently lying on the inside of your right wrist. As your arms move downward your head turns back to the front with your eyes looking forward.

Without stopping the flow, straighten your legs without locking your knees and at the same time circle your arms forward, upward, and slightly inward at mid-chest level. As your arms move inward, shift your weight onto your left foot and step out with your right foot to the right side while keeping your feet parallel.

From this position, imagine you are now holding a bow with your right hand and the string of the bow with your left hand. While slowly exhaling, nose or mouth, with the tip of your right index finger facing straight up, push the bow outward to the right side. Don't lock your elbow. As your right hand pushes to the side, follow your right index finger with your eyes by turning your head to the right. At the same time pull the string of the bow with your left hand to the left side in front of your shoulder. Your left arm is bent. Both arms are parallel to the ground. As you push and pull your arms, draw your shoulder blades together in your back. As you do this your chest will expand.

At the same time your arms are moving sideward, once again bend your knees and squat down. Make sure the tips of your knees do not protrude over your toes. While your upper body is stretching out horizontally, your lower body is dropping down on a vertical plane. As noted previously, this squatting-down posture is known in martials arts and qigong as a horse stance as it appears as if you could be riding a horse.

At this point, open your left hand as if releasing the string of the bow, causing the arrow to shoot outward, and begin inhaling slowly through your nose while letting your left hand circle upward and outward to the left side. Follow the movement of your left hand with your eyes and the turning of your head to the left. At the same time, your right hand opens up. Shifting your weight to your left foot, return your right foot to its original position next to the left foot. At the same time circle both your arms downward and inward to the front of your lower abdomen, about 3 inches below your hips. This completes one repetition. Perform seven more repetitions. On the last repetition as your arms circle downward let them come to rest on the sides of your legs. Take a few deep breaths, let them out, and walk away.

Upon finishing the sequence, how do you feel? Physically? Psychologically? What do you notice? Is your mind still and empty? Do you notice a difference between how you felt before you started and how you felt after you started? Were you distracted internally? Externally? The next time you practice the *Baduanjin*, begin with the first two preparation stages followed by both hands supporting heaven regulates the triple burners, and then pull the bow left and right as if shooting a vulture. Remember, to receive the long-term benefits of the *Baduanjin*, it must be practiced on a regular and consistent basis. This allows neuroplasticity to occur, which in turns allows you to learn about and explore the depth and many benefits of this ancient Chinese approach to addressing, managing, and eliminating chronic stress.

Remember, throughout the entire process, beginning with the preparation positions, always practice *guan*, a nonjudgmental self-awareness, regarding (a) your body, its position, and its movement in space (*proprioception*); (b) sensations generated from internal stimuli (*interoception*); and (c) sensations generated from external stimuli (*exteroception*)—all of which are fundamental for preventing and managing chronic stress and benefiting your overall health and well-being.

Benefits
According to Chinese qigong tradition, the pull the bow left and right as if shooting a vulture posture stretches the neck, chest, and the shoulders, strengthens the quads and buttock, rotates the spinal column, increases blood flow to these areas, opens up the associated meridians for *qi* to flow, improves balance, and massages the internal organs such as the lungs and heart (Chinese Health Qigong Association (CHQA), 2007; Lam, 1991; Liu, 2010).

KEY TERMS

sleep debt
sleep quantity
sleep deprivation
sleep quality
sleep deficiency
sleep disorders
sleep stages
circadian rhythm
homeostasis
sleep environment
lifestyle habits
irregular sleep schedule
medical conditions
medications

pain
overall poor health
chronic stress
extended wakefulness
vicious cycle of stress
processing and regulation of emotions
rapid eye movement (REM) sleep
non-rapid eye movement (NREM) sleep
light sleep
deep sleep
glymphatic system

oligodendrocyte precursor cells
oligodendrocytes
memory consolidation and learning
suprachiasmatic nucleus (SCN)
adenosine
pineal gland
melatonin
cortisol
yin and yang

1. How can the circadian rhythm and homeostasis be seen within the context of yin and yang?

2. What is the meaning of the phrase vicious cycle of sleep?

3. Given that both Confucius and Hui Hai focus on simplicity, how is simplicity relevant to restful sleep?

4. From the perspective of the *Zhuangzi* and the *Liezi*, why do people dream? What are your thoughts about why people dream?

5. Monitor you own sleep for a week for both quantity and quality. What did you discover?

6. Why is it important that you do not drive if you are sleep deprived?

7. How are REM sleep and psychological disorders intertwined?

8. How are cortisol, adenosine, and melatonin involved with the sleep-wake cycle?

9. Research recommendations/good habits for getting sufficient, quantity and quality, restful sleep. Get at least seven sources (using an Internet search is fine) and see how many commonalities you can find across the sources. Are you practicing these commonalities? As a starting point, see what information you can find regarding (a) the yoga corpse pose and (b) the practice of mindfulness relative to being useful strategies for getting restful sleep.

REFERENCES

American Academy of Sleep Medicine (AASM). (2016). Hidden health crisis costing America billions: Underdiagnosing and undertreating obstructive sleep apnea draining healthcare system. Retrieved from http://www.aasmnet.org/Resources/pdf/sleep-apnea-economic-crisis.pdf

American Heart Association (AHA). (2016, September 19). *Sleep disorders may influence heart disease risk factors: American heart association scientific statement.* Retrieved from http://newsroom.heart.org/news/sleep-disorders-may-influence-heart-disease-risk-factors

American Psychological Association (APA). (2014). *Stress in America: Are teens adopting adults' stress habits?* Retrieved from http://www.apa.org/news/press/releases/stress/2013/stress-report.pdf

American Sleep Association (ASA). (2017). *Sleep and sleep disorder statistics.* Retrieved from https://www.sleepassociation.org/sleep/sleep-statistics/

Anderson, C., & Platten, C. R. (2011). Sleep deprivation lowers inhibition and enhances impulsivity to negative stimuli. *Behavioral Brain Research, 217*(2), 463–466.

Anwar, Y. (2007). Sleep loss linked to psychiatric disorders. *UC Berkeley News.* Retrieved from http://www.berkeley.edu/news/media/releases/2007/10/22_sleeploss.shtml

Anxiety and Depression Association of America (ADAA). (2016a). *Sleep disorders*. Retrieved from https://www.adaa.org/understanding-anxiety/related-illnesses/sleep-disorders

Anxiety and Depression Association of America (ADAA). (2016b). *Stress and anxiety interfere with sleep*. Retrieved from https://www.adaa.org/understanding-anxiety/related-illnesses/other-related-conditions/stress/stress-and-anxiety-interfere

Arnedt, J. T., Wilde, G. J., Munt, P. W., & MacLean, A. W. (2001). How do prolonged wakefulness and alcohol compare in the decrements they produce on a simulated driving task? *Accident Analysis & Prevention, 33*(3), 337–344.

Assefa, S. Z., Diaz-Abad, M., Wickwire, E. M., & Scharf, S. M. (2015). The functions of sleep. *AIMS Neuroscience, 2*(2), 155–171.

Barclay, N. L., & Ellis, J. G. (2013). Sleep-related attentional bias in poor versus good sleepers is independent of affective valence. *Journal of Sleep Research, 22*(4), 414–421.

Barnes, C. M., & Drake, C. L. (2015). Prioritizing sleep health: Public health policy recommendations. *Perspectives in Psychological Science, 10*(6), 733–737.

Barone, D. A., & Krieger, A. C. (2015). The function of sleep. *AIMS Neuroscience, 2*(3), 71–90.

Basta, M., Chrousos, G. P., Vela-Bueno, A., & Vgontzas, A. N., (2007). Chronic insomnia and stress system. *Sleep Medicine Clinics, 2*(2), 279–291.

Bellesi, M., Pfister-Genskow, M., Maret, S., Keles S., Tononi, G., & Cirelli, C. (2013). Effects of sleep and wake on oligodendrocytes and their precursors. *Journal of Neuroscience, 33*(36), 14288–14300.

Blaxton, J. M., Bergeman, C. S., Whitehead, B. R., Braun, M. E., & Payne, J. D. (2015). Relationships among nightly sleep quality, daily stress, and daily affect. *Journals of Gerontology Series B: Psychological Sciences and Social Sciences, 72*(3), 263–372.

Blofeld, J. (1972). *The Zen teachings of Hui Hai on sudden illumination*. New York, NY: Samuel Weiser.

Bradl, M., & Lassmann, H. (2010). Oligodendrocytes: biology and pathology. *Acta Neuropathologica, 119*(1), 37–53.

Breus, M. J. (2012). Are sleep problems the next global health crisis: New study identifies worldwide sleep problems. *Psychology Today*. Retrieved from https://www.psychologytoday.com/blog/sleep-newzzz/201208/are-sleep-problems-the-next-global-health-crisis

Cappuccio, F. P., D'Elia, L., Strazzullo, P., & Miller, M. A. (2010). Sleep duration and all-cause mortality: A systematic review and meta-analysis of prospective studies. *Sleep, 33*(5), 585–592.

Centers for Disease Control and Prevention (CDC). (2011). *Unhealthy sleep-related behaviors—12 states, 2009*. Retrieved from https://www.cdc.gov/mmwr/preview/mmwrhtml/mm6008a2.htm

Centers for Disease Control and Prevention (CDC). (2014). *Key sleep disorders*. Retrieved from https://www.cdc.gov/sleep/about_sleep/key_disorders.html

Centers for Disease Control and Prevention (CDC). (2015). *Insufficient sleep is a public health problem*. Retrieved from https://www.cdc.gov/features/dssleep/index.html

Centers for Disease Control and Prevention (CDC). (2016). *Drowsy driving: Stay alert and unhurt*. Retrieved from https://www.cdc.gov/sleep/about_sleep/drowsy_driving.html

Centers for Disease Control and Prevention (CDC) (2017). *Are you getting enough sleep?* Retrieved from https://www.cdc.gov/features/sleep/index.html

Chang, C. Y. (1969). *Original teachings of Ch'an Buddhism*. New York, NY: Pantheon.

Chinese Health Qigong Association (CHQA). (2007). *Ba Daun Jin*. Beijing, China: Foreign Language Press.

Chinese Text Project (CTP). (2017). Huangdi Neijing Suwen. Translated from http://ctext.org/huangdi-neijing/suwen/zh

Colten, H. R., & Altevogt, B. M. (2006) (Eds.). *Sleep disorders and sleep deprivation: An unmet public health problem*. Washington, DC: National Academies Press. Retrieved from https://www.ncbi.nlm.nih.gov/books/NBK19960/

Cramer, S., & Espie, C. A. (2016). Waking up to the health benefits of sleep. *Royal Society of Public Health*. Retrieved from https://www.rsph.org.uk/resourceLibrary/waking-up-to-the-health-benefits-of-sleep.html

Czeisler, C. A. (2011). Impact of sleepiness and sleep deficiency on public health—Utility of biomarkers. *Journal of Clinical Sleep Medicine, 13*, s6–s8.

Dawson, D., & Reid. K., (1997). Fatigue, alcohol and performance impairment. *Nature, 388*(6639), 235.

Deliens, G., Gilson, M., & Peigneux, P. (2014). Sleep and the processing of emotions. *Experimental Brain Research*. Retrieved from http://dev.ulb.ac.be/ur2nf/reprints/Deliens-2014-Sleep%20and%20the%20processing%20of%20emoti.pdf

Dement, W. (1997). *What all undergraduates should know about how their sleeping lives affect their waking lives*. Retrieved from https://web.stanford.edu/~dement/sleepless.html

Eddy, R. (2005). Sleep deprivation among physicians. *British Columbia Medical Journal, 47*(4), 176–180.

Epstein, L. (Ed.) (2013). *Improving sleep: A guide to a good night's sleep*. Boston, MA: Harvard Health Publications.

Gallagher, J. (2013, October 17). Sleep "cleans" the brain of toxins. *BBC*. Retrieved from http://www.bbc.com/news/health-24567412

Gobin, C. M., Banks, J. B., Fins, A. I. & Tartar, J. L. (2015). Poor sleep quality is associated with a negative cognitive bias and decreased sustained attention. *Journal of Sleep Research, 24*(5), 535–542

Goldstein, A. N., & Walker, M. P. (2014). The role of sleep in emotional brain function. *Review of Clinical Psychology, 10*, 679. Retrieved from https://walkerlab.berkeley.edu/reprints/Goldstein-Walker_ARCP-Review_2014.pdf

Grandner, M. A., Chakravorty, S., Perlis, M. L., Oliver, L., & Gurubhagavatula, I. (2014). Habitual sleep duration associated with self-reported and objectively-determined cardiometabolic risk factors. *Sleep Medicine, 15*(1), 42–50.

Gruber, R., & Cassoff, J. (2014). The interplay between sleep and emotion regulation: Conceptual framework empirical evidence and future directions. *Current Psychiatry Reports, 16*(11), 500.

Guo, Q. F. (1974). Zhuangzi jishi, Vols 1 and 2. Taipei, Taiwan: Chung Hwa.

Hafner, M., Stepanek, M., Taylor, J., Troxel, W. M., & Van Stolk, C. (2016). Why sleep matters: The economic costs of insufficient sleep. *RAND*. Retrieved from https://www.rand.org/pubs/research_briefs/RB9962.html

Han, K. S., Kim, L., & Shim, I. (2012). Stress and sleep disorder. *Experimental Neurobiology, 21*, 141–150.

Harvard Medical School (HMS). (2008). Judgment and safety. Retrieved from http://healthysleep.med.harvard.edu/need-sleep/whats-in-it-for-you/judgment-safety

Harvard Medical School (HMS). (2019). *Sleep and mental health*. Retrieved from http://www.health.harvard.edu/newsletter_article/Sleep-and-mental-health

Health and Human Services (HHS). (2008). 2008 physical activity guidelines for Americans. Retrieved from https://health.gov/PAGuidelines/pdf/paguide.pdf

Health and Human Services & U.S. Department of Agriculture (HHS & USDA). (2005). *Dietary guidelines for Americans, 2005*. Retrieved from https://health.gov/dietaryguidelines/dga2005/document/

Health and Human Services & U.S. Department of Agriculture (HHS & USDA). (2015). *2015–2020 dietary guidelines for Americans*. Retrieved from http://health.gov/dietaryguidelines/2015/guidelines/

Hershock, P. D. (2005). *Chan Buddhism*. Honolulu, HI: University of Hawaii Press.

Hirshkowitz, M. (2014). 2014 Sleep health index. *National Sleep Foundation*. Retrieved from https://www.sleepfoundation.org/sleep-health-index-2014-highlights

Hui, H. (2017). *Zhu Fang Menren Can Wen Yulu*. Retrieved from http://tripitaka.cbeta.org/X63n1224_001

Jacobson, B. H., & Monaghan, T. M. (2015). Physical and psychological stress and sleep efficiency before and after introducing a new sleep surface. *Journal of Sleep Disorders & Therapy, 4*(3), 199. Retrieved from https://www.omicsgroup.org/journals/physical-and-psychological-stress-and-sleep-efficiency-before-and-after-introducing-a-new-sleep-surface-2167-0277-1000199.pdf

Jones, J. M. (2013). In U.S., 40% get less than recommended amount of sleep. *Gallup*. Retrieved from http://www.gallup.com/poll/166553/less-recommended-amount-sleep.aspx

Kahn, M., Sheppes, G., & Sadeh, A. (2013). Sleep and emotions: Bidirectional links and underlying mechanisms. *International Journal of Psychophysiology, 89*(2), 218–228.

Kendzerska, T., & Shapiro, C. M. (2013). Morbidity and mortality. *Encyclopedia of Sleep, 2*, 460–468. Retrieved from http://www.sciencedirect.com/science/article/pii/B9780123786104002333

Kim, E. J., & Dimsdale, J. E. (2007). The effect of psychosocial stress on sleep: A review of polysomnographic evidence. *Behavioral Sleep Medicine, 5*(4), 256–278.

Kondracki, N. L. (2012). The link between sleep and weight gain—Research shows poor sleep quality raises obesity and chronic disease risk. *Today's Dietitian, 14.* Retrieved from http://www.todaysdietitian.com/newarchives/060112p48.shtml

Krause, A. J., Simon, E. B., Mander, B. A., Greer, S. M., Saletin, J. M, Goldstein-Piekarski, A. N., & Walker, M. P. (2017). The sleep-deprived human brain. *Nature Reviews: Neuroscience, 18.* Retrieved from http://www.nature.com/nrn/journal/v18/n7/full/nrn.2017.55.html?foxtrotcallback=true

Krystal, A. D. (2012). Psychiatric disorders and sleep. *Neurologic Clinics, 30*(4), 1389–1413.

Lam, K. C. (1991). *The way of energy: Mastering the Chinese art of internal strength with chi kung exercises.* New York, NY: Simon & Schuster.

Lamond, N., & Dawson, D., (1999). Quantifying the performance impairment associated with fatigue. *Journal of Sleep Research, 8*(4), 255–262.

Landrigan C. P., Rothschild, J. M., Cronin, J. W., Kaushal, R., Burdick, E., Katz, J. T., ... & Czeisler, C. A. (2004). Effect of reducing interns' work hours on serious medical errors in intensive care units. *New England Journal of Medicine, 351*(18), 1838–1848.

Lee, S. H. W., Ng, K. Y., & Chin, W. K. (2017). The impact of sleep amount and sleep quality on glycemic control in type 2 diabetes: A systematic review and meta-analysis. *Sleep Medicine Reviews, 31*, 91–101.

Leger, D., Beck, F., Richard, J. B., Sauvet, F., & Faraut, B. (2014). The risks of sleeping "too much." Survey of a National Representative Sample of 24671 Adults (INPES Health Barometer). *PLoS ONE 9*, Retrieved from http://sommeilvdk.cluster020.hosting.ovh.net/wp-content/uploads/2016/03/Dormir-trop-Leger-2014.pdf

LeWine, H. (2014). Too little sleep, and too much, affect memory. *Harvard Health Publishing.* Retrieved from http://www.health.harvard.edu/blog/little-sleep-much-affect-memory-201405027136

Liu, T. (Ed.) (2010). *Chinese medical qigong.* London, UK: Singing Dragon.

Liu, Y., Wheaton, A. G., Chapman, D. P., Cunningham, T. J., Lu, H., & Croft, J. B. (2016). Prevalence of healthy sleep duration among adults—United States, 2014. *Centers for Disease Control and Prevention.* Retrieved from https://www.cdc.gov/mmwr/volumes/65/wr/mm6506a1.htm

Lockley, S. W., Cronin, J. W., Evans, E. E., Cade, B. E., Lee, C. J., Landrigan, C. P., ... & Cszeiler, C. A. (2004). Effect of reducing interns' weekly work hours on sleep and attentional failures. *New England Journal of Medicine, 351*, 1829–1837.

Luyster, F. S., Strollo, P. J., Zee, P. C., & Walsh, J. K. (2012). Sleep: A health imperative. *Sleep, 35*(6), 727–734.

Maquet, P. (2000). Sleep on it! *Nature Neuroscience, 3*(12), 1235–1236.

McCarthy, J., & Brown, A. (2015). Getting more sleep linked to higher well-being. *Gallup.* Retrieved from http://www.gallup.com/poll/181583/getting-sleep-linked-higher.aspx

Medina, J. (2014). *Brain rules: 12 principles for surviving and thriving at work, home, and school.* Seattle, WA: Pear Press.

Minkel, J. D., Banks, S., Htaik, O., Moreta, M. C., Jones, C. W., McGlinchey E. L., ... & Dinges, D. F. (2012). Sleep deprivation and stressors: Evidence for elevated negative affect in response to mild stressors when sleep deprived. *Emotion, 12*(5), 1015–1020.

Motomura, Y., Kitamura, S., Oba, K., Terasawa, Y., Enomoto, M., Katayose, Y., ... & Mishima, K. (2013). Sleep debt elicits negative emotional reaction through diminished amygdala anterior cingulate functional connectivity. *PloS ONE, 8.* Retrieved from http://journals.plos.org/plosone/article/file?id=10.1371/journal.pone.0056578&type=printable

National Heart, Lung, and Blood Institute (NHLBI). (2006). *Sleep, sleep disorders, and biological rhythms.* Retrieved from https://science.education.nih.gov/supplements/webversions/SleepDisorders/guide/info-sleep.html

National Heart, Lung, and Blood Institute (NHLBI). (2017a). *What are sleep deprivation and deficiency?* Retrieved from https://www.nhlbi.nih.gov/health/health-topics/topics/sdd/

National Heart, Lung, and Blood Institute (NHLBI). (2017b). *Why is sleep important?* Retrieved from https://www.nhlbi.nih.gov/health/health-topics/topics/sdd/why

National Heart, Lung, and Blood Institute (NHLBI). (2017c). *What makes you sleep?* Retrieved from https://www.nhlbi.nih.gov/health/health-topics/topics/sdd/whatmakes

National Highway Traffic Safety Administration (NHTSA). (2017). Asleep at the wheel: A national compendium of efforts to eliminate drowsy driving. Retrieved from https://www.nhtsa.gov/sites/nhtsa.dot.gov/files/documents/12723-drowsy_driving_asleep_at_the_wheel_031917_v4b_tag.pdf

National Institutes of Health (NIH). (2013a). Brain may flush out toxins during sleep: NIH-funded study suggests sleep clears brain of damaging molecules associated with neurodegeneration. Retrieved from https://www.nih.gov/news-events/news-releases/brain-may-flush-out-toxins-during-sleep

National Institutes of Health (NIH) (2013b). *How sleep clears the brain.* Retrieved from https://www.nih.gov/news-events/nih-research-matters/how-sleep-clears-brain

National Institutes of Health (NIH). (2013c). *Sleep on it: How snoozing strengthens memories.* Retrieved from https://newsinhealth.nih.gov/issue/Apr2013/feature2

National Institute of Neurological Disorders and Stroke (NINDS). (2017). *Brain basics: Understanding sleep.* Retrieved from https://www.ninds.nih.gov/Disorders/Patient-Caregiver-Education/Understanding-Sleep

National Sleep Foundation (NSF). (2014a). *Lack of sleep is affecting Americans, finds the National Sleep Foundation.* Retrieved https://sleepfoundation.org/media-center/press-release/lack-sleep-affecting-americans-finds-the-national-sleep-foundation

National Sleep Foundation (NSF). (2014b). *2014 sleep index.* Retrieved from https://www.sleepfoundation.org/sleep-health-index-2014-highlights

National Sleep Foundation (NSF). (2015). *2015 sleep and pain: Summary of findings.* Retrieved from https://sleepfoundation.org/sleep-polls-data/sleep-in-america-poll/2015-sleep-and-pain

National Sleep Foundation (NSF). (2017a). Backgrounder: *Later school start times.* Retrieved from https://sleepfoundation.org/sleep-news/backgrounder-later-school-start-times

National Sleep Foundation (NSF). (2017b). What happens when you sleep? Retrieved from https://sleepfoundation.org/how-sleep-works/what-happens-when-you-sleep

Ohkuma, T., Fujii, H., Iwase, M., Kikuchi, Y., Ogata, S., Idewaki, Y., ... & Kitazono, T. (2013). Impact of sleep duration on obesity and the glycemic level in patients with type 2 diabetes: The Fukuoka Diabetes Registry. *Diabetes Care, 36*(3), 611–617.

Palmer, C. A., & Alfano, C. A. (2017). Sleep and emotion regulation: An organizing, integrative review. *Sleep Medicine Reviews, 31*, 6–16.

Paruthi, S., Brooks, L. J., D'Ambrosio, C., Hall, W. A., Kotagal, S., Lloyd, R. M., ... & Wise, M. S. (2016). Consensus statement of the American Academy of Sleep Medicine on the recommended amount of sleep for healthy children: Methodology and discussion. *Journal of Clinical Sleep Medicine, 12*(6), 1549–1561.

Rasch, B., & Born, J. (2013). About sleep's role in memory. *Physiological Reviews, 93*(2), 681–766.

Santee, R. (2004, July 22). *A Daoist and an existential psychotherapist: A comparative study.* Paper presented at the First World Hong Ming Philosophy Conference. Honolulu, HI.

Santee, R. (2011). "The Zhuangzi: A Holistic Approach to Health Care," *Living Authentically: Daoist Contributions to Modern Psychology,* ed. Livia Kohn, pp. 44-45. Copyright © 2011 by Three Pines Press. Reprinted with permission.

Santee, R., & Zhang, X. (2015). Yangsheng (養生) and the yin style baguazhang of Wang Fu and Wang Shangzhi. *Empty Vessel: The Journal of Taoist Philosophy and Practice, 22*, 24–30.

Shahar, M. (2008). *The Shaolin Monastery: History, religion, and the Chinese martial arts.* Honolulu, HI: University of Hawaii Press.

Siegel, J. M. (2003). Why we sleep: The reasons that we sleep are gradually becoming less enigmatic. *Scientific American,* 92–97.

St-Onge, M. P., Grandner, M. A., Brown, D., Conroy, M. B., Jean-Louis, G., Coons, M., & Bhatt, D. L. (2016). Sleep duration and quality: Impact on lifestyle behaviors and cardiometabolic health: A scientific statement from the American heart association. *Circulation, 134*(18), 367–386. Retrieved from http://circ.ahajournals.org/content/early/2016/09/19/CIR.0000000000000444

Swaminathan, N. (2007, October 23). Can a lack of sleep cause psychiatric disorders? *Scientific American.* Retrieved from https://www.scientificamerican.com/article/can-a-lack-of-sleep-cause/

Tefft, B. C. (2014). *Prevalence of motor vehicle crashes involving drowsy drivers, United States, 2009–2013.* Retrieved from https://aaafoundation.org/wp-content/uploads/2017/12/PrevalenceofMVCDrowsyDriversReport.pdf

Thera, D. M. (2017). *What is vinaya?* Retrieved from http://www.budsas.org/ebud/whatbudbeliev/148.htm

Thomee, S., Härenstam, A., & Hagberg, M. (2011). Mobile phone use and stress, sleep disturbances, and symptoms of depression among young adults: A prospective cohort study. *BMC Public Health, 11.* Retrieved from https://bmcpublichealth.biomedcentral.com/articles/10.1186/1471-2458-11-66

Tononi, G., & Cirelli, C. (2014). Sleep and the price of plasticity: From synaptic and cellular homeostasis to memory consolidation and integration. *Neuron, 81*(1), 12–34.

van der Helm, E., & Walker, M. P. (2009). Overnight therapy? The role of sleep in emotional brain processing. *Psychological Bulletin, 135*(5), 731–748.

Vandekerckhove, M., & Cluydts, R. (2010). The emotional brain and sleep: An intimate relationship. *Sleep Medicine Reviews, 14*(4), 219–226.

Van Dongen H. P. A., Maislin, G., Mullington, J. M., & Dinges, D. F. (2003). The cumulative cost of additional wakefulness: Dose-response effects on neurobehavioral functions and sleep physiology from chronic sleep restriction and total sleep deprivation. *Sleep, 26*(2), 117–126.

Wahlstrom, K. (2016, September 19). Why teen brains need later school start time. *AP News.* Retrieved from https://apnews.com/3a07a0e9003a4def84fc3d4f02505489/why-teen-brains-need-later-school-start-time

Walch, O. J., Cochran, A., & Forger, D. B. (2016). A global quantification of "normal" sleep schedules using smartphone data. *Science Advances, 2*(5), 1–6. Retrieved from https://www.ncbi.nlm.nih.gov/pmc/articles/PMC4928979/

Walker, M. P. (2009). The role of sleep in cognition and emotion. *Annals of The New York Academy of Sciences, 1156*(1), 168–197.

Wang, R. R. (2012). *Yinyang: The way of heaven and earth in Chinese thought and culture.* New York, NY: Cambridge University Press.

Watson N. F., Badr, M. S., Belenky, G., Bliwise, D. L., Buxton, O. M., Buysse, D., ... & Tasali, E. (2015). Recommended amount of sleep for a healthy adult: A joint consensus statement of the American Academy of Sleep Medicine and Sleep Research Society. *Journal of Clinical Sleep Medicine, 11*(6), 591–592.

Williamson A. M., & Feyer, A. M. (2000). Moderate sleep deprivation produces impairments in cognitive and motor performance equivalent to legally prescribed levels of alcohol intoxication. *Occupational and Environmental Medicine, 57*(10), 649–655.

Weinhouse, B. (2017). America's sleep crisis is making us sick, fat, and stupid. But there's hope. *Reader's Digest.* Retrieved from http://www.rd.com/health/conditions/america-sleep-crisis/

Wong, W. S. & Fielding, R. (2011). Prevalence of insomnia among Chinese adults in Hong Kong: A population-based study. *Journal of Sleep Research, 20*(1), 117–126.

Woo, M. (2011). Why do we sleep? *Caltech.* Retrieved from http://www.caltech.edu/news/why-do-we-sleep-1863

Xie, L., Kang, H., Xu, Q., Chen, M. J., Liao, Y., Thiyagarajan, M., ... & Nedergaard, M. (2013). Sleep drives metabolite clearance from the adult brain. *Science, 342*(6156). Retrieved from https://www.ncbi.nlm.nih.gov/pmc/articles/PMC3880190/pdf/nihms540586.pdf

Xu, F. (Ed.). (2016). Nearly half of China's middle-income class suffer from insomnia. *CRI English.* Retrieved from http://english.cri.cn/12394/2016/03/21/195s921262.htm

Yang, J. L. (Ed.) (1972). *Lunyu zhu shu bu zheng.* Taibei, Taiwan: Shijie Shuju.

Yoo, S. S., Gujar, N., Hu, P., Jolesz, F. A., & Walker, M. P. (2007). The human emotional brain without sleep. *Current Biology, 17*(20), R877–R878.

Zhang, Z. (1972). *Liezi zhu. Taibei,* Taiwan: Shijie Shuju Yinxing.

Zohar, D., Tzischinsky, O., Epstein, R., & Lavie, P. (2005). The effects of sleep loss on medical residents' emotional reactions to work events: A cognitive-energy model. *Sleep, 28*(12), 47–54.

CREDITS

- Fig. 7.1: Copyright © 2012 Depositphotos/Hannamariah.
- Fig. 7.2: Copyright © 2017 Depositphotos/belchonock.
- Fig. 7.3: Copyright © 2012 Depositphotos/stockyimages.
- Fig. 7.4: Copyright © 2013 Depositphotos/cmeree.
- Fig. 7.5: Copyright © 2016 Depositphotos/racorn.
- Fig. 7.6: Copyright © 2015 Depositphotos/gpointstudio.
- Fig. 7.7: Copyright © 2014 Depositphotos/photographee.eu.
- Fig. 7.8: Copyright © 2014 Depositphotos/Siphotography.
- Fig. 7.9: Copyright © 2015 Depositphotos/AlexanderNovikov.
- Fig. 7.10: Copyright © 2010 Depositphotos/jcpjr1111.
- Fig. 7.11: Copyright © 2013 Depositphotos/stokkete.
- Fig. 7.12: Copyright © 2014 Depositphotos/platongkoh01.
- Fig. 7.13: Copyright © 2009 Depositphotos/shiyali.
- Fig. 7.14: Copyright © 2011 Depositphotos/philipus.
- Fig. 7.15: Copyright © by Jenai Kubo. Reprinted with permission.
- Fig. 7.16: Copyright © by Jenai Kubo. Reprinted with permission.
- Fig. 7.17: Copyright © by Jenai Kubo. Reprinted with permission.
- Fig. 7.18: Copyright © by Jenai Kubo. Reprinted with permission.
- Fig. 7.19: Copyright © by Jenai Kubo. Reprinted with permission.
- Fig. 7. 20: Copyright © by Jenai Kubo. Reprinted with permission.

CHAPTER 8

Nutrition

After finishing this chapter, you will be able to do the following:

- Indicate how chronic stress is linked to obesity and eating disorders
- Demonstrate how the HPA axis is linked to not only the stress response but also to eating behavior
- Explain how lack of exercise, sedentary behavior, inadequate restful sleep, problematic eating behaviors/choices, and inappropriate, threat-based psychosocial thinking are linked together in a vicious cycle/circle of chronic stress, which significantly compromises one's overall physical and psychological health and well-being
- Indicate how the practice of mindfulness may be beneficial for addressing problematic eating behaviors
- Explain how the process of evolution and the evolution of society and culture are linked to the problem of obesity and why obesity is a significant problem
- Explain why water is essential for our overall physical and psychological health and well-being and how dehydration threatens it
- Describe the Buddhist, Daoist, and Confucian approaches to stress free eating
- Describe the basic healthy, nutritional eating patterns proposed by the "2015–2020 Dietary Guidelines for Americans" document

No matter what we do, our body and brain require energy to do it. We need energy to stay alive and function in our various environmental contexts. All the numerous functions and processes our body and brain engage in, provided via the evolutionary process, to keep us alive and protect us, such as keeping us breathing and keeping our heart pumping, our blood flowing, our food digesting, our bowels

moving, our brains thinking, our immune system protecting us, our nose and eyes smelling and seeing, require energy. The amount of energy we need is contingent on the demands placed on us by our various environmental contexts. In other words, what we are doing—for example, sitting, watching TV, eating a meal, mind wandering, sitting in classroom listening to a professor, sleeping, driving a car, or exercising? The source and quality of our energy comes from what we eat and drink.

EVOLUTIONARY THEORY AND NUTRITION

As noted in chapter 6, our society and culture has evolved from our hunter-gather ancestors' environmental contexts, which required significant physical activity for survival through that of farming, agriculture, and domestication of plants and animals, which was obviously physically demanding, but from a more settled, essentially continually stationary location for survival, through the industrial revolution and its mass production requiring even less physical activity for survival, through the inventions and commercial use of the electric light bulb, refrigeration, automobile, airplanes and so on, all of which reduced physical activity, to the digital age of computers, mobile phones, tablets, which even further reduced physical activity. In other words, for most people in our current society, survival does not require much physical activity. Survival has, essentially, become sedentary in nature.

The problem is that we are evolved to adapt to the environment of our hunter-gather ancestors not our current environment (Malina, & Little, 2008; O'Keefe, Vogel, Lavie, & Cordain, 2010; Ratey & Hagerman, 2008). The consequences of this physical activity mismatch have significantly compromised our physical and psychological health and well-being (Malina, & Little, 2008; O'Keefe, Vogel, Lavie, & Cordain, 2010; Owen, Sparling, Healy, Dunstan, & Matthews, 2010; Ratey & Hagerman, 2008). In other words, as a result of our sedentary behavior and lack of physical exercise, our energy expenditure for survival is quite minimal when compared with our hunter-gather ancestors. As a result, our body and brain are compromised regarding how we evolved to adapt to our environment, thus contributing to being chronically stressed and susceptible to chronic diseases. One area where our minimal energy expenditure is quite evident is that of **obesity**.

Not only has our physical activity levels changed significantly from the time of our hunter-gather ancestors to current times, but so has our diet. The problem is, once again, we are evolved to adapt to the environment of our hunter-gather ancestors not our current environment (Carrera-Bastos et al., 2011; Cordain et al., 2005; Eaton, Konner, & Shostak, 1988; Jew, AbuMweis, & Jones, 2009; Ratey & Manning, 2014; Zucoloto, 2011). The consequences of this diet mismatch have significantly compromised our physical and psychological health and wellbeing (Carrera-Bastos et al., 2001; Cordain et al., 2005; Eaton, Konner, & Shostak, 1988; Jew, AbuMweis, & Jones, 2009; Ratey & Manning, 2014; Zucoloto, 2011).

With the advent of the agricultural age giving rise to farming, the domestication of plants, and the domestication of animals, the mass production of the industrial age evolving through a variety of ways of processing, refining, condensing, storing and preserving food; the enhancing of food by adding processed sugar; the increased amount of sodium used in foods; the easy access to meat and other types of food with a high fat content; the subsequent reduction in eating fruits and vegetables; the lessening of fiber, vitamins, and minerals in what we eat as a result of these various changes; and our diets being higher in carbohydrates and fats, which results for many people in excessive energy consumption; and lower consumption of protein than our hunter-gather ancestors, we have become vulnerable to a series of chronic diseases, illnesses, and disorders that compromise our overall physical and psychological health and well-being (Carrera-Bastos et al., 2001; Cordain et al., 2005; Eaton, Konner, & Shostak, 1988; Jew, AbuMweis, & Jones, 2009; Ratey & Manning, 2014; Zucoloto, 2011). In other words, as a result of our dietary changes, our body and brain are compromised regarding how we evolved to adapt to our environment, thus contributing to our being chronically stressed.

It is important to note that we are wired, via the evolutionary process, to seek out carbohydrates/sugars and fats for energy. The reason they generally taste good is our hunter-gather ancestors would eat them to get the nutrients they needed to survive. At the same time, this paring of energy consumption with the food tasting good has resulted in not only in **eating for energy** but also for **eating for pleasure and feeling good**.

Because carbohydrates/sugars and fats for energy were not both readily available to our hunter-gatherer ancestors, they had to engage in physical activity; in the case of hunting for animals it was most likely quite intense to obtain them, thus, the important link between physical activity, diet, and health.

We today have the same desire for carbohydrates/sugars and fats as our hunter-gather ancestors. The difference is that they are readily available to us and require minimal physical activity to obtain them. We don't even have to get up and move about very much at all if we want sugar and fat. We can simply get in our car and go to a drive-through at a fast-food place or, if that is asking too much, we can just make a phone call/order online and have someone deliver all the sugar and fat we want to consume.

Thus, for those of us living in highly developed industrial economies, there is no real, substantial physical requirement or energy expenditure to obtain all the sugar and fat we want. Our environment does not provide the same challenges or energy expenditures required of our hunter-gather ancestors to obtain sugar and fat. Given that we have, essentially, the same desire for sugar and fat as our hunter-gather ancestors, sugar and fat are readily available in an energy dense, processed form which requires minimal energy expenditure to be obtained, and as a result of our dietary changes, many of us consume more energy than we need. One area where our excessive energy consumption is quite evident is that of obesity.

OBESITY

According to the World Health Organization's (WHO, 2016) worldwide estimate, for 2014, (a) the prevalence of obesity has more than doubled between 1980 and 2014, (b) more than 1.9 billion adults (39%) 18 years and older were overweight (38% of men and 40% of women) with over 600 million (13%) of them being obese (11% men and 15% women), and (c) 41 million children under the age of 5 were overweight or obese with nearly half of them living in Asia. The WHO (2016) fact sheet indicated *most of the world's population live in countries where being overweight and obese kills more people than being underweight*, with the exceptions being parts of sub-Saharan Africa and Asia, and that being overweight or obese is not just a high-income country problem as it is on the rise in low- and middle-income countries, particularly in urban settings.

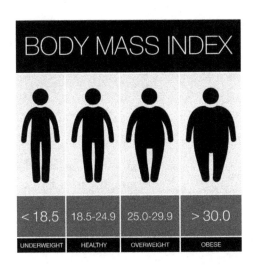

As indicated in chapter 6, the Centers for Disease Control and Prevention (CDC, 2016) in a 2013–2014 analysis of obesity and being overweight, indicated 70.7% of the adult population in the United States age 20 years and older were overweight or obese. Almost 38% of this group was obese. The Centers for Disease Control and Prevention (CDC, 2015) links obesity to body pain; osteoarthritis; all-cause mortality; hypertension, Type 2 diabetes; high LDL cholesterol; heart disease; joint functioning; strokes; gallbladder disease; breast, kidney, gallbladder, colon, and liver cancer; anxiety, depression, sleep disorders; breathing problems; and low quality of life. A Centers for Disease Control and Prevention report noted, among other statistics, a different relationship between wealth and obesity for women and men:

> Non-Hispanic blacks have the highest age-adjusted rates of obesity (48.1%) followed by Hispanics (42.5%), non-Hispanic whites (34.5%), and non-Hispanic Asians (11.7%). Obesity is higher among middle age adults age 40–59 years (40.2%) and older adults age 60 and over (37.0%) than among younger adults age 20–39 (32.3%). Among non-Hispanic black and Mexican-American men, those with higher incomes are more likely to have obesity than those with low income. Higher income women are less likely to have obesity than low-income women. There is no significant relationship between obesity and education among men. Among women, however, there is a trend—those with college degrees are less likely to have obesity compared with less educated women (Centers for Disease Control and Prevention (CDC), 2017a).

The Centers for Disease Control and Prevention (CDC, 2017a) report noted that the annual medical costs of obesity, in 2008 dollars, was estimated to be $147 billion. This report also noted that the annual lost productivity due to obesity or obesity-related absenteeism was between $3.3 and 6.38 billion. In order to address these concerns, it is necessary to address nutritional guidelines.

2015–2020 DIETARY GUIDELINES FOR AMERICANS

The Health and Human Services and U.S. Department of Agriculture's (HHS & USDA, 2015) "**2015–2020 Dietary Guidelines for Americans**" primary focus is encouraging healthy eating patterns and preventing chronic diseases. These guidelines are quite clear that many of these chronic diseases are linked to lifestyle, especially poor diet and lack of physical activity. Of specific concern in this context is obesity.

Obesity is most prevalent in those ages 40 years and older and in African American adults, and is least prevalent in adults with highest incomes. Prevalence is higher with increasing age and varies by sex and race/ethnicity. In 2009–2012, 65% of adult females and 73% of adult males were overweight or obese. In 2009–2012, nearly one in three youth ages 2 to 19 years were overweight or obese (Health and Human Services & U.S. Department of Agriculture, 2015).

Healthy Eating Patterns

- Follow a healthy eating pattern across the lifespan.
- Focus on variety, nutrient density, and amount.
- Limit calories from added sugars and saturated fats and reduce sodium intake.
- Shift to healthier food and beverage choices.
- Support healthy eating patterns for all. (Health and Human Services & U.S. Department of Agriculture, 2015)

WATER

Water is fundamental to life. We cannot function or live without water. Although our primary source of water should be plain drinking water, water is also consumed in the foods we eat and the other liquids we drink (Kavouras & Anastasiou, 2010; Riebel & Davy, 2013). On average, based on body mass, more than half, between 50–60%, of the adult body weight is made up of water, with males generally being composed of more water than females (Benelam & Wyness, 2010; Bushman, 2017; Kavouras & Anastasiou, 2010; Popkin, D'Anci, &

Rosenberg, 2010; Zelman, 2008). Water is necessary for absorption, body fluids, saliva, sweat, tears, removal of waste, and blood volume for the cells and organs to function properly and to maintain normal temperature, for the joints to function properly, and to protect spinal column and tissue, physical activity, cognitive performance, mood, and metabolism (Benelam & Wyness, 2010; Bushman, 2017; Kavouras & Anastasiou, 2010; Popkin, D'Anci, & Rosenberg, 2010; Zelman, 2008).

Given that adequate amounts of water are necessary for all these processes and functions, dehydration, depending on the degree, compromises their normal processing/functioning (Benelam & Wyness, 2010; Bushman, 2017; Kavouras & Anastasiou, 2010; Popkin, D'Anci, & Rosenberg, 2010). Essentially, if you are dehydrated, your body and brain are being stressed as they are not being allowed to perform in the manner in which they evolved. This is a significant problem for overall physical and psychological health and well-being. Not only can being severely dehydrated be fatal, but if you are severely overhydrated, although quite rare, your normal body and brain functioning is severely compromised, stressed, and can be fatal (ACEP, 2017; Farrell & Bower, 2003).

Although there are recommendations regarding how much water you should drink each day, such as twelve 8-ounce glasses a day or half your body weight in ounces, there is no agreed-on amount due to individual differences, environments, and activity levels for daily consumption of water per day in the research literature (Benelam & Wyness, 2010; Popkin, D'Anci, & Rosenberg, 2010; Riebel & Davy, 2013).

As a rule of thumb, the lighter the color of your urine, such as clear pale yellow, and your urine being odorless is indicative of being hydrated (Cleveland Clinic, 2013; Kavouras & Anastasiou, 2010; Riebel & Davy, 2013; Zelman, 2008). Urine that is darker and smells is indicative of dehydration, but color and odor may be influenced by other causes such as vitamins, medications, diet, exercise, and weather. Bottom line: Make sure you stay hydrated!

GLYCEMIC INDEX AND GLYCEMIC LOAD

Given the strong link between obesity and type 2 diabetes (HHS & USDA, 2015; CDC, 2015), it is important to have an understanding of **glycemic index** and **glycemic** load (Craig, 2012; Harvard Medical School (HMS), 2017; Sheard et al., 2004). Glycemic index refers to how fast a particular carbohydrate changes/affects the blood glucose/sugar level after ingestion. The glycemic index, where pure glucose has a value of 100, goes from low, 55 or less, to medium, 56–69, with high being 70 or above (American Diabetes Association (ADA), 2014; Craig, 2012; Mendosa, 2008). Glycemic load refers to how much of a particular carbohydrate is in a serving. The glycemic load, which is determined by both the GI value and the total grams of carbohydrate in the serving and then dividing by 100, ranges from a GL of 10 and below being low, 11 to 19 being medium, and 20 and above being high (Craig, 2012; Mendosa, 2008). There are numerous tables that allow you to assess each food regarding both index and load (HMS, 2015; Mendosa, 2008). Concerns have been raised whether you need to focus on both GI and GL, just GI, just GL, or neither (HMS, 2017). The bottom line is that both obesity and type 2 diabetes compromise the normal, evolved functioning of the body and brain and thus provide another source of chronic stress.

EATING DISORDERS

As noted in the previous chapter on sleep, there are, in addition to the major problems regarding adequate, restful, quantity and quality of sleep, specific sleep disorders which are also linked to chronic stress. In the same sense, there are, in addition to the major problems regarding adequate nutrition and obesity, specific eating disorders that are also linked to chronic stress. When your focus on food consumption, weight, and body form is to the extent that it significantly compromises your normal daily interactions and threatens your overall health and well-being, it is indicative of psychological stress and may indicate an eating disorder such as (a) **anorexia nervosa,** which is being excessively thin to the point of being unhealthy due to a severe reduction of food consumption along with various forms of purging; (b) **bulimia nervosa** which, although maintaining a normal weight, is essentially binge eating with purging; and (c) **binge eating disorder,** which is episodic consuming of huge amounts of food without purging, thus resulting in being overweight or obese (National Institute of Mental Health (NIMH), 2016; National Alliance of Mental Illness (NAMI), 2015). Research suggests that these disorders are linked to chronic stress (Hardaway, Crowley, Bulik, & Kash, 2015; Rojo, Conesa, Bermudez, & Livianos, 2006). As these eating disorders significantly compromise the normal functioning of the brain and body, passed down, via evolution, the brain and body are chronically stressed. Thus, like sleep there is a vicious cycle/circle of chronic stress.

In addition to the eating disorders noted, there is a problematic eating behavior known as orthoexia nervosa, which refers to, essentially, being obsessed with eating only healthy food to the point that it becomes unhealthy (APA, 2016; Kratina, 2016). At this point, due to a lack of research, defining characteristics, and statistics regarding age, gender, occurrences, complications, and so on, it has not been incorporated into the Diagnostic and Statistical Manual-Fifth Edition or DSM-5 (APA, 2016; Kratina, 2016).

OBESITY AND CHRONIC STRESS

If you do not eat and drink adequately and provide, relative to your specific energy needs to optimally function, your body and brain with an appropriate, harmonious distribution of nutrients (carbohydrates, protein, fats, minerals, vitamins, and water), you significantly compromise the natural evolved functioning of both your brain and body. Essentially, your brain and body will be chronically stressed simply due to your feeding behavior. On the other hand, if you are chronically stressed due to, for example, inappropriate threat-based psychosocial thinking, this chronic stress will negatively impact your eating and drinking behavior. Once again, there is a vicious cycle/circle of chronic stress.

In the previous chapter on sleep it was noted that chronic stress negatively impacts, physically and psychologically, the quantity and quality of sleep, resulting in individuals either not getting enough sleep or getting too much sleep. As the majority of individuals had problems with not getting enough sleep, the primary focus of the research has been on that issue. In the same sense, the impact of chronic stress on eating behavior is a double-edged sword as it causes, depending on the type and severity of the stressor, one's coping skills, personality, life experiences, genetics, and so on, problems for some people, resulting in them eating less food and, for most people, in eating more food (Adam & Epel, 2007; Block, Zaslavsky, Ding & Ayanian, 2009; Ilari & Elena, 2016; Sapolsky, 1998; Tahir, 2016; Torres & Nowson, 2007). Given the data regarding the number of people who are overweight or obese, concerns of the World Health Organization (WHO, 2016) regarding this issue, and the 2015–2020 Dietary Guidelines regarding obesity, the focus will be on chronic stress and eating too much.

Poor nutrition chronically stresses your body and brain.

During acute stress, appetite is suppressed via the **hypothalamus, pituitary, adrenal axis (HPA)**, which is the neuro-endocrine component of the stress response, by the release of **corticotropin releasing factor (CRF)** from the **hypothalamus** (HMS, 2012; Sapolsky, 1998; Yau & Potenza, 2013) while digestion is suppressed by the release of cortisol, which increases during the stress response, from the adrenal cortex (LLari & Elena, 2016; Mayo Clinic, 2016) as the brain redistributes/increases energy to the large muscles associated with an activated stress response in order to address the perceived threat. In this situation, as appetite and digestion are not relevant to addressing and resolving the perceived threat, energy is redirected away from these processes. Once the threat has been resolved the body and brain return, via negative feedback messages from cortisol to the HPA axis to stop producing cortisol or terminate the stress response, to its previous state (Adam & Epel, 2007; Adeniyi, 2015; LLari & Elena, 2016; Singh, 2016; Sapolsky 1998; Scott, Melhorn, & Sakai, 2012; Yau & Potenza, 2013). However, as the activation of the stress response is the mobilization and utilization of energy, this energy needs to be replaced/stored and, via the cortisol still in the blood stream, one's appetite/hunger is stimulated by feedback to the hypothalamus (HMS, 2012; Sapolsky, 1988; Sominsky & Spencer, 2014). In addition to cortisol stimulating appetite, the levels of **ghrelin**, an appetite-stimulating hormone found in the stomach, are also increased as a result of stress (Adams, Greenway, & Brantley, 2010; Bose, Olivan, & Laferre, 2009; Spencer & Tilbrook, 2011). Thus, there is a clear link between the stress response and eating behavior via the HPA axis.

As noted in the last chapter, cortisol levels vary throughout the day. As part of your wake/sleep cycle, circadian rhythm, cortisol usually peaks in the morning soon after waking up, begins its descent, and then starts to rise again a few hours before you awake (National Heart, Lung, and Blood Institute (NHLBI), 2017; National Sleep Foundation (NSF), 2017). During the acute stress response, cortisol becomes elevated and then, once the situation is resolved, gradually returns to pre-stress levels and its natural circadian rhythm.

The problem is that during chronic stress the cortisol levels stay elevated. For most people, it is not so much one ongoing stressor that is the problem as it is a series of intermittent stressors/daily hassles/perceived psychosocial threats that results in the continuing turning on and turning off of the stress response (Sapolsky, 1988). The stress response did not evolve to be yoyoed throughout the day. This continual activation and deactivation of the stress response compromises the normal functioning of the HPA axis, possibly interfering with the negative feedback of turning off the stress response (Adam & Epel, 2007; Bose, Olivan, & Laferre, 2009; Yau & Potenza, 2013). As a result of this yoyoing, cortisol does not have the opportunity to completely return to a pre-stress level and thus remains elevated.

When the normal variation in cortisol levels is compromised, as result of chronic stress, and remains elevated, this may result, as cortisol stimulates appetite, in chronic feeding behavior, cravings for calorie-dense food containing high sugar and fat content, and taking in more energy than is needed, resulting in it being stored as fat (Scott, Melhorn, & Sakai, 2012; Sominsky & Spencer, 2014). Research (Adam & Epel, 2007; HMS, 2012; Scott, Melhorn, & Sakai, 2012; Sominsky & Spencer, 2014; Spudich, 2007; Yau & Potenza, 2013) suggests that this craving for and eating of high-content sugar and fat food relieves the symptoms of chronic stress by linking into the reward center of the brain, hence, the notion of **comfort food** and/or **food being used to self-medicate**. Individuals who are emotionally distraught and in a negative state such as experiencing anger, depression, anxiety, and so on, all of which are directly linked to chronic stress, have a tendency to crave and eat food that is high in sugar and fat content as it reduces the chronic stress and hence the negative state (Yau & Potenza, 2013). This using of food, in a negative state, to self-medicate or comfort oneself is known as emotional eating (HMS, 2012; Yau & Potenza, 2013), once again demonstrating the clear link, via the HPA axis, between the stress response and eating behavior.

Individuals who chronically, consciously, and purposefully control or restrain what and how much they eat to maintain or lose weight, **restrained eating**, have a tendency to increase their eating behavior, especially for food with high sugar and fat content, when under stress (Yau & Potenza, 2013; Tahir, 2016). This may be due to a loss of control during stress (Tahir, 2016).

Given the evolutionary structuring of the stress response for our hunter-gatherer ancestors regarding the replacing of the energy that was actually physically utilized, running away to address and resolve an acute physical stressor or predator by increasing appetite after the situation has been resolved, a significant problem arises in the case of chronic stress. The daily yoyoing of the stress response relative to, essentially, perceived/imagined psychosocial threats, does not usually require physical energy–utilizing responses to address them. Nonetheless, remember our brain does not make a distinction between a real physical threat or a self-generated/imagined psychosocial threat; our appetite, for most of us, will be stimulated to replace physical energy that we did not actually utilize. In other words, an energy imbalance will occur as a result excess energy consumption and deficient energy expenditure. You gain weight!

NUTRITION, PHYSICAL ACTIVITY, SEDENTARY BEHAVIOR, SLEEP, CHRONIC STRESS, AND OBESITY

As already noted, inadequate nutrition chronically stresses your body and brain. In chapter 6, it was noted that inadequate daily physical exercise chronically stresses the body and brain and is linked to obesity. As also noted in chapter 6, even though you may meet your daily requirement for physical exercise, if you are essentially sedentary for the rest of the day, this behavior chronically stress the brain and the body and is linked to obesity. Chapter 7 indicated that inadequate, restful sleep chronically stresses the brain and the body and is linked to obesity. Research has indicated that inadequate restful sleep increases the levels of ghrelin, the hormone that stimulates appetite, while decreasing the levels of **leptin**, produced in fat cells, the hormone that reduces appetite (Harvard School of Public Health (HSPH), 2017a; Liu, Wheaton, Chapman, & Croft, 2013; Patel & Hu, 2008; Patel, Malhotra, White, Gottlieb, & Hu 2006; WebMD, 2013). This being the case, metabolism and the circadian rhythm are both compromised, leading to potential weight gain. It has also been suggested that inadequate restful sleep results in fatigue, which compromises the motivation to exercise, which in turn increases sedentary behavior, and that sedentary behavior is conducive to snacking, especially on calorie-dense foods containing sugar and fat, all of which results in potential weight gain (HSPH, 2017b; Patel & Hu, 2008; Patel et al., 2006).

The chronic stress that is caused by self-generated/imagined threat-based, problematic psychosocial thinking, beliefs, judgments, and the framing of the situation negatively compromises eating behavior, physical activity, and sleep. For example, excessive eating to self-medicate because of worrying (stress) about an imagined perception that your boss dislikes you leads to excessive weight gain, which leads to inadequate restful sleep, which in turn causes a lack of energy such that the individual does not engage in exercise and in fact becomes quite sedentary, resulting in additional weight gain, all of which become additional sources of chronic stress. This entire process compromises one's overall cognitive processing, perceiving, and mood. Thus, there is this integrated, interdependent, vicious reciprocal, cycle/circle of chronic stress that significantly compromises overall physical and psychological health and well-being.

> **No exercise, sedentary** behavior, inadequate restful sleep, poor nutrition, dehydration, and self-generated/imagined threat-based, problematic, psychosocial thinking = vicious circle/cycle of chronic stress

This being the case, it is imperative when addressing chronic stress and the various physical and psychological problems associated with it you not only manage self-generated/imagined threat-based, problematic psychosocial thinking, beliefs, judgments, and the framing of the situation, you also need to integrate and address issues of exercise, sedentary behavior, sleep, and nutrition. You need to recognize and address, holistically, the integrated, interdependent, reciprocal, vicious cycle/circle of chronic stress.

MINDFULNESS AND EATING

In order to address and eliminate *dukkha* or what this text translates as chronic stress, Buddha advocated the practice of **mindfulness** in all aspects of life, including eating. In the case of eating, you would simply be in the present, aware of and fully engaged in all aspects of the process of eating without making any judgments or being distracted by anything outside of the process of eating. All of your senses, including your mind, are fully engaged in the present, in the process of eating such as chewing, tasting, smelling, visually observing, and listening. Your fast-paced life is slowed down through the process of mindfulness as you eat in a more deliberate, attentive, and focused manner. You simply eat. Nothing else!

No cell-phones, e-mails, tablets, computers, TV, mind wandering, eating while working, and so on. No distractions. You are simply eating.

This being the case, there is no threat-based psychosocial thinking occurring and thus no continual/yoyoing activation of the stress response. As this behavior is continually practiced and reinforced on a daily basis, it will literally begin wiring in your brain, via neuroplasticity, and eventually result in a functional, positive, stress-free eating behavior that is readily assessible and conducive to your overall physical and psychological health and well-being.

Research by Robinson and colleagues (2013) suggests that distractions during eating increases the amount of food you initially ingest, at say breakfast, and increases the amount you take in even more so at later meals and that being attentive while eating may result in eating less during meals, which, in turn, may be beneficial for maintaining and/or losing weight.

Research (Daubenmier et al., 2011; HMS, 2011; Khan & Zadeh, 2014; Kristeller & Wolever, 2011) has noted that applying mindfulness while eating may not only be beneficial for weight loss and maintaining a desired weight, but also for digestion, food choices, eating disorders, chronic stress, and psychological health. O'Reilly, Cook, Spruijt-Metz, and Black (2014) found that the practice of mindfulness was beneficial for addressing obesity and food behavior patterns.

> **Buddha, speaking to** Jivaka/Qi Po, said, "I say there are three circumstances in which you can eat meat. If it is not seen (kanjian 看見), heard (tingwen 聽聞) or suspected (yilu 疑慮) [that it was specifically killed for a monk]. Qi Po, I say that in these three circumstances meat can be eaten by a monk" (Translated by Robert Santee. Chinese text can be found at http://agama.buddhason.org/MN/MN055.htm).

BUDDHISM, DAOISM, CONFUCIANISM, AND EATING BEHAVIOR

This section will look at how Buddhism, Daoism, and Confucianism address eating behavior in the context of managing chronic stress. The practices of mindfulness, moderation, and structured eating are offered as practices to consider incorporating for healthy, stress-free eating.

Buddhism

For Buddha, in order to eliminate *dukkha* or chronic stress and all that is entailed with it across all aspects of life, the practice of mindfulness (*sati, nian*念) needs to be applied to everything at all times. As noted in chapters 3 and 4, mindfulness is a nonjudgmental awareness of all aspects of the here and now. It is to experience/be aware of whatever you are engaged in without being controlled by insatiable desires, greed, feelings/emotions, passions, beliefs, thoughts, and judgments

> **When you eat,** practice mindfulness.

There are no exceptions! In *The Dwellings of Mindfulness Sutra* (*Satipatthanasutta*) of the *Majjhima Nikaya* or *Middle Length Sayings*, Buddha's explanation is quite clear regarding the practice of mindfulness, in which he also specifies its application to eating and drinking.

> Monks! For all to become clear and pure, in order to overcome worry and grieving, in order to eliminate bitterness, anxiety, and depression, in order to achieve the path of attainment, in order to experience the release of nirvana, there is this one way: the four dwellings of mindfulness (*si nian zhu* 四念住). What are these four? Here! Monks, nonjudgmentally observing the body as the body, enthusiastically, truly aware with mindfulness (*nian*念), being able to tame and regulate the greed, insatiable desires, anxiety, and depression of the world ... nonjudgmentally observing sensations as sensations ... nonjudgmentally observing feelings/emotions as feelings/emotions ... and nonjudgmentally observing mental objects as mental objects. (Santee, 2007, p. 103, 106; Agama, 2019).
>
> Monks, again! Perhaps a monk is walking; knowing this he says, "I am walking." Perhaps he is standing; knowing this he says, "I am standing." Perhaps he is sitting; knowing this he says, "I am sitting." Perhaps he is lying down; knowing this he says, "I am lying down." Whatever aspect of the body is indicated, he knows it is such. In this way, he follows along nonjudgmentally observing the body ... without dependency or attachments. This, monks, is nonjudgmentally observing the body as the body. Monks, again! A monk is going off, returning, truly aware, nonjudgmentally observing the front and the back, truly aware, desiring to bend or stretch, truly aware, desiring to hold his top coat, robe, or alms bowl, he is truly aware. Eating, drinking, chewing, tasting, he is truly aware. At the time of defecating or urinating, he is truly aware. (Santee, 2007, 108)

In the teachings of the Tang dynasty (618–907), Chan Buddhist Master Hui Hai's (8th century CE), analysis regarding sleep and eating are discussed in the last chapter and are clearly consistent with Buddha's focus as he essentially is saying that people interfere with themselves and go mind wandering regarding their concerns instead of just eating. In other words, they are not practicing mindfulness while they eat. This being the case, they are fragmented and thus chronically stressed. In the *Records of Various Question Based Dialogues* (*zhu fang menren shen wen yulu* 諸方門人參問語錄) of Hui Hai there is a question-based dialogue between a *Vinaya* master, an individual concerned with/controlled by abstract, absolute rules, regulations, ceremonies, and rituals, and Master Hui Hai.

> On one occasion, a Master/Teacher of *Vinaya* asked Master Hui Hai (慧海), "Does your cultivating the Dao require effort and hard work?" Master Hui Hai said, "It requires effort and hard work." The *Vinaya* Master said, "What do you do?" Hui Hai said, "When hunger comes, I eat. When tiredness comes, I sleep." The *Vinaya* Master said," Everybody behaves in that manner. Are they not acting the same as you?" Master Hui Hai said, "They are not the same." The *Vinaya* Master said, "How are they are not the same?" Master Hui Hai said, "When they eat, they are not willing to just eat. There are a hundred concerns that they feel they must ponder. When they go to sleep, they are not willing to simply go to sleep. There are a thousand apprehensions they feel they must evaluate. Thus, they are not the same." The *Vinaya* Master said no more. (C Beta, n.d.a.)

The teachings of the Tang dynasty Chan Buddhist Master Huang Bo (黃檗), who lived during the 9th century CE, make a distinction between those who eat mindfully, wise eating, and those who do not, discriminatory eating. Those who eat mindfully eat when they are hungry, do not interfere with themselves, are not greedy, and know when to stop eating. They are not chronically stressed when eating. On the other hand, those who are controlled by their emotions and passions when they eat, discriminatory eating, are fragmented, greedy and do not know when enough food is enough food. They simply do not know when to stop. They are chronically stressed while eating. In the *Essential Method of the Transmission of the Mind* (*chuan xin fa yao* 傳心法要) of Huang Bo it states,

> There is discriminatory eating and wise eating. When your body, of the four elements, is disturbed because of hunger pains, and you then eat without being greedy, this is called wise eating. If you give free rein to your emotions and passions regarding what your taste desires, this gives rise to fragmentation. If you only seek that which is tasty and do not know when to stop eating, this is called discriminatory eating. (C Beta, n.d.b.)

The teachings of the Tang dynasty Chan Buddhist Master Linji (臨濟), who lived during the 9th century CE and was a disciple of Huang Bo, are quite consistent with the teachings of Buddha, Hui Hai, and Huang Bo regarding eliminating chronic stress by not interfering with yourself as you engage all aspects of world around you. Keep it simple. Stay in the present. Practice mindfulness. Know when enough is enough. Know when to stop. Do not get entangled in the activities of the world. In *The Recorded Sayings of Linji* (*Linjilu* 臨濟錄), these practices are clearly expressed and, as Hui Hai noted, when you are hungry, eat.

> Linji (臨濟) instructing all present said, "Followers of the Way (Dao 道), the Buddha's method (dharma, fa 法) does not engage in irrelevant activities. Just act in an ordinary manner and do not get entangled in the activities of the world (*wushi* 無事). Defecate, urinate, put on your clothes, eat your food, and if you are tired lay down. The foolish will laugh at me while the wise will understand." (C Beta, n.d.c.)
>
> Linji said, "There is no better method (*dharma, fa* 去) than stopping and not getting entangled in the activities of the world (*wushi* 無事). When you become hungry, eat. When you become tired, go to sleep. The fools will laugh at me, while the wise will understand." (C Beta, n.d.d.)

The teachings of Buddha, Hui Hai, Huang Bo, and Linji all recognize the importance of a natural, holistic, integrated, mindfulness-based approach to the removal of what we refer to as chronic stress. If we interfere with our self while eating we end up stressing the **When you eat,** just eat! natural processes associated with simply eating. This, in turn, negatively impacts all other areas of our lives, which, in turn, negatively impacts our eating behavior, and on goes another vicious cycle of chronic stress.

Daoism

Although tradition traces the roots of Daoism back to the *Daodejing*, research has suggested that there are earlier texts such as the *Neiye* (內業) or *Engaging the Interior*, compiled mid-late 4th century BCE, which appears to serve as source material for aspects of the *Daodejing* and the *Zhuangzi*, and for Daojiao sects or what is known as later or religious Daoism (Kirkland, 2004; Roth, 1999). The *Neiye* is embedded in the late 4th century BCE compilation the *Guanzi* (管子), a repository of writings of many different schools, which received its apparent final arrangement in the late 1st century BCE by Liu Xiang (劉向) a court librarian (Kirkland, 2004; Roth, 1999; Theobald, 2010).

The *Neiye* is a text that provides guidelines for mind/body self-cultivation where physical and psychological health and well-being must be established as part of or be a prerequisite for a holistic and integrated approach to engaging life and spiritual awareness. It describes causes, **When you eat** and drink, such as an agitated mind, desires, and not eating correctly, and practice moderation.

symptoms, such as improper breathing, misaligned body, anger, anxiety, depression, worry, and obsession, of chronic stress, which is linked to problematic health and well-being. It in turn offers solutions for addressing these causes and symptoms and thus eliminating chronic stress and establishing overall physical and psychological health and well-being. In the case of eating behavior, it notes that the key to eating, and essentially all of life, is moderation.

> The Dao of natural eating: If you eat too much, the body will be harmed and stressed. If you eat too little your bones will weaken and your blood flow will be compromised. To be between these two extremes, is called achieving harmony. (Sangle, 2007)

> If hunger or fullness is excessive, then create a strategy to address it. If full, it is urgent that you begin moving. If hungry don't waste time thinking about it. When old, forget about worrying. If full and you don't begin to move with any sense of urgency, then your vital energy or qi (氣) will be obstructed in your four limbs. If you are hungry and you waste time thinking about it, then when you do eat, you will gorge yourself. When you are old and you don't forget about worrying, then you will quickly drain yourself. (Sangle, 2007)

The *Records of Nourishing Your Nature and Extending your Life* (*Yangxing Yanming Lu* 養性延命録) is a collection of selections on the art and various practices of nourishing life for overall health, well-being, and longevity that appears to have been constructed during the late Tang dynasty (618–907) as its authorship is unclear (Santee & Zhang, 2015). The connection between illness and death with what you eat and drink is clearly established in this text. As has been indicated earlier in this chapter, improper eating and drinking chronically stresses your body and leads to multiple physical and psychological illnesses, diseases, and problems. Thus, for all intents and purposes, the *Yangxing Yanming Lu* is a holistic, integrative guide to addressing, healing, and preventing chronic stress, with its goal being achieving optimal physical and psychological health and well-being. Fundamental to its perspective is practicing moderation across all aspects of life. It notes,

> The hundred illnesses and unnatural death, much of it is caused by food and drink. The health problems caused by food and drink far exceeds those caused by sights and sounds. Sights and sounds may be given up for years, but food and drink cannot be given up for even a day. (Chinese Text Project (CTP), n.d.)

Thus, the basic guidelines when eating and drinking are practice moderation and, as noted in chapter 4 regarding the *zhenren* or authentic person, don't relish, be controlled by, or overwhelmed by your desires and senses when you eat and drink. In addition, Daoism has a long history of what to eat and drink relative to the occasion, weather, location, and season of the year, and is guided by yin and yang, simplicity, and quality of food (Kohn, 2010; Saso, 1994). As with all aspects of life for Daoists, physical and psychological illnesses and diseases are due to a disharmony of the flow of *qi*. Aside from the primordial vital energy or *yuan qi* (元氣), which you are born with, breathing, eating, and drinking are the sources of replenishing the *qi*, which you lose throughout your daily activities. In addition to appropriate eating and drinking, in order to enhance the flow of unobstructed *qi* throughout your body and achieve optimal physical health and well-being and be free from chronic stress, you need, guided by moderation, regular and consistent exercise, *qi* circulation practices such as *qigong and taijiquan*, adequate restful sleep, meditation, and positive reciprocal interaction with others.

Confucianism

In Chapter 10 of the *Analects* of Confucius (*Lunyu*), his approach to eating and drinking is described. His approach is very structured and very controlled without a hint of chronic stress. His guidelines include quality of the food, safety, preparation, decorum, moderation, and when eating, his focus was on just eating. No mind wandering by engaging in discussions. He was fully engaged with just eating!

> Confucius did not satiate himself on fine rice. He did not satiate himself on exquisite meat. He did not eat sour rice, spoiled fish, or decayed meat. If the color was bad, he did not eat it. If the smell was bad, he did not eat it. If it was cooked improperly, he did not eat it. If it was not seasonal, he did not eat it. If it was not cut correctly, he did not eat it. If the proper sauce was not present, he did not eat it. Even if there was a lot of meat, he did not eat more than his rice. Only wine was without a specific restriction, but he did not drink to confusion. Although the ginger was not removed from the meal, he did not eat excessively … . When he ate, he did not engage in discussion. When he went to bed, he did not talk. (Chinese Classic, n.d.)

When you eat and drink, practice moderation and just eat and drink.

PRACTICAL APPLICATION

Baduanjin: Regulating Spleen and Stomach with Single-Arm Raise (*tiáolǐ píwèi xū dān jǔ* 調理脾胃須單舉)

Breathe naturally. Begin by standing with your feet parallel, pointing forward, and touching. The weight is evenly distributed on both feet. Your feet are flat and there is no leaning or rolling of them to the sides, forward or backward. Bend your knees slightly. Your arms hang naturally on your sides with your palms facing your thighs. Relax. Your eyes look straight forward. To align your body, gently push both feet down and gently push your head up. Imagine you are a puppet being suspended by a string, centered on the top of your head, from above. Your shoulders will naturally sink. Your spine will align. Your jaw is parallel to the ground, and your tongue gently touches the roof of your mouth behind your upper teeth.

Let your arms arc slightly forward staying thigh-width apart until your hands, palms facing each other, are about 3 or so inches below your hips. Slowly bring your fingertips toward each other until they are an inch or so apart. Your palms face up and toward each other. Visualize you are holding a large beach ball with your hands, arms, and lower abdomen/pelvic area gently holding it in place. This is the **transition position** between repetitions of this posture.

From the **transition position**, inhale as you slowly pull up both hands, palms up, along the centerline of your body. When your palms reach the height of your solar plexus/lower chest slowly rotate both palms inward toward your chest and then keep rotating until both palms face downward. Begin to slowly exhale as you slowly start pushing the left palm downward while at the same continuing to rotate your right palm outward so the back of the right hand faces your chest. Pushing your right hand upward, continue to rotate your right hand inward so your right palm begins to face up. With both hands moving together and pushing in opposite directions, begin straightening your legs, but don't lock your knees, while extending your arms upward and downward until your right hand is above the center of your head with the back of your right hand facing toward the top of your head. At the same time, your left hand with the palm facing down comes to rest on the left side of your body, about hip height, with your fingers facing forward. Visualize your left palm pushing down on a table while your right palm is pushing on the ceiling. You should feel a stretch across your shoulders, arms, and back.

From this extended position, inhale slowly as you rotate your right hand outward and downward, palm now facing down, while beginning to lower your right hand down your centerline. At the same time rotate your left hand inward until your palm faces up while moving it toward the centerline of your body, at the same height, and then begin to raise your left hand up. As both hands move toward the solar plexus/lower chest begin to bend your knees. When both hands pass by each other at the solar plexus/lower chest level begin to exhale, rotating your left hand outward and upward, continuing to push your left palm upward. At the same time continue to push your right palm down. As you once again are pushing upward and downward, straighten out your legs. Upon completion, your left palm is facing up with the back of your hand over the center of your head while your right hand with the palm facing down comes to rest on the right side of your body, about hip height, with your fingers facing forward. Visualize your left palm pushing on the ceiling while your right palm is pushing on a table. **From this position repeat the process seven more times.** At the end of the eighth repetition, begin inhaling and circle your left arm, the left hand above your head, outward, downward and inward while rotating your right hand inward and return to the **transition position.** Exhale. Take a few more complete breaths and let your arms return to your sides. Walk away.

As with the previous postures what did you notice going on internally (**interoception**)? What did you notice while your arms and legs moved through space (**proprioception**)? Given this is the third posture, how did each of these postures affect your body and mind? Is your mind empty and clear?

Benefits

According to Chinese qigong tradition, the posture regulating spleen and stomach with single-arm raise stretches the muscles and tendons in your arms, chest shoulders, and back, loosens your joints, massages your spleen and stomach, stimulates the spleen and stomach meridians, and stimulates your spine.

KEY TERMS

eating for energy	anorexia nervosa	ghrelin
eating for pleasure and feeling good	bulimia nervosa	leptin
obesity	binge-eating disorder	restrained eating
water	hypothalamus, pituitary, adrenal axis (HPA)	comfort food
glycemic Index	corticotropin-releasing factor (CRF)	food being used to self-medicate
glycemic Load	hypothalamus	emotional eating
2015–2020 dietary guidelines for Americans	cortisol	mindfulness
	adrenal cortex	

EXERCISES

1. Why are being overweight and obesity problems? Why are they linked to chronic stress?

2. In a notebook or on your computer or cell phone, record and analyze your eating behavior, what, how much, where, when, and why you eat and drink for the next 3 days. Don't modify your eating patterns, just observe. Is it consistent with the healthy eating patterns presented in the 2015–2020 guidelines? What patterns do you notice in your eating behavior?

3. Why is an understanding of the glycemic index and glycemic load important when addressing the problem of obesity and its relationship to chronic stress? Diabetes?

4. Explain how lack of exercise, sedentary behavior, inadequate restful sleep, problematic eating behaviors/choices, and inappropriate, threat-based

psychosocial thinking are linked together in a vicious cycle/circle of chronic stress that significantly compromises one's overall physical health and well-being. How can this vicious cycle/circle of chronic stress be addressed?

5. List three ways in which the practice of mindfulness may be beneficial for addressing problematic eating behaviors and the chronic stress associated with them.

6. Describe the Buddhist, Daoist, and Confucian approaches to eating, indicating how they are linked together and how they address chronic stress.

REFERENCES

Adam, T. C., & Epel, E. S. (2007). Stress, eating and the reward system. *Physiology and Behavior, 91*(4), 449–458.

Adams, C. E., Greenway, F. L. & Brantley, P. J. (2011). Lifestyle factors and ghrelin: Critical review and implications for weight loss maintenance. *Obesity Reviews, 12*(5), e211–e218.

Adeniyi, P.O. (2015). Stress, a major determinant of nutritional and health status. *American Journal of Public Health Research, 3*(1), 15–20.

Agama. (2019). *Middle length sayings.* Translated from http://agama.buddhason.org/MN/MN010.htm

American College of Emergency Physicians (ACEP) (2017). Dehydration comes on fast and can be fatal. Retrieved September 11, 2017 from http://www.emergencycareforyou.org/Health-Tips/Dehydration-comes-on-fast-and-can-be-fatal/

American Diabetes Association (ADA). (2014). *Glycemic index and diabetes.* Retrieved from http://www.diabetes.org/food-and-fitness/food/what-can-i-eat/understanding-carbohydrates/glycemic-index-and-diabetes.html

American Psychiatric Association (APA). (2016). *Orthorexia: Can healthy eating become unhealthy?* Retrieved from https://www.psychiatry.org/news-room/apa-blogs/apa-blog/2016/06/orthorexia-can-healthy-eating-become-unhealthy

Benelam, B., & Wyness, L. (2010). Hydration and health: A review. *Nutrition Bulletin, 35*(1), 3–25.

Bose, M., Olivan, B., & Laferrere, B. (2009). Stress and obesity: The role of the hypothalamic–pituitary–adrenal axis in metabolic disease. *Current Opinion in Endocrinology, Diabetes, and Obesity, 16*(5), 340– 346.

Block, J. P., He, Y., Zaslavsky, A. M., Ding, L., & Ayanian, J. Z. (2009). Psychosocial stress and change in weight among US adults. *American Journal of Epidemiology, 170*(2), 181–192.

Bushman, B. (Ed.) (2017). *American college of sports medicine complete guide to fitness & health.* Champaign, IL: Human Kinetics.

C Beta. (n.d.a.). *Records of various question-based dialogues.* Retrieved from http://tripitaka.cbeta.org/X63n1224_001

C Beta. (n.d.b.). *Essential method of the transmission of the mind.* Retrieved from http://tripitaka.cbeta.org/T48n2012A_001

C Beta. (n.d.c.). *The recorded sayings of Linji.* Retrieved from http://tripitaka.cbeta.org/T47n1985_001

C Beta. (n.d.d.). Section 0502c10. *The recorded sayings of Linji.* Retrieved from http://tripitaka.cbeta.org/T47n1985_001

Chinese Text Project (CTP). (n.d.). *Yangxing Yanming Lu.* Translated from http://ctext.org/wiki.pl?if=gb&chapter=87845&remap=gb#

Carrera-Bastos, P., Fontes-Villaba, M., O'Keefe, J. H., Lindeberg, S., & Cordain, L. (2011). The western diet and lifestyle and diseases of civilization. *Research Reports in Clinical Cardiology, 2,* 15–35.

Centers for Disease Control and Prevention (CDC). (2015). *The health effects of overweight and obesity.* Retrieved from https://www.cdc.gov/healthyweight/effects/index.html

Centers for Disease Control and Prevention (CDC). (2016). *Obesity and overweight.* Retrieved from https://www.cdc.gov/nchs/fastats/obesity-overweight.htm

Centers for Disease Control and Prevention (CDC). (2017a). *Adult obesity causes & consequences.* Retrieved from https://www.cdc.gov/obesity/adult/causes.html

Centers for Disease Control and Prevention (CDC). (2017b). *Adult obesity facts.* Retrieved from https://www.cdc.gov/obesity/data/adult.html

Chinese Classic. (n.d.). *Analects.* Retrieved from http://www.chineseclassic.com/13jing/LeungYu/LeungYu01.htm

Cleveland Clinic. (2013). The color of pee. Retrieved from https://2rdnmg1qbg403gumla1v9i2h-wpengine.netdna-ssl.com/wp-content/uploads/sites/3/2013/10/13-HHB-1407-The-Color-of-Pee-Infographic_FNL-finalnm.pdf

Cordain, L., Eaton, S. B., Sebastian, A., Mann, N., Lindeberg, S., Watkins, B. A., O'Keefe, J. H., & Brand-Miller, J. (2005). Origins and evolution of the Western diet: Health implications for the 21st century. *American Journal of Clinical Nutrition, 81*(2), 341–354.

Craig, J. (2012). *Carbohydrate counting, glycemic index, glycemic load: Putting them all together.* Retrieved from https://www.diabetesselfmanagement.com/nutrition-exercise/meal-planning/carbohydrate-counting-glycemic-index-and-glycemic-load-putting-them-all- together/

Daubenmier, J., Kristeller, J., Hecht, F. M., Maninger, N., Kuwata, M., Jhaveri, K., … & Epel, E (2011). Mindfulness intervention for stress eating to reduce cortisol and abdominal fat among overweight and obese women: an exploratory randomized controlled study. *Journal of Obesity*, 2011.

Eaton, S. B., Konner, M., & Shostak, M. (1988). Stone agers in the fast lane: Chronic degenerative diseases in evolutionary perspective. *American Journal of Medicine, 84*(4), 739–49.

Farrell, D. J., & Bower, L. (2003). Fatal water intoxication. *Journal of Clinical Pathology, 56*(10), 803–804.

Hardaway, J. A., Crowley, N. A., Bulik, C. M., & Kash, T. L. (2015). Integrated circuits and molecular components for stress and feeding: Implications for eating disorders. *Genes, Brain, and Behavior, 14*(1), 85–97.

Harvard Medical School (HMS). (2011, February). *Mindful eating.* Retrieved from https://www.health.harvard.edu/staying-healthy/mindful-eating

Harvard Medical School (HMS). (2012, February). *Why stress causes people to overeat.* Retrieved from https://www.health.harvard.edu/newsletter_article/why-stress-causes-people-to-overeat

Harvard Medical School (HMS). (2015). *Glycemic index and glycemic load for 100+ foods: Measuring carbohydrate effects can help glucose management.* Retrieved from https://www.health.harvard.edu/diseases-and-conditions/glycemic-index-and-glycemic-load-for-100-foods

Harvard Medical School (HMS). (2019). *The lowdown on glycemic index and glycemic load.* Retrieved from https://www.health.harvard.edu/diseases-and-conditions/the-lowdown-on-glycemic-index-and-glycemic-load

Harvard School of Public Health (HSPH). (2017a). *Obesity prevention source: Sleep.* Retrieved from https://www.hsph.harvard.edu/obesity-prevention-source/obesity-causes/sleep-and-obesity/

Harvard School of Public Health (HSPH). (2017b). *The nutrition source: Sleep deprivation and obesity.* Retrieved from https://www.hsph.harvard.edu/nutritionsource/sleep/

Health and Human Services & U.S. Department of Agriculture (HHS & USDA). (2015). *2015–2020 dietary guidelines for Americans.* Retrieved from http://health.gov/dietaryguidelines/2015/guidelines/

Ilaria, D., & Elena, G. (2016). Stress-related weight gain: Mechanisms involving feeding behavior, metabolism, gut microbiota and inflammation. *Journal of Nutrition & Food Sciences*, 6.

Jew, S., AbuMweis, S. S., & Jones, P. J. H. (2009). Evolution of the human diet: Linking our ancestral diet to modern functional foods as a means of chronic disease prevention. *Journal of Medicinal Food, 12*(5), 925–934.

Khan, Z., & Zadeh, Z. F. (2014). Mindful eating and its relationship with mental well-being. *Procedia—Social and Behavioral Sciences, 159*, 69–73.

Kavouras S. A., & Anastasiou, C. A. (2010). Water physiology: Essentiality, metabolism, and health implications. *Nutrition Today, 45*, S27–S32.

Kirkland, R. (2004). *Taoism: The enduring tradition*. New York, NY: Routledge.

Kratina, K. (2016). Orthoexia nervosa. *National Eating Disorders Association.* Retrieved from https://www.nationaleatingdisorders.org/orthorexia-nervosa

Kristeller, J. L. &Wolever, R. Q. (2011). Mindfulness-based eating awareness training for treating binge eating disorder: The conceptual foundation. *Eating Disorders, 19*(1), 49–61.

Liu, Y., Wheaton, A. G., Chapman, D. P., &Croft, J. B. (2013). Sleep duration and chronic diseases among US adults age 45 years and older: Evidence from the 2010 behavioral risk factor surveillance system. *Sleep, 36*(10), 1421–1427.

Malina, R. B., &Little L. B. (2008). Physical activity: The present in the context of the past. *American Journal of Human Biology, 20*(4), 373–391.

Mayo Clinic. (2016). *Stress management: Chronic stress puts your health at risk*. Retrieved from http://www.mayoclinic.org/healthy-lifestyle/stress-management/in-depth/stress/art-20046037

Mendosa, D. (2008). *Revised international table of glycemic index (GI) and Glycemic Load (GL) Values—2008.* Retrieved from http://www.mendosa.com/gilists.htm

National Alliance of Mental Illness (NAMI). (2017). Eating disorders. Retrieved from https://www.nami.org/Learn-More/Mental-Health-Conditions/Eating-Disorders/Overview

National Heart, Lung, and Blood Institute (NHLBI). (2017). What makes you sleep? Retrieved from https://www.nhlbi.nih.gov/health/health-topics/topics/sdd/whatmakes

National Institute of Mental Health (NIMH). (2016). *Eating disorders*. Retrieved from https://www.nimh.nih.gov/health/topics/eating-disorders/index.shtml

National Sleep Foundation (NSF). (2017). *What happens when you sleep?* Retrieved from https://sleepfoundation.org/how-sleep-works/what-happens-when-you-sleep

O'Keefe, J. H., Vogel, R., Lavie, C. J., &Cordain, L. (2010). Organic fitness: Physical activity consistent with our hunter-gatherer heritage. *The Physician and Sports Medicine, 38*(4), 11–18.

O'Reilly, G. A., Cook, L., Spruijt-Metz, D., &Black, D. S. (2014). Mindfulness-based interventions for obesity-related eating behaviors: A literature review. *Obesity Reviews: An Official Journal of the International Association for the Study of Obesity, 15*(6), 453–461.

Owen, N., Sparling, P. B., Healy, G. N., Dunstan, D. W., &Matthews, C. E. (2010). Sedentary behavior: Emerging evidence for a new health risk. *Mayo Clinic Proceedings, 85*(12), 1138–1141.

Patel, S. R., Malhotra, A., White, D. P., Gottlieb, D. J., &Hu, F. B. (2006). Association between reduced sleep and weight gain in women. *American Journal of Epidemiology, 164*(10), 947–954.

Patel, S. R., &Hu, F. B. (2008). Short sleep duration and weight gain: A systematic review. *Obesity* (Silver Spring, Md.), *16*(3), 643–653.

Popkin, B. M., D'Anci, K. E., &Rosenberg, I. H. (2010). Water, hydration, and health. *Nutrition Reviews, 68*(8), 439–458.

Ratey, J. J., &Hagerman, E. (2008). *Spark: The revolutionary new science of exercise and the brain*. New York, NY: Little, Brown and Company.

Ratey, J. J., &Manning, R. (2014). *Go Wild: Free your body and mind from the afflictions of civilization*. New York, NY: Little, Brown, and Company.

Riebel, S. K., &Davy, B. M. (2013). The hydration equation: Update on water balance and cognitive performance. *ACSM's Health & Fitness Journal, 17*(6), 21–28.

Robinson, E., Aveyard, P., Daley, A., Jolly, K., Lewis, A., Lycett, D., &Higgs, S. (2013). Eating attentively: A systematic review and meta-analysis of the effect of food intake memory and awareness on eating. *American Journal of Clinical Nutrition, 97*(4), 728–742.

Rojo, L., Conesa, L., Bermudez, O., &Livianos, L. (2006). Influence of stress in the onset of eating disorders: Data from a two-stage epidemiologic controlled study. *Psychosomatic Medicine, 68*(4), 628–635.

Roth, H.D. (1999). *Original Tao: Inward training (Nei Yeh)*. New York, NY: Columbia University Press.

Sangle. (2007). Guanzi Neiye chapter 49. Retrieved from http://sangle.web.wesleyan.edu/etext/pre-qin/neiye-corrected.html

Santee, R. (2007). *An Integrative Approach to Counseling: Bridging Chinese Thought, Evolutionary Theory, and Stress Management*. Copyright © 2007 by SAGE Publications. Reprinted with permission.

Santee, R., & Zhang, X. (2015). Yangsheng 養生 and the yin style baguazhang of Wang Fu and Wang Shangzhi. *The Empty Vessel: The Journal of Taoist Philosophy and Practice*, 24–30.

Sapolsky, R. M. (1998). *Why zebras don't get ulcers: An updated guide to stress, stress-related diseases, and coping.* New York, NY: W.H. Freeman and Company.

Scott, K. A., Melhorn, S. J., & Sakai, R. R. (2012). Effects of chronic social stress on obesity. *Current Obesity Reports, 1*(1), 16–25.

Sheard, N. F., Clark, N. G., Brand-Miller, J. C., Franz, M. J., Pi-Sunyer, X., Mayer-Davis, E., Kulkarni, K., & Geil, P. (2004). Dietary carbohydrate (amount and type) in the prevention and management of diabetes: A statement by the American diabetes association. *Diabetes Care, 27*(9), 2266–2271. Retrieved from http://care.diabetesjournals.org/content/27/9/2266

Singh, K. (2016). Nutrient and stress management. *Journal of Nutrition & Food Sciences, 6*. Retrieved from https://www.omicsonline.org/open-access/nutrient-and-stress-management-2155-9600-1000528.php?aid=76425

Sominsky, L., & Spencer, S. J (2014). Eating behavior and stress: A pathway to obesity. *Frontiers in Psychology, 5*, 434.

Spencer, S. J., & Tilbrook, A. (2011). The glucocorticoid contribution to obesity. *Stress, 14*(3), 233–246.

Spudich, T. (2007). *Cortisol and weight.* Retrieved from https://project-aware.org/Resource/articlearchives/cortisol_weight.shtml

Tahir, U. (2016) Stress and eating behaviour. *Advances in Obesity, Weight Management, & Control, 4*(4). Retrieved from http://medcraveonline.com/AOWMC/AOWMC-04-00095.pdf

Theobald, U. (2010). Chinese literature: Guanzi 管子 master guan. Retrieved from http://www.chinaknowledge.de/Literature/Diverse/guanzi.html

Torres, S. T., & Nowson, C. A. (2007). Relationship between stress, eating behavior and obesity. *Nutrition, 23*(11–12), 887–894.

WebMD. (2013). Sleep and weight gain: Will better sleep help you avoid extra pounds? Retrieved from http://www.webmd.com/sleep-disorders/features/lack-of-sleep-weight-gain#1

World Health Organization. (WHO) (2016). *Obesity and overweight.* Retrieved from http://www.who.int/mediacentre/factsheets/fs311/en/

Yau, Y. H. C., & Potenza, M. N. (2013). Stress and eating behaviors. *Minerva Endocrinologica, 38*(3), 255–267.

Zelman, K. M. (2008). 6 reasons to drink water. *WebMD.* Retrieved from http://www.webmd.com/diet/features/6-reasons-to-drink-water#1

Zucoloto, F. S. (2011). Evolution of the human feeding behavior. *Psychology & Neuroscience, 4*(1), 131–141.

CREDITS

CHAPTER 9

The Immune System

After finishing this chapter, you will be able to do the following:

- Indicate the two basic purposes of the immune system
- Compare the innate immune system with the adaptive/acquired immune system
- Compare the humoral and cellular arms of the adaptive/acquired immune system
- Explain the basic function of inflammation
- Describe the Ader and Cohen experiment, indicate how it is related to learning, and specify how it is related to psychoneuroimmunology
- Explain how chronic stress compromises the immune system and how the HPA axis and the SPA axis are involved in this process
- Describe chronic inflammation and its relationship to both physical and psychological diseases and disorders
- Indicate the relationship between chronic stress, immune system dysregulation, exercise, sedentary behavior, nutrition, sleep, and mind-body therapies/mind-body interventions

Organs of the Immune System

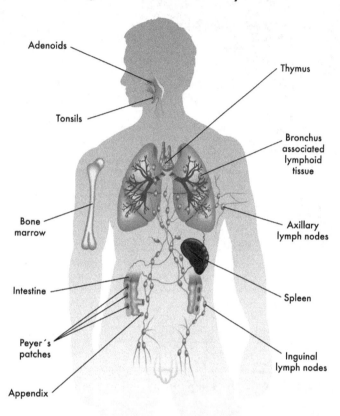

As part of our evolutionary toolkit, we have a healing system that protects us from infection by pathogens such as bacteria, viruses, parasites, and fungi (Nesse, & Williams, 1994; NIH, 2003; PubMed, 2016; Sapolsky, 2004). This system is known as the immune system. It consists of various immune cells, some of which circulate throughout the blood stream; some that reside in various tissues; and some that reside, waiting to be alerted and respond to an infection or invasion, in lymph nodes and lymph vessels and lymphatic components such as bone marrow, the tonsils, the spleen, the thymus, and the appendix (ACS, 2017; CDC, 2017; Delves, 2017a; Douketis, 2017, LLS, 2017). The basic purpose of the lymphatic system is to store and transport, via lymph fluid, various immune cells, drain fluid from tissues, and dispose of/filter out viruses, bacteria, cancer cells, and damaged cells (ACS, 2017; CDC, 2017; Delves, 2017a; Douketis, 2017; LLS, 2017; PubMed, 2017).

THE TWO BASIC PURPOSES OF THE IMMUNE SYSTEM

The two basic purposes/functions of the immune system are to (a) distinguish between what is our self and what is not our self and (b) eliminate/destroy what is not our self (Kiecolt-Glaser & Glaser, 1993; NIH, 2003; Sapolsky, 2004). The cells that are uniquely us have a distinct marker due to the **major histocompatibility complex (MHC)**, while foreign cells/invaders do not have this same marker (Chaplin, 2010; Gonzalez et al., 2011, NIH, 2003, 2014; Sapolsky, 2017).

Two Lines or Levels of Defense of the Immune System

The immune system has, essentially, two lines or levels of defense against invaders. The levels move from nonspecific/general to very specific/specialized. They are the evolutionary, older, innate/preexisting, quicker-responding, nonspecific immune system and the slower-responding, adaptive/acquired specific immune system (Chaplain 2010; Janeway, Travers, Walport, & Shlomchik, 2001; Mogensen, 2009; NIH, 2003; Sapolsky, 2004; PubMed, 2016). It is important to note that these two immune systems work together.

Innate Immune System

The innate immune system provides the initial and quickest response to invaders (Janeway, Travers, Walport, & Shlomchik, 2001; NIH, 2016; Mogensen, 2009). It consists of physical, mechanical, and chemical barriers and the general, nonspecific immune cell defense system against invading microbes/micro-organisms such as certain types bacteria and viruses. The physical/mechanical barriers include such areas as the skin and mucous membranes at body openings, which also line the respiratory tract, gastrointestinal tract, and the reproductive tract, the cilia or hair-like structures of the respiratory tract and lungs, which propel invaders stuck in mucous toward body openings, the hair in the nose, sneezing, urinating, peristalsis/defecating, vomiting, and coughing (Chaplain 2010; Janeway, Travers, Walport, & Shlomchik, 2001; MedlinePlus, 2016; Mogensen, 2009; NIH, 2003; 2016). Examples of chemical barriers are the enzyme lysozyme, which can be found in the tears and saliva, and the acidic digestive enzymes (Janeway, Travers, Walport, & Shlomchik, 2001; NIH, 2016; Perdue, & Humphrey, 2017).

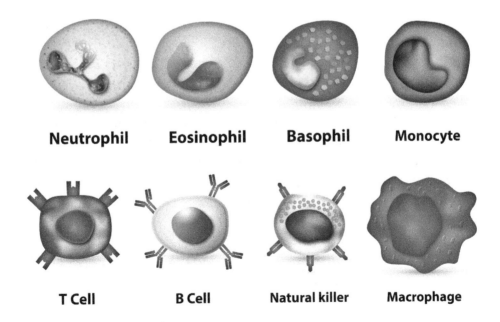

Neutrophil   **Eosinophil**   **Basophil**   **Monocyte**

T Cell   **B Cell**   **Natural killer**   **Macrophage**

If the invaders get past the physical, mechanical and chemical barriers, they then will be met by the following:

- The general, nonspecific immune cell defense system cells, which do not look for specific antigen markers
- White blood cells or **leukocytes** (white/clear blood cells), such as **monocytes,** which, once they leave the circulatory system and enter the tissue, become
  - **macrophages**, which consumes, **phagocytosis**, microbes and dead tissue;
  - **neutrophils,** usually the first to respond and also consume the microbes;
  - **basophils** which release histamines and address parasites; and
  - **eosinophils**, which not only can consume microbes and release toxic substances against microbes too large to consume, but also destroy parasites and natural killer cells, which look for and destroy cancer and virus-infected cells (Chaplin, 2010; Delves, 2017a, 2017b; Janeway, Travers, Walport, & Shlomchik, 2001; NIH, 2003, 2016; Perdue, & Humphrey, 2017; Segerstrom & Miller, 2004).

Inflammation

Inflammation is the innate/preexisting immune system's response to infection, cell death, and/or tissue damage, such as a twisted ankle or a splinter (Barton, 2008; MedlinePlus, 2016; Newton, & Dixit, 2012; PubMed, 2015; Rock & Kono, 2008). Its functions are (a) to protect the body by walling off/isolating the area of concern, (b) to eradicate the invader, (c) to remove any compromised tissue, and (d) to allow healing to take place (Anft, 2016; Janeway, Travers, Walport, & Shlomchik, 2001; Perdue & Humphrey, 2017). The inflammatory process, stimulated by the **sympathetic adrenal meduallary axis (SAM)** via epinephrine and norepinephrine (Barnes, Carson & Nair, 2015; Rontgen, Sablotzki, Simm, Silber, & Czeslick, 2004; Shields, Moons, & Slavich, 2017) results in immune cells such as macrophages releasing the messenger/cell signaler **proinflammatory cytokines,** which, in turn, begins the inflammatory process, resulting in the four basic signs/symptoms of inflammation: swelling, warmth/heat, redness, and pain (Janeway, Travers, Walport, & Shlomchik, 2001; PubMed, 2015; Segerstrom & Miller, 2004; Slavich & Irwin, 2014). All four symptoms/signs of inflammation are essentially the body's indication that there is a problem and that it is being addressed.

Basically, the inflammatory response increases circulation to the injured /infected site (redness and warmth/heat) and vessels dilate, allowing immune cells, nutrients, hormones, and fluid circulating in the blood to pass through the vessels to the injured/infected site (swelling and pain) and begin both the process of

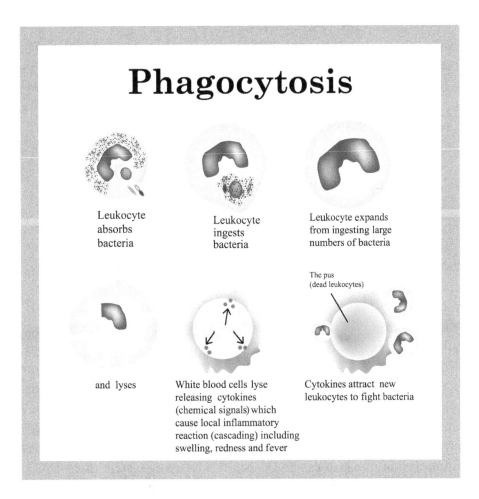

eliminating the invader and removing damaged/dead issue and of regeneration and healing (Janeway, Travers, Walport, & Shlomchik, 2001; Lawrence & Gilroy, 2007; Rock & Kono, 2008). The inflammatory process itself does some tissue damage and thus it is stopped, via anti-inflammatory mediators, as soon as the situation is under control (Lawrence & Gilroy, 2007; Rock & Kono, 2008; Urso, 2013).

Cortisol regulates, via the **hypothalamus-pituitary-adrenal cortex axis (HPA axis)**, the inflammatory process by suppressing it when it is determined that further inflammation is not necessary and to prevent any further tissue damage (Barrett, 2017; Coutinho & Chapman, 2011; Wolkow, Aisbett, Reynolds, Ferguson, & Main, 2015; Sapolsky, 2004; Shields, Moons, & Slavich, 2017).

Research has demonstrated that these proinflammatory cytokines also induce sickness behaviors via contact with the brain, such as disengagement/withdrawal from/loss of interest in physical and social contexts, sad mood, anhedonia, low motivation, muscle and joint pain, discomfort, uneasiness, feeling nauseous, feeling irritable, a general feeling of not being well, feeling cold, feeling feverish, sleepiness, tiredness, lack of energy, reduced/loss of appetite, anger, hostility, psychomotor retardation and cognitive impairments such as attention difficulties and self-regulation. While these behaviors and sensations are all adaptive, insofar as they conserve energy and generally force individuals to slow down and rest so they will heal, they are often experienced as unpleasant by the affected individual (Dantzer, 2009; Dantzer & Kelley, 2007; Glaser & Kiecolt-Glaser, 2005; Raison, Capuron, & Miller, 2005; Shields, Moons, & Slavich, 2017; Slavich & Irwin, 2014).

Adaptive/Acquired Immune System

If the innate immune system is unable to resolve the threat presented by the invaders, it alerts the **adaptive/acquired immune system** via messages from immune cells such as the macrophages (Janeway, Travers, Walport, & Shlomchik, 2001; Alberts et al., 2002; NIAID, 2014; Nauta, 2011). While the innate immune system responds quite quickly to an invader, the adaptive/acquired immune system response time is slower, taking a number of days (Chaplin, 2010; NIAID, 2014; NIH, 2016; Segerstrom & Miller, 2004). The adaptive/acquired immune system, unlike the innate immune system, develops and continues to develop specific immune cell responses to recognize and address the unique/specific markers of foreign invaders/**antigens** and retain information, **memory cells**, allowing for a quicker response if the same antigen invades again in the future (Chaplin, 2010; MedlinePlus, 2016; NIAID, 2014; NIH, 2003, 2016; Perdue & Humphrey, 2017). The adaptive/acquired immune system consists of two arms or branches: the **humoral immune system** and the **cellular immune system** (Kiecolt-Glaser & Glaser, 1993; NIH, 2016). It is important to note that the innate and the adaptive/acquired immune systems work together (Chaplin, 2010; PubMed, 2016).

PLASMA CELL

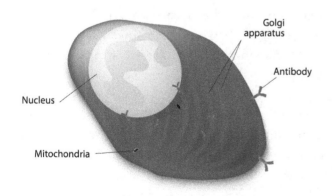

Golgi apparatus

Antibody

Nucleus

Mitochondria

Humoral Immune System

The humoral immune system addresses antigen-specific markers of invaders/microbes such as bacteria and viruses that are found in the body fluids (Kiecolt-Glaser & Glaser, 1993; NIH, 2003; Nauta, 2011; Perdue & Humphrey, 2017). The humoral immune system response relies on a type of white blood cell known as a **B lymphocyte/B cell,** which produces **antibodies** for each specific, unique antigen. Essentially, there is only one type of B cell for each unique antigen. When the B cell recognizes and links to the only specific antigen it can connect with, it is assisted by a **helper T cell**, which attaches to the B cell and releases the cytokines messenger **interleukins,** resulting in the B cell becoming a **plasma cell,** which generates identical antibodies that search for and eliminate the specific invading antigen, which in turn is then shut down by **suppressor T-cells** (Delves, 2017a; Kiecolt-Glaser & Glaser, 1993; Nauta, 2011; Perdue & Humphrey, 2017; Sapolsky, 2004; Segerstrom & Miller, 2004).

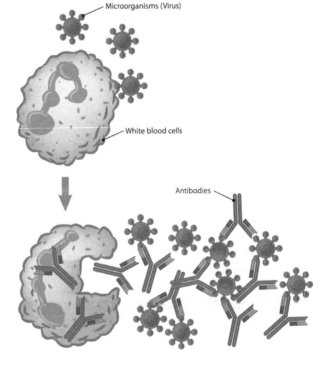

Cellular Immune System

The cellular immune system response relies on a type of white blood cell known as a **T lymphocyte/T cell** to directly eliminate (it does not create antibodies but instead replicates itself) the invader that has taken up residence in the cell itself (Chaplin, 2010; Kiecolt-Glaser & Glaser, 1993; Perdue & Humphrey, 2017; Segerstrom & Miller, 2004). Like the various types of B cells, which are each antigen specific and are thus only able to recognize and connect to one specific type of antigen, the various types of **T cells,** with assistance from helper T cells, also recognize only one specific type of antigen and address the cells infected by the specific virus or cancer by lysis or simply destroying the entire cell (Chaplin, 2010; Kiecolt-Glaser & Glaser, 1993; Nauta, 2011; Perdue & Humphrey, 2017; Sapolsky, 2004; Segerstrom & Miller, 2004).

WE CAN LEARN TO GET SICK

For quite some time it was believed that the immune system was, essentially, independent and functionally autonomous (Ader & Cohen, 1995; Dantzer & Kelley, 2007; Goleman & Gurin, 1993; Kiecolt-Glaser & Glaser, 1993; Sapolsky, 2004; Segerstrom, 2007; Segerstrom & Miller, 2004; Zachariae, 2009). Research published in the mid-1970s demonstrated that this was not the case (Ader & Cohen, 1975, 1995; Goleman & Gurin, 1993; Kiecolt-Glaser & Glaser, 1993). The researchers

T-cell activation

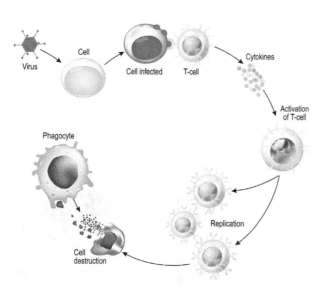

discovered that the immune system can learn via behavioral conditioning and proposed an evidence-based link between the immune system and behavioral conditioning (Ader & Cohen, 1975).

The Ader and Cohen Experiment and Psychoneuroimmunology (PNI)

Robert Ader and Nicholas Cohen devised an experiment to behaviorally condition rats to avoid saccharin-flavored water (Ader & Cohen, 1975; Goleman & Gurin, 1993; Kiecolt-Glaser & Glaser, 1993). As the rats liked to drink saccharin-flavored water or **neutral stimulus**, the researchers paired it, after drinking the saccharin-flavored water, with an injection of the drug cyclophosphamide or **unconditioned stimulus,** which gave the rats a stomach ache or an **unconditioned response**. When the injection was eliminated, the saccharin-flavored water/**conditioned stimulus** alone resulted in the rats getting a stomach ache or a **conditioned response** and thus they avoided drinking the saccharin-flavored water. In other words, the rats had become **classically/Pavlovian conditioned** and had learned the behavior of avoiding the saccharin-flavored water. Given this occurrence, can you think of any examples where humans can learn to become sick? If so, how would this occur in everyday life?

The problem with the study, which the researchers did not expect, was that some of the rats died. It turns out that the drug cyclophosphamide was an immunosuppressant. Thus, not only were the rats conditioned to avoid the saccharin-flavored water, but they were also conditioned to suppress their immune system (Ader & Cohen, 1975; Goleman & Gurin, 1993).

Subsequent research/evidence has established a clear, reciprocal relationship between the immune system, the central nervous system/brain and spinal cord, and the endocrine system, such that these three systems clearly communicate with each other (Ader & Cohen, 1995; Bovbjerg, Ader, & Cohen, 1982; Glaser & Kiecolt-Glaser, 2005; Goleman & Gurin, 1993; Kiecolt-Glaser & Glaser, 1993; Zachariae, 2009). Thus, when combined with the results from these later studies, the

Ader and Cohen study provided the foundation for a paradigm shift (the initial evidence that the immune system can learn) and for the creation of a new discipline known as **psychoneuroimmunology** or **PNI.**

Psychoneuroimmunology

Psychoneuroimmunology (the term was coined by Robert Ader (URMC, 2011) is the study of the reciprocal relationship between the nervous system, endocrine system, and the immune system in the context of stress, psychological factors, behavior, health, and disease (Ader & Cohen, 1995; Glaser & Kiecolt-Glaser, 2005; Kiecolt-Glaser, 2009; Kiecolt-Glaser & Glaser, 1993; Kiecolt-Glaser, McGuire, Robles, & Glaser, 2002; Nassau, Tien, & Fritz, 2008; Zachariae, 2009). Essentially, PNI is a holistic, integrative approach to health and well-being that is built in to the healthy human body.

STRESS AND THE IMMUNE SYSTEM

While a normal PNI response is ongoing, stress can change that response in important ways. The research is quite clear that acute stress enhances certain aspects of innate/natural immunity such as the following:

- The increasing of certain leukocyte activity/redistribution regarding potential injury and/or infection/invasion
- Maintaining the humoral component while suppressing the cellular component of the adaptive/specific immune system (Cohen, Janicki-Deverts, & Miller, 2007; Dhabhar, 2008; Dhabhar & McEwen, 1997; Glaser & Kiecolt-Glaser, 2005; Reiche, Nunes, & Morimoto, 2004; Segerstrom & Miller, 2004; Slavich & Irwin, 2014; Tian, Hou, Li, & Yuan, 2014).

On the other hand, *chronic* stress dysregulates/compromises various immune cells and the functioning of both the innate/natural immune system and the adaptive/specific immune system's humoral and cellular components and thus is detrimental to both physical and psychological health and well-being (Cohen, Janicki-Deverts, & Miller, 2007; Cohen et al., 2012; Dhabhar, 2008; Glaser

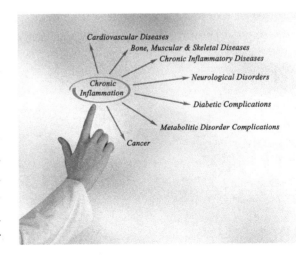

&Kiecolt-Glaser, 2005; Reiche, Nunes, &Morimoto, 2004; Segerstrom &Miller, 2004; Tian, Hou, Li, &Yuan, 2014).

Of concern regarding chronic stress, immune dysfunction/dysregulation, disease and health is chronic/systemic inflammation. Chronic/systemic inflammation occurs as part of the normal aging process as our immune system weakens (hence the importance on an integrated holistic stress-management program) and/or the ongoing presence of an infection, injury, or disease that chronically stresses the body (Franceschi &Campisi, 2014; Freund, Orjalo, Desprez, &Campisi, 2010; Irwin, &Olmstead, 2012; Reig-Ferrer et al., 2014). In addition, and of particular concern, is that research indicates that proinflammatory cytokines, hence inflammation, can be elicited by chronic psychosocial/psychological stress independent of any infection, tissue damage, or injury (Berk et al., 2013; Bierhaus et al., 2003; Glaser &Kiecolt-Glaser, 2005; Kiecolt-Glaser, Gouin, &Hantsoo, 2010; Kiecolt-Glaser, McGuire, Robles, &Glaser, 2002a, 2002b; Raison, Capuron, &Miller, 2005; Slavich &Irwin, 2014; Stellar et al., 2015). This is a major concern because **chronic/systemic inflammation** is linked to chronic tissue/cellular damage, damage to DNA, dysregulation of the SAM axis, the HPA axis, the immune system, impaired healing of wounds and infections, autoimmune diseases/disorders where the immune system attacks the host such as rheumatoid arthritis, Type 1 diabetes, asthma and allergies, cardiovascular disease, hypertension, stroke, obesity, upper-respiratory infections, arthritis, the common cold, asthma, herpes, Type 2 diabetes, osteoporosis, certain cancers, periodontal disease, psoriasis, depression, anxiety, and PTSD (Cohen, Janicki-Deverts, &Miller, 2007; Cohen et al., 2012; Franceschi &Campisi, 2014; Furtado &Katzman, 2015; Ioannidou, Goulielmaki, &Garinis, 2016; Kiecolt-Glaser, McGuire, Robles, &Glaser, 2002a; Kiecolt-Glaser et al., 1995; Kiecolt-Glaser et al., 2003; Morey, Boggero, Scott, &Segerstrom, 2015; NCI, 2015; Robles, Glaser, &Kiecolt-Glaser, 2005; Slavich, 2015; Slavich, &Irwin, 2014; Shields, Moons, &Slavich, 2017; Steptoe, Hamer, &Chida, 2007; Tedeschi &Asero, 2008; Tian, Hou, Li, &Yuan, 2014; Vogelzangs, Beekman, de Jonge, &Penninx, 2013; Vogelzangs, de Jonge, Smit, Bahn, &Penninx, 2016; Zotova, Chereshnev, &Gusev, 2016). Consider which of these disorders/diseases are most relevant to you. What can you do to address/prevent them?

As previously noted, the inflammatory process is initiated by various immune cells, such as the macrophages, which release proinflammatory cytokines, which in turn stimulate the inflammatory process.

However, when a person is under stress, the inflammatory process is shut down/ regulated by the release of cortisol via the HPA axis. This is all well and good in response to an acute situation. The problem arises in situations of chronic stress, especially chronic psychosocial/psychological stress, where cortisol is continually present. In these situations, the yoyoing of the stress response results in the cells becoming insensitive to cortisol's anti-inflammatory effect, which in turn keeps the proinflammatory cytokine levels elevated, resulting in a dysregulation of the immune system and ongoing inflammation, unnecessary tissue damage, the continual presence of various symptoms of sickness behavior, and eventually, if not successfully addressed, the diseases and disorders previously discussed (Cohen et al., 2012; Dantzer, 2009; Dantzer & Kelley, 2007; Dantzer et al., 2008; Glaser & Kiecolt-Glaser, 2005; Morey, Boggero, Scott, & Segerstrom, 2015; Raison, Capuron, & Miller, 2005). In other words, the HPA axis has been dysregulated and is unable perform its function of regulating proinflammatory cytokines, thus *creating*, rather than alleviating, disease.

Chronic Stress, the Immune System, Depression, and Anxiety

This chronic eliciting, SAM axis, of the inflammatory response by psychosocial/ psychological stress, the associated presence of sickness behaviors, many of which describe symptoms accompanying depression, the subsequent dysregulation of the HPA axis, and the resulting ongoing inflammation all suggest that depression may be best understood in the context of a dysregulation within the immune system (Anft, 2016; Dantzer, 2009; Dantzer et al., 2008; Raison, Capuron, & Miller, 2006; Robles, Glaser, & Kiecolt-Glaser, 2005; Shields, Moons, & Slavich, 2017; Slavich & Irwin, 2014). Of particular note is research indicates that anti-depressants decrease pro-inflammatory cytokines—usually present during a heighted immune or stress response—while anti-inflammatory medication not only reduces inflammation, but also relieves symptoms of depression (Slavich & Irwin, 2014).

Anxiety disorders are also being linked to chronic psychosocial/psychological stress, dysregulation of the HPA axis, inflammation, and dysregulation within the immune system (Furtado & Katzman, 2015; Vogelzangs, Beekman, de Jonge, & Penninx, 2013; Vogelzangs, de Jonge, Smit, Bahn, & Penninx, 2016). As with depression, research is suggesting that anxiety disorders may be best understood within the context of dysregulation within the immune system.

EXERCISE AND THE IMMUNE SYSTEM

As previously noted in chapter 6, exercise/physical activity is beneficial in reducing and preventing chronic stress and is quite important for overall physical and psychological health and well-being. Given the issues with physical and psychological disorders within the context of inflammation, moderate to vigorous, consistent, regular, and ongoing exercise/physical activity has been shown to reduce inflammation and disease rates while improving immunity (Berk et al., 2013; Gleeson et al., 2011; Kiecolt-Glaser, Gouin, & Hantsoo, 2010; Nieman, 2011; Ratey, 2008; Pruimboom, Raison, & Muskiet, 2015; Vella et al., 2017).

Sedentary behavior, on the other hand, has been linked to problematic levels of inflammation (Allison, Jensky, Marshall, Bertoni, & Cushman, 2012; Handschin & Spiegelman, 2008). This link may be a reason why, as indicated in chapter 6, sedentary behavior is associated with chronic stress and numerous physical and psychological disorders. The message is quite clear: Meeting our daily requirement of exercise and reducing sedentary behavior is necessary for the immune system to efficiently and effectively perform its job of protecting our physical and psychological health and well-being.

NUTRITION AND THE IMMUNE SYSTEM

For the immune system to function properly it needs adequate energy. Thus, diet is clearly linked to the proper functioning of the immune system as a diet that does not provide the appropriate nutrients, one that is excessive in caloric intake, or one that is deficient in caloric intake clearly compromises/stresses its ability to function properly (Karacabey & Ozdemir, 2012; Kiecolt-Glaser, 2010; Kiecolt-Glaser, Gouin, & Hantsoo, 2010; Kiecolt-Glaser et al., 2017; Ponton, Wilson, Cotter, Raubenheimer, & Simpson 2011; Vetvicka & Vetvickova, 2016). Foods that are continually consumed and that are high in saturated fats, trans-fats, and sugar, are highly processed and refined, and fast foods, basically the good old American diet, are all conducive to obesity and chronic inflammation, which clearly chronically stresses not only our immune system but our overall physical and psychological health and well-being (Kiecolt-Glaser, 2010; Kiecolt-Glaser, Gouin, & Hantsoo, 2010; Kiecolt-Glaser et al., 2017). In fact, obesity is viewed as a chronic inflammatory condition (Dandona, Aljada, & Bandyopadhyay, 2004; Fantuzzi, 2005; Kiecolt-Glaser, Gouin, & Hantsoo, 2010).

On the other hand, a diet that incorporates antioxidants, such as beans, fruits, nuts, vegetables, omega-3 fatty acids (such as certain seafood, spinach, broccoli, and walnuts) and foods fortified with it, monosaturated fats like olive oil, are anti-inflammatory in nature (Kiecolt-Glaser, 2010; Kiecolt-Glaser et al., 2017; WebMD, 2005, 2017). Of course, one needs to also reduce and/or eliminate foods that are inflammatory in nature. A diet that incorporates olive oil and is being promoted for being anti-inflammatory and beneficial for physical and psychological disorders such as cardiovascular disease and depression is the Mediterranean style diet (AHA, 2014; Kiecolt-Glaser, 2010; Kiecolt-Glaser et al., 2017; Mayo Clinic, 2017; Vetvicka & Vetvickova, 2016). Again, the message is quite clear: Appropriate nutrition is necessary for the immune system to efficiently and effectively perform its job of protecting our physical and psychological health and well-being. In other words, as our parents told us, we really should eat our fruits and vegetables!

SLEEP AND THE IMMUNE SYSTEM

As noted in chapter 7, chronic stress disrupts the quality, quantity, sequencing, and patterns of restful sleep, thus compromising its ability to perform its beneficial functions. This in turn creates additional stress as our body and mind, upon awakening, are hampered, tired and fatigued, as we attempt to navigate through our new day. This additional stress then affects our next night of sleep. This vicious circle is associated with a variety of physical and psychological disorders.

A number of these disorders, such as cardiovascular disease, Type 2 diabetes, obesity, and depression are also associated with chronic/systemic inflammation and thus a dysregulation of the immune system (Cohen et al., 2012; (Kiecolt-Glaser, Gouin, & Hantsoo, 2010; Kiecolt-Glaser, McGuire, Robles, & Glaser, 2002; Segerstrom, & Miller, 2004). Research has indicated that sleep loss, disruption, deprivation, and deficiency are directly linked to an increase in inflammatory markers such as proinflammatory cytokines (Interlukin-6/IL-6) and C-reactive protein (CRP), which is produced in the liver, thus associating inadequate restful sleep with immune dysregulation (Irwin, Olmstead, & Carroll, 2016; Irwin, Olmstead, Ganz, & Haque, 2013; Kiecolt-Glaser, Gouin, & Hantsoo, 2010; Kinnucan, Rubin, & Ali, 2013; Mullington, Simpson, Meier-Ewert, & Haack, 2010; Ranjbaran, Keefer, Stepanski, Farhadi, & Keshavarzian, 2007). The message is quite clear: Adequate restful sleep is necessary for the immune system to efficiently and effectively perform its job of protecting our physical and psychological health and well-being.

MIND-BODY THERAPIES/MIND-BODY INTERVENTIONS AND THE IMMUNE SYSTEM

Meta-analysis, systematic review, and descriptive review research suggests that both physical movement and primarily nonmovement mind-body therapies/mind-body interventions are beneficial in reducing chronic stress, reducing inflammation, and strengthening the immune system (Bower, & Irwin, 2016; Buric et al., 2017; Morgan, Irwin, Chung, & Wang, 2014). Yoga, taijiquan, and qigong are examples of movement-based mind-body therapies/mind-body interventions, while mindfulness and the technique called relaxation response, saying a word or short phrase when you exhale, are examples of, essentially, nonmovement-based mind-body therapies/mind-body interventions. All of these approaches share the commonality of a nonjudgmental awareness, being in and staying focused in the present moment—in other words not mind wandering, paying attention to deep, slow, refined breathing, and the necessity of commitment, effort, and continual and consistent practice. All of these approaches activate the physiologically innate response, which Herbert Benson called the **relaxation response**, and is the opposite of the stress response (AIS, 2012; Benson, 2001; Santee, 2007). Essentially, what is being engaged/elicited is the parasympathetic nervous system, which calms down the arousal of the sympathetic nervous system (AIS, 2012; Pelletier, 1993; Sapolsky, 2004).

Yoga and the Immune System

The Hindu-associated ancient practice of yoga, which was previously taught in this text, uses asanas or postures, breathing exercises, and/or meditation and is linked to reducing and preventing chronic stress and to enhancing positive physical and psychological health and well-being (Kiecolt-Glaser et al., 2010; Khalsa, & Elson; 2016; Khalsa, & Gould, 2012; Lim & Cheong, 2015; Ross, & Thomas, 2010; Twal, Wahlquist, & Balasubramanian, 2016; Wei, & Groves, 2017; Woodyard, 2011). Research has indicted that the practice of yoga is related to a decrease in inflammation and the strengthening of the immune system (Cahn, 2017; Khalsa & Elson; 2016; Kiecolt-Glaser, 2014; Lim & Cheong, 2015; Pullen et al., 2008; Ross & Thomas, 2010; Twal, Wahlquist, & Balasubramanian, 2016; Wei & Groves, 2017). As opposed to a strictly spiritual practice, many who practice yoga in the U.S. do so to attain these benefits.

Qigong, Taijiquan, and the Immune System

The Daoist/Taoist linked ancient practice known as daoyin (導引), or stretching the body and guiding/leading vital energy/breath (*qi*), minus its spiritual, religious, and cultural context, was essentially renamed during the late 1940s as qigong/chi kung (氣功), or working with/cultivating *qi*, and standardized to meet the needs of the Chinese government (Palmer, 2007). Practices such as *Zhan zhuang,* which was previously taught in this text, and *Baduanjin,* which is now being taught in this text, are examples of qigong. Taijiquan/Tai Chi Chuan is an ancient practice, attributed to Chen Wangting (circa 16th–17th century), which was created approximately 350 years ago as a martial art (Shahar, 2008). It was later modified during the 19th and 20th centuries (Wile, 1996) with a strong focus on moving meditation and physical and psychological health and well-being. It consists of slow motion, choreographed rhythmic patterns of stepping, kicking, blocking, striking, and, sometimes, jumping. The consistent and regular practice of it is associated with reducing and preventing chronic stress and enhancing positive physical and psychological health and well-being (Abbott & Lavretsky, 2013; Irwin et al., 2015; Jahnke, Larkey, Rogers, Etnier, & Lin, 2010; Liu, 2010; Oh et al., 2010; Wayne, & Fuerst, 2013). In addition, research has also demonstrated that these practices are linked to enhancing the immune system and reducing inflammation (Abbott & Lavretsky, 2013; Irwin et al., 2014; Jahnke et al., 2010; Lin et al., 2017; Oh et al., 2010; Wayne & Fuerst, 2013)

MINDFULNESS, THE RELAXATION RESPONSE, AND THE IMMUNE SYSTEM

The Buddhist practice of mindfulness and Benson's relaxation response technique, both of which were previously taught in this text, are linked to reducing and preventing chronic stress, enhancing the immune system, and reducing inflammation (Benson, 2001; Bhasin et al., 2013; Black & Slavich, 2016; Davidson et al., 2003; Dusek & Benson, 2009; Holzel, 2011; Kabat-Zinn, 2005; Santee, 2007; Witek-Janusek, 2008).

TAKE AWAY

Chronic threat-based psychosocial thinking, lack of exercise, sedentary behavior, poor nutrition, and inadequate restful sleep are all integrated, interdependent, and linked to chronic stress, chronic/systemic inflammation, immune system dysregulation, and a wide variety of physical and psychological disorders and illnesses. In order to address these issues and develop and maintain optimal physical and psychological health and well-being, it is necessary to create and implement a holistic, integrated stress-management program that is guided by moderation and incorporates appropriate cognitive restructuring/reframing, positive psychology, exercise, nutrition, sleep, and mind-body therapies/mind-body interventions.

PRACTICAL APPLICATION

Baduanjin: Prevent Illness and Emotional Stress by Looking Backward (*wǔláo qīshāng wǎng hòu qiáo* 五劳七伤往後瞧)

Upon finishing the previous posture, let your hands return to the transition posture. From this position, take a deep breath and slowly exhale as you gradually twist both hands, arcing outward, to the sides and to the rear, finishing behind your hips. Your palms are at a 45-degree angle. At the at same time and in tune with your breathing and movement, gently turn your head to the right and look over your right shoulder. Your shoulder blades will have come together in your back and your chest will have expanded. It is important that your breathing and movements are coordinated together. Pause for a moment and then begin to slowly inhale as you reverse the process, returning to the transition posture. Your head will now be facing forward, your chest will be contracted, and your shoulder blades will be expanded outward. Again, it is important that your breathing and all movements are coordinated together.

Repeat the same process on the left side. Slowly exhale as you gradually twist both hands, arcing outward, to the sides and to the rear, finishing behind your hips. Your palms are at a 45-degree angle. At the same time and in tune with your breathing and movement, gently turn you head to the left and look over your left shoulder. Your shoulder blades will have come together in your back and your chest will have expanded. Pause for a moment and then begin to slowly inhale as you reverse the process, returning to the transition posture. Again, it is important that your breathing and all movements are coordinated together. Repeat the sequence, right and left, seven more times. Upon finishing, let your arms slowly drop to your sides, gently exhale, and slowly walk away, letting your breathing return to normal. Remember, the fundamental component of qigong is the coordination of slow, gentle movement with your breathing while maintaining a nonjudgmental, focused awareness in the present.

What did you notice? How do you feel physically? Psychologically? What did you discover? What did you learn about the relationship between your breathing, movement, and awareness? Being aware of internally generated sensations is called **interoception**. Being aware of your body moving through space is **proprioception**. Given these two concepts, describe your experience interoceptively and proprioceptively.

Within the context of traditional Chinese medicine, *wulao* (五劳) literally means the five laboring/straining/stressing, which symbolically refers to overworking/stressing, hence illness/disorders of the heart (*xin* 心), liver (*gan* 肝), spleen (*pi* 脾), lungs (*fei* 肺), and kidneys (*shen* 肾) or the five yin organs (Kaptchuk, 1983; Huangdi Neijing, 2017; Shen-nong, 2006; SINA, 2017). *Qishang* (七傷) literally means seven ways of injuring/wounding, which symbolically refers to happiness (*xi* 喜), anger/hostility (*nu* 怒), anxiety/worry (*you* 憂), longing for/pining for (*si* 思), sadness, grieving, melancholy (*bei* 悲), fear (*kong* 恐), and surprise (*jing* 驚) or the seven emotions being excessive (Kaptchuk, 1983; Huangdi Neijing, 2017; Shen-nong, 2006; SINA, 2017).

Essentially, this specific posture appears to regulate the emotions and the physical body and, as a result, it is believed to benefit your internal organs and the muscles and tendons of your neck, back, shoulders, arms, and chest. What did you specifically notice about your body and mind when you completed the posture? The following translation/quote links emotions to illness and emphasizes the important of practicing regularly and consistently to not only treat but prevent a wide variety of diseases and illnesses. Essentially, this posture, like all of the eight postures of the *Baduanjin*, appears to be structured to treat and prevent what we today refer to as chronic stress, as the focus throughout is relaxing the entire body and calming the mind (CHQGA, 2007; CWS-CMA, 2017; Yang; 1997).

> To prevent the emotions from weakening the five organs, you must consistently and regularly practice and work hard to make your body firm and strong. Your body suffers because your emotions weaken your internal organs. Expand your chest, twist your neck, and look to the rear. Squeezing your waist and chest inwards, your body is aligned. This posture is especially beneficial for treating your internal disorders. (CWS-CMA, 2017; Yang, 1997)

KEY TERMS

two basic purposes/functions of the immune system

major histocompatibility complex (MHC)

innate immune system

leukocytes

monocytes

macrophages

neutrophils

basophils

eosinophils

phagocytosis

natural killer cells

inflammation

SAM axis

HPA axis

proinflammatory

cytokines

cortisol

adaptive/acquired immune system

antigens

lymphocytes

B-cells

antibodies

T-cells

cytotoxic T-Cells

helper T-cells

suppressor T-cells

memory cells

interleukins

plasma cell

neutral stimulus

unconditioned stimulus

unconditioned response

conditioned stimulus

conditioned response

classically/Pavlovian conditioned

psychoneuroimmunology chronic/systemic inflammation

relaxation response

introception

proprioception

1. Compare the innate immune system with the adaptive acquired immune system.

2. Why is the Ader and Cohen experiment so important within the context of psychoneuroimmunology?

3. Describe the relationship between these factors: chronic psychosocial stress, lack of exercise, sedentary behavior, poor nutrition, inadequate restful sleep, and immune system dysregulation.

4. Why is it so important to eliminate chronic/systemic inflammation?

5. Why is an understanding of/implementing of a stress-management program that incorporates mind-body therapies/interventions important for addressing chronic stress, chronic/systemic inflammation, and immune system dysregulation?

6. Why is an understanding of/implementing of a stress-management program that incorporates appropriate exercise, sedentary behavior, sleep, and nutrition important for addressing chronic stress, chronic/systemic inflammation, and immune system dysregulation?

7. Describe and indicate how you would implement a holistic, integrative stress-management program to address chronic stress, chronic/systemic inflammation, and immune system dysregulation.

REFERENCES

Abbott, R., & Lavretsky, H. (2013). Tai chi and qigong for the treatment and prevention of mental disorders. *Psychiatric Clinics of North America, 36*(1), 109–119.

Ader, R., & Cohen, N. (1975). Behaviorally conditioned immunosuppression. *Psychosomatic Medicine, 37*(4), 333–340.

Ader, R., & Cohen, N. (1995). Psychoneuroimmunology: Interaction between the nervous system and the immune system. *The Lancet, 345*(8942), 99–103.

Alberts, B., Johnson, A., Lewis, J., Raff, M., Roberts, K., & Walter, P. (2002). *Molecular biology of the cell* (4th ed.). New York, NY: Garland Science.

Allison, M. A., Jensky, N. E., Marshall, S. J., Bertoni, A. G., Cushman, M. (2012). Sedentary behavior and adiposity-associated inflammation: The multi-ethnic study of atherosclerosis. *American Journal of Preventive Medicine, 42*(1), 8–13.

American Cancer Society (ACS). (2018). Normal bone marrow, blood, and lymphoid tissue. Retrieved from https://www.cancer.org/cancer/chronic-lymphocytic-leukemia/about/normal-tissue.html

American Heart Association (AHA). (2014). Mediterranean-style diet details. Retrieved from http://www.heart.org/HEARTORG/Affiliate/Mediterranean-style-diet-details_UCM_461758_Article.jsp#.WfVVTLpFyUk

American Institute of Stress (AIS). (2012). Take a deep breath. Retrieved from https://www.stress.org/take-a-deep-breath/

Anft, M (2016). Understanding inflammation. Retrieved from https://www.johnshopkinshealthreview.com/issues/spring-summer-2016/articles/understanding-inflammation

Barnes, M. A., Carson, M. J. & Nair, M.G. (2015). Non-traditional cytokines: How catecholamines and adipokines influence macrophages in immunity, metabolism and the central nervous system. *Cytokine, 72*(2), 210–219.

Barrett, L. F. (2017). *How emotions are made: The secret life of the brain.* New York, NY: Houghton Mifflin Harcourt.

Barton, G. M. (2008). A calculated response: Control of inflammation by the innate immune system. *Journal of Clinical Investigation, 118*(2), 413–420.

Bennett, J. M., Fafundes, C. P., & Kiecolt-Glaser, J. K. (2013). The chronic stress of caregiving accelerates the natural aging of the immune system. In J. A. Bosch, A. C. Phillips, & J. M. Lord (Eds.), *Immunosenescence: Psychosocial and behavioral determinants* (pp. 35–46). New York, NY: Springer.

Benson, H., & Klipper, M. Z. (2001). *The relaxation response.* New York, NY: Harper.

Berk, M., Williams, L. J., Jacka, F. N., O'Neil, A., Pasco, J. A., Moylan, S., ... & Maes, M. (2013). So depression is an inflammatory disease, but where does the inflammation come from? *BioMed Central, 11.* Retrieved from https://www.ncbi.nlm.nih.gov/pmc/articles/PMC3846682/

Bhasin, M. K., Dusek, J. A., Chang, B. H., Joseph, M. G., Denninger, J. W., Fricchione, G. L., ... Libermann, T. A. (2013). Relaxation response induces temporal transcriptome changes in energy metabolism, insulin secretion and inflammatory pathways. *PLoS ONE, 8.* Retrieved from https://www.ncbi.nlm.nih.gov/pmc/articles/PMC3641112/pdf/pone.0062817.pdf

Bierhaus, A., Wolf, J., Andrassy, M., Rohleder, N., Humpert, P.M., Petrov, D., ... Nawroth, P. P. (2003). A mechanism converting psychosocial stress into mononuclear cell activation. *Proceedings of the National Academy of Sciences of the United States of America, 100*(4), 1920–1925.

Black, D.S., & Slavich, G.M. (2016). Mindfulness meditation and the immune system: A systematic review of randomized controlled trials. *Annals of the New York Academy of Sciences, 1373*(1), 13–24.

Bovbjerg, D., Ader, R., & Cohen, N. (1982). Behaviorally conditioned suppression of a graft-versus-host response. *Proceedings of the National Academy of Sciences of the United States of America, 79*(2), 583–585.

Bower, J. E., & Irwin, M. R. (2016). Mind-body therapies and control of inflammatory biology: A descriptive review. *Brain, Behavior, and Immunity, 51,* 1–11.

Buric, I., Farias, M., Jong, J., Mee, M., & Brazil, I. A. (2017). What is the molecular signature of mind-body interventions? A systematic review of gene expression changes induced by meditation and related practices. *Frontiers in Immunology.* Retrieved from https://www.frontiersin.org/articles/10.3389/fimmu.2017.00670/full

Cahn, B. R., Goodman, M. S., Peterson, C. T., Maturi, R., & Mills, P. J. (2017). Yoga, meditation and mind-body health: Increased BDNF, cortisol awakening response, and altered inflammatory marker expression after a 3-month yoga and meditation retreat. *Frontiers in Human Neuroscience, 11.* Retrieved from https://www.ncbi.nlm.nih.gov/pmc/articles/PMC5483482/pdf/fnhum-11-00315.pdf

Centers for Disease Control and Prevention (CDC) (2017). *Your immune system.* Retrieved from https://www.cdc.gov/bam/diseases/immune/immunesys.html

Chaplin, D. D. (2010). Overview of the immune response. *Journal of Allergy and Clinical Immunology, 125,* S3–23.

Chinese Health Qigong Association (CHQGA). (2007). *Baduanjin.* Beijing, China: Foreign Language Press.

Cohen, S., Janicki-Deverts, D., & Miller, G. E. (2007). Psychological stress and disease. *Journal of the American Medical Association, 298*(14), 1685–1687.

Cohen, S., Janicki-Deverts, D., Doyle, W. J., Miller, G. E., Frank, E., Rabin, B. S., & Turner, R. B. (2012). Chronic stress, glucocorticoid receptor resistance, inflammation, and disease risk. *Proceedings of the National Academy of Sciences of the United States of America, 109*(16), 5995–5999.

Coutinho, A. E., & Chapman, K. E. (2011). The anti-inflammatory and immunosuppressive effects of glucocorticoids, recent developments and mechanistic insights. *Molecular and Cellular Endocrinology, 335*(1), 2–13.

CWS-CMA (2017). Yangsheng bojian neigong chujie: Baduanjin (養生保健內功(初階)-八段錦). Retrieved from http://cws-cma.com/index.php?option=com_content&view=article&id=49&Itemid=67

Dandona, P., Aljada, A., & Bandyopadhyay, A. (2004). Inflammation: The link between insulin resistance, obesity and diabetes. *Trends in Immunology, 25*(1), 4–7.

Dantzer, R. (2009). Cytokine, sickness behavior, and depression. *Immunology and Allergy Clinics of North America, 29*(2), 247–264.

Dantzer, R., & Kelley, K. W. (2007). Twenty years of research on cytokine-induced sickness behavior. *Brain, Behavior, and Immunity, 21*(2), 153–160.

Dantzer, R., O'Connor, J. C., Freund, G. G., Johnson, R. W., & Kelley, K. W. (2008). From inflammation to sickness and depression: When the immune system subjugates the brain. *Nature Reviews Neuroscience, 9*(1), 46–56.

Davidson, R. J., Kabat-Zinn, J., Schumacher, J., Rosencranz, M., Miller, D., Santorelli, S. F., ... & Sheridan, J. (2003). Alterations in brain and immune function produced by mindfulness meditation. *Psychosomatic Medicine, 65*(4), 564–570.

Delves, P. J. (2017a). Overview of the immune system. *Merck Manual.* Retrieved from http://www.merckmanuals.com/home/immune-disorders/biology-of-the-immune-system/overview-of-the-immune-system

Delves, P.J. (2017b). Innate immunity. *Merck Manual.* Retrieved from http://www.merckmanuals.com/home/immune-disorders/biology-of-the-immune-system/innate-immunity

Dhabhar, F. S. (2008). Enhancing versus suppressive effects of stress on immune function: Implications for immunoprotection versus immunopathology. *Allergy, Asthma, and Clinical Immunology: Official Journal of the Canadian Society of Allergy and Clinical Immunology, 4,* 2–11.

Dhabhar, F. S., & McEwen, B. S. (1997). Acute stress enhances while chronic stress suppresses cell-mediated immunity in vivo: a potential role for leukocyte trafficking. *Brain, Behavior and Immunity, 11*(4), 286–306.

Douketis, J. D. (2017). Overview of the lymphatic system. *Merck Manual.* Retrieved from http://www.merckmanuals.com/home/heart-and-blood-vessel-disorders/lymphatic-disorders/overview-of-the-lymphatic-system

Dusek, J. A., & Benson, H. (2009). Mind-body medicine: A model of the comparative clinical impact of the acute stress and relaxation responses. *Minnesota Medicine, 92*(5), 47–50.

Fantuzzi, G. (2005) Adipose tissue, adipokines, and inflammation. *Journal of Allergy and Clinical Immunology, 115*(5), 911–919.

Franceschi, C., & Campisi, J., (2014). Chronic inflammation (inflammaging) and its potential contribution to age-associated diseases. *Journals of Gerontology: Biological Sciences, 69*(1), S4–S9.

Freund, A., Orjalo, A. V., Desprez, P. Y., & Campisi, J. (2010). Inflammatory networks during cellular senescence: causes and consequences. *Trends in Molecular Medicine, 16*(5), 238–246.

Furtado M., & Katzman, M.A. (2015). Neuroinflammatory pathways in anxiety, posttraumatic stress, and obsessive compulsive disorders. *Psychiatry Research, 229*(1–2), 37–48.

Glaser, R., Kiecolt-Glaser, J. K. (2005) Stress-induced immune dysfunction: Implications for health. *Nature Reviews Immunology, 5*(3), 243–251.

Gleeson, M., Bishop, N. C., Stensel, D. J., Lindley, M. R., Mastana, S. S., & Nimmo, M. A. (2011) The anti-inflammatory effects of exercise: Mechanisms and implications for the prevention and treatment of disease. *Nature Reviews: Immunology, 11*(9), 607–615.

Goleman, D., & Gurin, J. (1993). What is mind body medicine? In D. Goleman & J. Gurin (Eds.), *Mind body medicine: How to use your mind for better health* (pp. 3–18). Yonkers. NY: Consumer Reports Books.

Gonzalez, S., González-Rodríguez, A. P., Suárez-Álvarez, B., López-Soto, A., Huergo-Zapico, L., & Lopez-Larrea, C. (2011). Conceptual aspects of self and nonself discrimination. *Self Nonself, 2*(1), 19–25.

Handschin, C., & Spiegelman, B. M. (2008). The role of exercise and PGC1α in inflammation and chronic disease. *Nature, 454*(7203), 463–469.

Holzel, B. K., Lazar, S. W., Gard, T., Schuman-Olivier, Z., Vago, D. R., & Ott, U. (2011). How does mindfulness meditation work? Proposing mechanisms of action from a conceptual and neural perspective. *Perspectives Psychological Sciences, 6*(6), 537–559.

Huangdi Neijing (2017). *Huangdi neijing suwen* (黃帝內經素問). Translated from http://ctext.org/huangdi-neijing/zh

Ioannidou, A., Goulielmaki, E., & Garinis, G. A. (2016). DNA damage: From chronic inflammation to age-related deterioration. *Frontiers in Genetics, 7.* Retrieved from https://www.ncbi.nlm.nih.gov/pmc/articles/PMC5078321/pdf/fgene-07-00187.pdf

Irwin, M. R., & Olmstead, R. (2012). Mitigating cellular inflammation in older adults: A randomized controlled trial of tai chi chih. *American Journal of Geriatric Psychiatry: Official Journal of the American Association for Geriatric Psychiatry, 20*(9), 764–772.

Irwin, M. R., Olmstead, R., Breen, E. C., Witarama, T., Carrillo, C., Sadeghi, N., … & Cole, S. (2015). Cognitive behavioral therapy and tai chi reverse cellular and genomic markers of inflammation in late life insomnia: A randomized controlled trial. *Biological Psychiatry, 78*(10), 721–729.

Irwin, M. R., Olmstead, R., Breen, E. C., Witarama, T., Carrillo, C., Sadeghi, N., … & Cole, S. (2014). Tai chi, cellular inflammation, and transcriptome dynamics in breast cancer survivors with insomnia: A randomized controlled trial. *Journal of the National Cancer Institute. Monographs, 2014*(50), 295–301.

Irwin, M. R., Olmstead, R., & Carroll, J. E. (2016). Sleep disturbance, sleep duration, and inflammation: A systematic review and meta-analysis of cohort studies and experimental sleep deprivation. *Biological Psychiatry, 80*(1), 40–52.

Irwin, M. R., Olmstead, R. E., Ganz, P. A., & Haque, R. (2013). Sleep disturbance, inflammation and depression risk in cancer survivors. *Brain, Behavior, and Immunity, 30,* S58–S67.

Jahnke, R., Larkey, L., Rogers, C., Etnier, J., & Lin, F. (2010). A comprehensive review of health benefits of qigong and tai chi. *American Journal of Health Promotion, 24*(6), e1–e25. Retrieved from https://www.ncbi.nlm.nih.gov/pmc/articles/PMC3085832/pdf/nihms281835.pdf

Janeway, C. A., Travers, P., Walport, M., & Shlomchik, M. J. (2001). *Immunobiology: The immune system in health and disease* (5th ed.). New York, NY: Garland Science; 2001.

Kabat-Zinn, J. (2005). *Full catastrophe living: Using the wisdom of the body and mind to face stress, pain, and illness.* New York, NY: Delta.

Kaptchuk, T. J. (1983). *The web has no weaver: Understanding Chinese medicine.* Chicago, IL: Congdon & Weed.

Karacabey, K., & Ozdemir, N. (2012). The effect of nutritional elements on the immune system. *Journal of Obesity & Weight Loss Therapy, 2.* Retrieved from https://www.omicsonline.org/open-access/the-effect-of-nutritional-elements-on-the-immune-system-2165-7904.1000152.pdf

Khalsa, S. B. S., & Gould, J. (2012). *A Harvard Medical School guide: Your brain on yoga.* New York, NY: RosettaBooks.

Khalsa, S. B. S., & Elson, L. E. (Eds.) (2016). *A Harvard Medical School special health report: An introduction to yoga: Improve your strength, balance, flexibility, and well-being.* Boston, MA: Harvard Medical School.

Kiecolt-Glaser, J. K. (2009). Psychoneuroimmunology: Psychology's gateway to the biomedical future. *Perspectives on Psychological Science, 4*(4), 367–369.

Kiecolt-Glaser, J. K. (2010). Stress, food, and inflammation: Psychoneuroimmunology and nutrition at the cutting edge. *Psychosomatic Medicine, 72*(4), 365–369.

Kiecolt-Glaser, J. K., Bennett, J. M., Andridge, R., Peng, J., Shapiro, C. L., Malarkey, W. B., … & Glaser, R. (2014). Yoga's impact on inflammation, mood, and fatigue in breast cancer survivors: A randomized controlled trial. *Journal of Clinical Oncology, 32*(10), 1040–1049.

Kiecolt-Glaser, J. K., Christian, L., Preston, H., Houts, C. R., Malarkey, W. B., Emery, C. F., & Glaser, R. (2010). Stress, inflammation, and yoga practice. *Psychosomatic Medicine, 72*(2), 113. Retrieved from https://www.ncbi.nlm.nih.gov/pmc/articles/PMC2820143/pdf/nihms172911.pdf

Kiecolt-Glaser, J. K., Fagundes, C. P., Andridge, R., Peng, J., Malarkey, W. B., Habash, D., & Belury, M. A. (2017). Depression, daily stressors, and inflammatory responses to high-fat meals: When stress overrides healthier food choices. *Molecular Psychiatry, 22*(3), 476–482.

Kiecolt-Glaser, J.K. & Glaser, R. (1993). Mind and immunity. In D. Goleman & J. Gurin, J. (Eds.), *Mind body medicine: How to use your mind for better health,* (pp. 39–61). Yonkers. NY: Consumer Reports Books.

Kiecolt-Glaser, J. K., Gouin, J. P., & Hantsoo, L. (2010). Close relationships, inflammation, and health. *Neuroscience and Biobehavioral Reviews, 35*(1), 33–38.

Kiecolt-Glaser, J. K., Marucha, P. T., Mercado, A. M., Malarkey, W. B., & Glaser, R. (1995). Slowing of wound healing by psychological stress. *The Lancet, 346*(8984), 1194–1196.

Kiecolt-Glaser, J. K., McGuire, L., Robles, T. F., & Glaser, R. (2002). Psychoneuroimmunology: Psychological influences on immune function and health. *Journal of Consulting and Clinical Psychology, 70*(3), 537–547.

Kiecolt-Glaser, J. K., McGuire, L., Robles, T. F., & Glaser, R. (2002a). Emotions, morbidity, and mortality: New perspectives from psychoneuroimmunology. *Annual Review of Psychology, 53*, 83–107.

Kiecolt-Glaser, J. K., Preacher, K. J., MacCallum, R. C., Atkinson, C., Malarkey, W. B., & Glaser, R. (2003). Chronic stress and age-related increases in the proinflammatory cytokine IL-6. *Proceedings of the National Academy of Sciences of the United States of America, 100*(15), 9090–9095.

Kinnucan, J. A., Rubin, D. T., & Ali, T. (2013). Sleep and Inflammatory bowel disease: Exploring the relationship between sleep disturbances and inflammation. *Gastroenterology & Hepatology, 9*(11), 718–727.

Lawrence, T., & Gilroy, D. W. (2007). Chronic inflammation: A failure of resolution? *International Journal of Experimental Pathology, 88*(2), 85–94.

Leukemia and Lymphoma Society (LLS) (2017). The lymphatic system. Retrieved from https://www.lls.org/managing-your-cancer/understanding-blood-marrow-and-the-lymphatic-system/the-lymphatic-system

Lin, H. C., Lin, H. P., Yu, H. H., Wang, L. C., Lee, J. H., Lin, Y. T., … & Chiang, B. L. (2017). Tai-chi-chuan exercise improves pulmonary function and decreases exhaled nitric oxide level in both asthmatic and nonasthmatic children and improves quality of life in children with asthma. *Evidence-Based Complementary and Alternative Medicine.* Retrieved from https://www.ncbi.nlm.nih.gov/pmc/articles/PMC5406730/pdf/ECAM2017-6287642.pdf

Lim, S. A., & Cheong, K. J. (2015). Regular yoga practice improves antioxidant status, immune function, and stress hormone releases in young healthy people: A randomized, double-blind, controlled pilot study. *Journal of Alternative and Complementary Medicine, 21*(9), 530–538.

Liu, T. J. (Ed.) (2010). *Chinese medical qigong.* Philadelphia, PA: Singing Dragon.

Mayo Clinic (2017). *Mediterranean diet: A heart-healthy eating plan.* Retrieved from https://www.mayoclinic.org/healthy-lifestyle/nutrition-and-healthy-eating/in-depth/mediterranean-diet/art-20047801

MedlinePlus (2016). *Immune response.* Retrieved from https://medlineplus.gov/ency/article/000821.htm

Mogensen, T. H. (2009). Pathogen recognition and inflammatory signaling in innate immune defenses. *Clinical Microbiology Reviews, 22*(2), 240–273.

Morey, J. N., Boggero, I. A., Scott, A. B., & Segerstrom, S. C. (2015). Current directions in stress and human immune function. *Current Opinion in Psychology, 5*, 13–17.

Morgan, N., Irwin, M. R., Chung, M., & Wang, C. (2014). The effects of mind-body therapies on the immune system: Meta-analysis. *PLoS ONE, 9.* Retrieved from https://www.ncbi.nlm.nih.gov/pmc/articles/PMC4079606/pdf/pone.0100903.pdf

Mullington, J. M., Simpson, N. S., Meier-Ewert, H. K., & Haack, M. (2010). Sleep loss and inflammation. *Best Practice & Research: Clinical Endocrinology & Metabolism, 24*(5), 775–784.

Nassau, J. H., Tien, K. & Fritz, G. K. (2008). Review of the literature: Integrating psychoneuroimmunology into pediatric chronic illness interventions. *Journal of Pediatric Psychology, 233*, 195–207.

National Cancer Institute (NCI). (2015). *Chronic inflammation.* Retrieved from https://www.cancer.gov/about-cancer/causes-prevention/risk/chronic-inflammation

National Institute of Allergy and Infectious Diseases (NIAID) (2014). *Features of an immune response.* Retrieved from https://www.niaid.nih.gov/research/immune-response-features

National Institutes of Health (NIH). (2003). *Understanding the immune system: How it works.* Retrieved from http://www.imgt.org/IMGTeducation/Tutorials/ImmuneSystem/UK/the_immune_system.pdf

National Institutes of Health (NIH). (2014). *Immune cells.* Retrieved from https://www.niaid.nih.gov/research/immune-cells

National Institutes of Health (NIH). (2016). *The innate and adaptive immune systems.* Retrieved from https://www.ncbi.nlm.nih.gov/pubmedhealth/PMH0072580/

Nauta, J. (2011) Humoral and cellular immunity. In *Statistics in clinical vaccine trials (pp. 13-18.* New York, NY: Springer.

Nesse, R. M., & Williams, G. C. (1994). *Why we get sick: The new science of Darwinian medicine.* New York, NY: Vintage Books.

Newton, K., & Dixit, V. M. (2012). Signaling in innate immunity and inflammation. *Cold Spring Harbor Perspectives in Biology, 4.* Retrieved from https://www.ncbi.nlm.nih.gov/pmc/articles/PMC3282411/pdf/cshperspect-SIG-a006049.pdf

Nieman, D.C. (2011). Moderate exercise improves immunity and decreases illness rates. *American Journal of Lifestyle Medicine, 5*(4), 338–345.

Oh, B., Butow, P., Mullan, B., Clarke, S., Beale, P., Pavlakis, N., ... & Rosenthal, D. (2010). Impact of medical qigong on quality of life, fatigue, mood and inflammation in cancer patients: A randomized controlled trial. *Annals of Oncology, 21*(3), 608–614.

Palmer, D. (2007). *Qigong fever: Body, science, and utopia in China.* New York, NY: Columbia University Press.

Pelletier, K. R. (1993). Between mind and body: Stress, emotions and health. In D. Goleman & J. Gurin (Eds.), *Mind body medicine: How to use your mind for better health* (pp. 39–61). New York, NY: Consumer Reports Books.

Perdue, S. S., & Humphrey, J. H. (2017). Immune system. Encyclopædia Britannica. Retrieved from https://www.britannica.com/science/immune-system

Ponton, F., Wilson, K., Cotter, S. C., Raubenheimer, D., & Simpson, S. J. (2011). Nutritional immunology: A multi-dimensional approach. *PLoS Pathogens, 7.* Retrieved from https://www.ncbi.nlm.nih.gov/pmc/articles/PMC3228798/pdf/ppat.1002223.pdf

Pruimboom, L., Raison, C. L., & Muskiet, F. A. J. (2015). Physical activity protects the human brain against metabolic stress induced by a postprandial and chronic inflammation. *Behavioural Neurology.* Retrieved from https://www.hindawi.com/journals/bn/2015/569869/

PubMed. (2015). *What is an inflammation?* Retrieved from https://www.ncbi.nlm.nih.gov/pubmedhealth/PMH0072482/

PubMed. (2016). *How does the immune system work?* Retrieved from https://www.ncbi.nlm.nih.gov/pubmedhealth/PMH0072548/

PubMed. (2017). *Lymphatic system.* Retrieved from https://www.ncbi.nlm.nih.gov/pubmedhealth/PMHT0024459/

Pullen, P. R., Nagamia, S. H., Mehta, P. K., Thompson, W. R., Benardon, D., Hammoud R., Parrot, J. M., Sola, S., & Khan, B. V. (2008). Effects of yoga on inflammation and exercise capacity in patients with chronic heart failure. *Journal of Cardiac Failure, 14*(5), 407–413.

Raison, C. L., Capuron, L., & Miller, A. H. (2006). Cytokines sing the blues: Inflammation and the pathogenesis of depression. *Trends in Immunology, 27*(1), 24–31.

Ranjbaran, Z., Keefer, L., Stepanski, E., Farhadi, A., & Keshavarzian, A. (2007). The relevance of sleep abnormalities to chronic inflammatory conditions. *Inflammation Research, 56*(2), 51–57.

Ratey, J. J., & Hagerman, E. (2008). *Spark: The revolutionary new science of exercise and the brain.* New York, NY: Little, Brown and Company.

Reiche, E. M., Nunes, S. O., & Morimoto, H. K. (2004). Stress, depression, the immune system, and cancer. *Lancet Oncology, 5*(10), 617–25.

Reig-Ferrer, A., Ferrer-Cascales, R., Santos-Ruiz, A., Campos-Ferrer, A., Prieto-Seva, A., Velasco-Ruiz, I., ... & Albaladejo-Blazquez, N. (2014). A relaxation technique enhances psychological well-being and immune parameters in elderly people from a nursing home: A randomized controlled study. *BMC Complementary and Alternative Medicine, 14.* Retrieved from https://www.ncbi.nlm.nih.gov/pmc/articles/PMC4153914/pdf/12906_2013_Article_1886.pdf

Robles, T. F., Glaser, R., & Kiecolt-Glaser, J. K. (2005). Out of balance: A new look at chronic stress, depression, and immunity. *Current Directions in Psychological Science, 14*(2), 111–115.

Rock, K. L., & Kono, H. (2008). The inflammatory response to cell death. *Annual Review of Pathology, 3,* 99–126.

Rontgen, P., Sablotzki, A., Simm, A., Silber, R. E., & Czeslick, E. (2004). Effect of catecholamines on intracellular cytokine synthesis in human monocytes. *European Cytokine Network, 15*(1), 14–23.

Ross, A., & Thomas, S. (2010). The health benefits of yoga and exercise: A review of comparison studies. *Journal of Alternative and Complementary Medicine, 16*(1), 3–12.

Santee, R. (2007). *An Integrative Approach to Counseling: Bridging Chinese Thought, Evolutionary Theory, and Stress Management.* Copyright © 2007 by SAGE Publications. Reprinted with permission.

Sapolsky, R. M. (2004). *Why zebras don't get ulcers* (3rd ed.). New York, NY: Henry Holt and Company.

Sapolsky, R. M. (2017). *Behave: The biology of humans at our best and worst.* New York, NY: Penguin.

Segerstrom, S. C. (2007). Stress, energy, and immunity: An ecological view. *Current Directions in Psychological Science, 16*(6), 326–330.

Segerstrom, S. C., & Miller, G. E. (2004). Psychological stress and the human immune system: A meta-analytic study of 30 years of inquiry. *Psychological Bulletin, 130*(4), 601–630.

Shahar, M. (2008). *The Shaolin monastery: History, religion, and the Chinese martial arts.* Honolulu, HI: University of Hawaii Press.

Shen-nong. (2006). *What are the seven emotions?* Retrieved from http://www.shen-nong.com/eng/principles/sevenemotions.html

Shields, G. S., Moons, W. G., & Slavich, G. M. (2017). Inflammation, self-regulation, and health: An immunologic model of self-regulatory failure. *Perspectives on Psychological Science 12*(4), 588–612.

SINA. (2017). *Jianshen qigong baduanjin* (健身气功八段锦). Retrieved from http://blog.sina.com.cn/s/blog_b00686d90102wu07.html

Slavich, G. M. (2015). Understanding inflammation, its regulation, and relevance for health: A top scientific and public priority. *Brain, Behavior, and Immunity, 45*, 13–14.

Slavich, G. M., & Irwin, M. R. (2014). From stress to inflammation and major depressive disorder: A social signal transduction theory of depression. *Psychological Bulletin, 140*(3), 774–815.

Stellar, J. E., John-Henderson, N., Anderson, C. L., Gordon, A. M., McNeil, G. D., & Keltner, D. (2015, January 19). Positive affect and markers of inflammation: Discrete positive emotions predict lower levels of inflammatory cytokines. *Emotion, 15*(2), 129–133.

Steptoe, A., Hamer, M., & Chida, Y. (2007). The effects of acute psychological stress on circulating inflammatory factors in humans: A review and meta-analysis. *Brain, Behavior, and Immunity, 21*(7), 901–912.

Tedeschi, A., & Asero, R. (2008). Asthma and autoimmunity: A complex but intriguing relation. *Expert Review of Clinical Immunology, 4*(6), 767–776.

Tian, R., Hou, G., Li, D., & Yuan, T. F. (2014). A possible change process of inflammatory cytokines in the prolonged chronic stress and its ultimate implications for health. *Scientific World Journal, 2014.* Retrieved from https://www.ncbi.nlm.nih.gov/pmc/articles/PMC4065693/pdf/TSWJ2014-780616.pdf

Twal, W.O., Wahlquist, A. E., & Balasubramanian, S. (2016). Yogic breathing when compared to attention control reduces the levels of pro-inflammatory biomarkers in saliva: A pilot randomized controlled trial. *BMC Complementary and Alternative Medicine, 16*, 294. Retrieved from https://www.ncbi.nlm.nih.gov/pmc/articles/PMC4991069/pdf/12906_2016_Article_1286.pdf

University of Rochester Medical Center (URMC) (2011). Robert Ader, founder of psychoneuroimmunology, dies. Retrieved from https://www.urmc.rochester.edu/news/story/3370/robert-ader-founder-of-psychoneuroimmunology-dies.aspx

Urso, M.L. (2013). Anti-inflammatory interventions and skeletal muscle injury: Benefit or detriment? *Journal of Applied Physiology, 115*, 920–928.

Vella, C. A., Allison, M. A., Cushman, M., Jenny. N. S., Miles, M. P., Larsen, B., … & Blaha, M. J. (2017). Physical activity and adiposity-related inflammation: The MESA. *Medicine & Science in Sports & Exercise, 49*(5), 915–921.

Vetvicka, V., & Vetvickova, J. (2016). Concept of immuno-nutrition. *Journal of Nutrition and Food Science, 6.* Retrieved from https://www.omicsonline.org/open-access/concept-of-immunonutrition-2155-9600-1000500.pdf

Vogelzangs, N., Beekman, A. T. F., de Jonge, P., & Penninx, B. W. J. H. (2013). Anxiety disorders and inflammation in a large adult cohort. *Translational Psychiatry, 3.* Retrieved from https://www.ncbi.nlm.nih.gov/pmc/articles/PMC3641413/pdf/tp201327a.pdf

Vogelzangs, N., de Jonge, P., Smit, J. H., Bahn, S., & Penninx, B. W. (2016). Cytokine production capacity in depression and anxiety. *Translational Psychiatry, 6*. Retrieved from https://www.ncbi.nlm.nih.gov/pmc/articles/PMC5070051/pdf/tp201692a.pdf

Wayne, P. M., & Fuerst, M. L. (2013). *The Harvard Medical School guide to tai chi: 12 weeks to a healthy body, strong heart and sharp mind*. Boston, MA: Shambala.

WebMD. (2005). *20 common foods with the most antioxidants*. Retrieved from https://www.webmd.com/food-recipes/20-common-foods-most-antioxidants

WebMD. (2017). *Your omega-3 family shopping list*. Retrieved from https://www.webmd.com/diet/guide/your-omega-3-family-shopping-list#1

Wei, M. & Groves, J. (2017). The Harvard Medical School guide to yoga: Eight weeks to strength, awareness, and flexibility. Boston, MA: Da Capo Lifelong.

Wile, D. (1996). *Lost tai-chi classics from the late Ching dynasty*. New York, NY: State University of New York Press.

Witek-Janusek, L., Albuquerque, K., Chroniak, K. R., Chroniak, C., Durazo, R., & Mathews, H. L. (2008). Effect of mindfulness-based stress reduction on immune function, quality of life, and coping in women newly diagnosed with early stage breast cancer. *Brain, Behavior, and Immunity, 22*(6), 969–981.

Wolkow, A., Aisbett, B., Reynolds, J., Ferguson, S. A., & Main, L. C. (2015). Relationships between inflammatory cytokine and cortisol responses in firefighters exposed to simulated wildfire suppression work and sleep restriction. *Physiological Reports, 3*. Retrieved from https://www.ncbi.nlm.nih.gov/pmc/articles/PMC4673634/

Woodyard, C. (2011). Exploring the therapeutic effects of yoga and its ability to increase quality of life. *International Journal of Yoga, 4*(2), 49–54.

Yang, J. M. (1997). *Eight simple qigong exercises for health: The eight pieces of brocade*. Jamaica Plain, MA: YMAA Publication Center.

Zachariae, R. (2009). Psychoneuroimmunology: A bio-psycho-social approach to health and disease. *Scandinavian Journal of Psychology, 50*(6), 645–651.

Zotova, N. V., Chereshnev, V. A., & Gusev, E. Y. (2016). Systemic inflammation: Methodological approaches to identification of the common pathological process. *PLoS ONE, 11*. Retrieved from https://www.ncbi.nlm.nih.gov/pmc/articles/PMC4859514/pdf/pone.0155138.pdf

CREDITS

CHAPTER 10

Time Management

After finishing this chapter, you will be able to do the following:

- Understand why you are not really managing time but managing yourself
- Explain why self-management is important, within the context of sedentary behavior, exercise, sleep, and eating and drinking behavior, for addressing chronic stress
- Indicate how wasting time is conducive to chronic stress
- Explain how mind wandering, procrastinating, using social media, negative thinking and judgments, and making excuses can all be conducive to wasting time and chronic stress
- Discuss why the perception of being in control of your time is important in addressing chronic stress
- Describe why establishing priorities, generating goals, creating action plans, setting timelines, self-monitoring, and flexibility are all fundamental to self-management, increasing your perception of being in control of how you use your time, and eliminating chronic stress
- Why learning to say no is important in self-management, your perception of being in control of how you use your time, and in eliminating chronic stress
- Compare Buddhist, Daoist, and Confucian perspectives regarding self-management

How important is your physical and psychological health and well-being to you? How much time during the day do you spend engaged in behaviors that are beneficial to your own physical and psychological health and well-being? Not that much? Do you ever get a sense of not having enough time during your day? Do you seem to be chasing after time? How much time during the day do you waste?

TIME

Time only moves one way. Forward! You are born, grow older, and then die. This is inevitable! It does not matter how rich you are, what status you have, what you own, who you know, how much power you have, how much control you have over others and/or the world around you, or what you believe in. The passing of time cannot be stopped. So, let's stop trying to stretch, control, or otherwise manage time and turn toward things that we can manage.

SELF-MANAGEMENT

Time management is about how you live your life before you die. Truth of the matter is, you are not really managing time. Time just flows along. You are, essentially, managing your behavior, physical, psychological, and interpersonal, within the context of time. In other words, self-management (Claessens, van Eerde, Rutte, & Roe, 2007). So, the fundamental question is, how do you want to live your life and manage your behavior before you are dead?

Time management/self-management is about helping you optimize your overall experience within the time interval between where you are at now and your

eventual death. Research cited in this text so far has raised considerable concerns about chronic stress and our overall physical and psychological health/well-being. In other words, our physical, psychological, and interpersonal behavior can significantly compromise our experience of how we move through time. In some cases, we spend **too much time** engaged in certain behaviors, while in other cases we spend **too little time** engaged in other behaviors. In either case, the result is that the natural, evolved state of our body and mind is compromised and, as indicated in previous chapters, we end up chronically stressed. Is your overall physical, psychological, and interpersonal health and well-being important to you? If so, it is of utmost importance to examine your physical, psychological, and interpersonal behavior within the context of time.

Sedentary Behavior

In developed economies, **too much time** is often spent engaged in sedentary behavior. Sedentary behavior, such a sitting or lying down, is waking behavior with minimal energy output (Owen, Sparling, Healy, Dunstan, & Matthews, 2010). Excessive time spent engaged in sedentary behavior, as previously cited in this text, is detrimental, physically and psychologically, to our overall health and well-being. The American Psychological Association's Stress in America Survey (2014) for 2013 indicated that adults spend, on average, per day

- 3.4 hours sitting at a desk,
- 3.7 hours online, and
- 3.9 hours watching TV.

In a subsequent report, the American Psychological Association's Stress in America Survey (2016) for 2015 indicated the average amount of time adults engage

How Sitting Too Long Affects Body

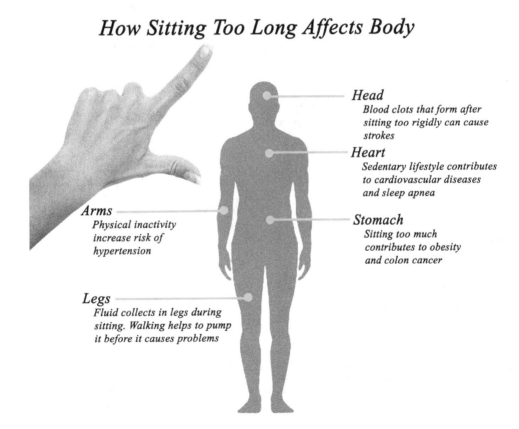

Head
Blood clots that form after sitting too rigidly can cause strokes

Heart
Sedentary lifestyle contributes to cardiovascular diseases and sleep apnea

Arms
Physical inactivity increase risk of hypertension

Stomach
Sitting too much contributes to obesity and colon cancer

Legs
Fluid collects in legs during sitting. Walking helps to pump it before it causes problems

in sedentary behavior (watching TV, sitting at a desk, on the computer) per day is 6.4 hours, with 45% of adults spending 6–12-plus hours per day engaged in sedentary behavior. As we are wired, via evolution, to engage in physical activity on a regular basis, excessive sedentary behavior compromises our natural physical and psychological well-being and health (Ratey, & Hagerman, 2008). We see the effects of this shift all around us.

Exercise

As previously cited in this text, although the evidence is clear that a well-rounded exercise program (aerobic, anaerobic, stretching, neuromotor/neuromuscular) is beneficial for preventing/reducing chronic stress and the various physical and psychological disorders associated with it, **too little time** is spent exercising in such a manner on a regular basis. The American Psychological Association's Stress in America Survey (2014) for 2013 indicated that 43% of adults engaged in exercise to address stress, 37% either don't exercise or if they do it averages less than one time per week, 39% reported during the past month that if they felt stressed they have not engaged in exercise/physical activity, and just 17% exercised every day. Their report for 2015 (APA, 2016) noted that

- 22% of adults do not exercise and
- 50% of adults do exercise, a few times a week, to the point of exertion (sweating, breathing hard).

As we are wired, via evolution, to engage in physical activity on a regular basis, inadequate/no exercise compromises our natural physical and psychological well-being and health (Spark, & Hagerman, 2008).

Sleep

As previously cited in this text, **too little time** engaged in restful sleep compromises our overall physical and psychological health and well-being, and, as the research demonstrated,

most of us are clearly not getting enough restful sleep. The American Psychological Association's Stress in America Survey (2014) for 2013 noted, for adults, regarding **too little time** spent sleeping, the following:

- 6.7 hours a night is the average
- 42% rate sleep as poor/fair
- 43% have, during the past month, laid in bed awake
- Upon waking,
    - 53% felt sluggish/lazy,
    - 38% felt irritable,
    - 29% had problems concentrating, and
    - 25% lacked motivation to address obligations.

The American Psychological Association's Stress in America Survey (2016) for 2015, regarding **too little time** spent sleeping, notes the following:

- 6.7 hours a night is the average
- 46% rate sleep as poor/fair
- 46% have, during the past month, laid in bed awake

Eating

Given the adult overweight and obesity problem previously cited in this text, 70.7% (for 2013–2014) are overweight or obese (Centers for Disease Control and Prevention, 2016), it is clear that **too much time** is being spent eating and drinking calorie-dense food and drink. The American Psychological Association's Stress in America Survey (2014) for 2013 noted the following for adults during the month previous to the survey:

- 38% have eaten too much/ate unhealthy foods due to stress
- 49% of this group do so at least one time or more a week
- 33% of this group do so as it diverts them from their stress
- 34% of this group do so because it has become a habit
- 30% indicated that stress caused them to skip a meal
- 41% of this group did so at least one time or more a week
- 26% of this group did so because of lack of time

The American Psychological Association's Stress in America Survey (2016) for 2015 noted the following for adults during the month previous to the survey:

- 39% have eaten too much/ate unhealthy foods due to stress
- 31% indicated that stress caused them to skip a meal

It is important to note, as was the case in the last chapter, that sedentary behavior, lack of exercise, lack of sleep, and excessive eating are all interdependent, all cause the body and mind to be chronically stressed, all are directly linked to a wide variety of physical and psychological disorders/illnesses, all are directly influenced by chronic psychosocial stress, and all are indictive of mismanaging behavior within a contextual time frame.

WASTING TIME

There are certain types of behaviors that, if ongoing, waste time—time that you cannot get back. This wasting of time contributes to the perception that you do not have enough time to do what you need to do, and as a result that you do not have control over your time. As was previously noted you do not have control over time. It simply moves onward. You *are* able, however, to control/manage your behavior within a contextual time frame. There are a number of behaviors that waste time, are directly linked to chronic stress, and thus compromise your ability to manage/control your behavior within a contextual time frame.

Mind Wandering

As previously cited in this text, we spend approximately half of our waking life mind wandering, and, for all intents and purposes, when we mind wander we are essentially unhappy (Killingsworth & Gilbert, 2010). While mind wandering, as noted in chapter 1, clearly is beneficial for our survival, it can also be quite detrimental. Obsessing and ruminating about past events that cannot be undone, and continually worrying about future events that may or may not happen, are all threat based. This in turn activates and maintains our stress response, which eventually results in chronic stress, hence, the research demonstrating that we are essentially unhappy when we mind wander. This type of **mind wandering is clearly not beneficial and wastes a considerable amount of time that you cannot get back.**

Procrastination

Procrastination is the behavior of intentionally putting off a task until the very last moment or not doing it all (Gafni & Geri, 2010; Zarick & Stonebraker, 2009).

While there are many explanations for why people procrastinate, it seems that the task may be perceived, in one way or another, as a threat and thus is stressful (Chapman & Rupured, n.d.; Marano, 2003; Shellenbarger, 2014; UC Santa Cruz, 2016; WebMD, 2018). In so far as the task evokes uncomfortable stress for the procrastinator, the task is avoided. By avoiding the task, the perceived threat, the stress associated with

it, and the feeling of being uncomfortable disappears. This thus reinforces the behavior of procrastinating.

The problem is that procrastination is quite often dysfunctional such that the cost appears to outweigh the benefit, and this is especially observable in academic performance (exams, papers, projects) of college students (Marano, 2003; UC Santa Cruz, 2016; Zarick & Stonebraker, 2009). From the perspective of self-management within the context of a time frame, **procrastination clearly wastes time—time that you cannot get back!** Then, as the deadline for your task is upon you, you get stressed because you have not completed the task, you realize you don't have much time to complete the task, and you have the perception that you do not have any control over the situation as you rush to complete the task, all of which leads to more stress—another vicious circle of chronic stress!

Social Media and Technology

According to Statista's (2017a) data on **social media**, there are, worldwide, over 2 billion active users of Facebook, 1.5 billion active users of YouTube, 700 million active users of Instagram, and 328 million active users of Twitter. Data from the Pew Research Center (Perrin, 2015) indicates, for adults in the United States, 65% of all adults (68% of all women and 62% of all men), 90% between the ages of 18–29, 35% of those 65 years and older, 56% in the lowest SES, 65% of Caucasians, 65% of Hispanics, and 56% of African Americans use social media.

A Gallup poll (Gallup, 2015) indicated 46% of adults (41% men and 51% women), 51% between the ages of 18–29, 48% between the ages of 30–49, 42% between the ages of 50–64, and 40% of those 65 and older are attached to their smart phones and essentially believe they cannot live without it. The American Psychological Association's Stress in America Survey (2017) for 2016 identified a new behavior pattern referred to as a "**constant checker**," categorizing 43% of adults in the United States who continually check social media, texts, and e-mails on a daily basis and is indicative of higher levels of stress. Eighty-six percent of adults indicate they continually/often check these three areas on a daily basis (APA, 2017,2). Forty-eight percent of millennials (18–34), 37% of gen Xers (35–50), 22% of boomers (51–69), and 15% of matures (70 or greater) strongly/somewhat agree, regarding their physical and psychological health and well-being, that they are worried about the detrimental effects of social media (APA, 2017).

A national survey of adults in the United States by the Pew Research Center (Greenwood, Perrin, & Duggan, 2016) indicated that 79% of online adults (68% of all adults) use Facebook. Research (Kross et al., 2013) has previously noted that increased Facebook use, from a sample of young adults (N = 82, mean = 19.52, SD = 2.17), was indicative of self-reported negative decline in life satisfaction and how they felt in the moment.

Data (Statista, 2017b) indicates that American adults on average, spend about 2 hours a day online via laptop and desktop computers. It is estimated that American adults spend, on average, between 4 to 5 hours a day on mobile devices,

smartphones, and tablets, with the smartphones counting for most of the time (Gregoire; 2015; Hackernoon, 2017; Harper, 2015; Khalaf, & Kesiraju, 2017; Perez, 2017). A research study (Andrews, Ellis, Shaw, & Piwek, 2015) in England found that the participants averaged 5 hours a day on their smartphone, with average utilization being 85 times a day.

How much time, during a day, do you spend using **digital devices** such as an iPhone/mobile phone, iPad/tablet, and/or a computer to surf the Web, play games, text, talk with another person, read a book, watch a movie and/or a TV show, access social media, and so on? How much time, during that same day, do you spend on social media such as Facebook, YouTube, Instagram, or Twitter? Be honest with yourself; how much total time do you spend a day engaged in those activities? How attached are you to your digital devices? How long do you think you can go without using your digital devices? How would you rate your stress level when you are not using your digital devices? When you are using them?

How much of that daily time using your digital devices is directed toward meeting your nonleisure time/non-playtime goals such as work, school, eating, paying bills, purchasing necessities, solving problems, completing tasks, and so on? How much of that daily time using your digital devices allows you to avoid attending to problems, completing tasks, fulfilling obligations, and so on. In other words, how much **time during the day is wasted** using your digital devices relative to not attending to problems, completing tasks, fulfilling obligations, and so on? **This is time you cannot get back!**

Negativity

How much time during the day do you spend complaining, criticizing, whining, moaning, awfulizing, catastrophizing, worrying, obsessing, engaging in rumination, grumbling, fault-finding, engaging in negative self-thought, engaging in negative thought about others, putting yourself down, putting others down, doubting, letting your **negativity** bias run wild, negatively judging yourself and others, feeling mad, and feeling guilty? All of these are threat based and thus activate and maintain your stress response, eventually, if ongoing, resulting in chronic stress.

All of them are a **waste of time—time that you cannot get back! Time** that could be used more constructively to examine and address the source of this type of behavior. **Time** that can be used more constructively to address and resolve your problems, fulfill your obligations, and complete your tasks for the day. In other words, you need to be in control of yourself and manage yourself. Discover that you have a timeframe to enjoy yourself without feeling stressed about it.

Excuses

How much time during the day do you spend making excuses why you cannot exercise, cannot meditate, must stay up late, don't really need much sleep, cannot eat and drink in a manner that is beneficial to you, cannot address your tasks now, resolve your problems now, and so on? Do these excuses sound familiar? It's too hard, it's too early, it's too late, I don't have any time, I don't know how, it's too complicated, it's too hot, it's too cold, I can't do it by myself, I am too tired, I don't have any energy, I am too busy, I don't feel motivated right now, it's boring, there is too much to do, I will do it later, I don't want to talk about it, I am fine the way I am, and so on. To differentiate between a legitimate reason and an excuse, generally, excuses are a way to avoid doing something that is viewed as a threat, which makes you uncomfortable/stressed even thinking about it. The problem is that the more you engage in excuses to not do something, the stronger this behavior becomes and the more **time you waste** relative to addressing and reducing your stress.

GUIDELINES FOR SELF-MANAGEMENT

Fundamental to managing yourself within the context of a time frame is being organized. There are numerous websites, apps, blogs, books, articles, practitioners, and programs all oriented to teach you how to best manage/organize yourself within the context of time. Examine them and decide which **strategy** best fits your personality and needs. There is a lot of overlap between them. However, how and when they are implemented, the specific **tactics**, may differ. Focus on keeping your self-management/organization process as **simple** as possible. The more **complex** the self-management/organization process, the more potential problems with control and stress. Keep it simple! Research (Claessens, van Eerde, Rutte, & Roe, 2007; Hafner, Stock, & Oberst, 2014; Macan, Shahani, Dipboye, & Phillips, 1990) has indicated the **self-management strategies** that are most successful are those that increase one's perceived sense of control, which then, in turn, reduces stress. Specific tactics to obtaining these results, which are fairly consistent across research studies, are establishing concrete **goals**, **action plans**, **timelines**, **priorities**, and **self monitoring** (Claessens, van Eerde, Rutte, & Roe, 2007; Hafner, Stock, & Oberst, 2014; Macan, Shahani, Dipboye, & Phillips, 1990; WebMD, 2018).

Goals, Action Plans, and Timelines

Fundamental to constructing priorities, goals, action plans, and timelines is the necessity of being **flexible**. Life often gets in the way and you need to be able to adapt to an ever-changing environment. Give yourself the space to modify, and if necessary, change priorities, goals, action plans, and timelines based on the challenges life presents to you.

Goals

Concrete, **short-term** and **long term**, specific goals give you direction, let you know where you are going, provide a context, focus your energy, put you in control, motivate you, get you in the present, and get you organized.

Action Plans

While goals tell you where you are going, concrete, specific action plans tell you how you are going to get there. Actions plans are all about what you need to do to attain your goals. Action plans allow you to be further organized as they provide specific details and focus regarding how you are going to reach your goal.

Timelines

While action plans tell you how you are going to reach your goals, concrete, specific timelines tell you when you are going to reach your goal. Timelines even further organize your behavior relative to when you are going to achieve your goal.

Priorities

In order to set goals, you need to clarify your **priorities**. You need to determine what is most important. Create a descending, hierarchical list of the tasks that need to be completed relative to importance and deadlines. The problem, however, is there is a tendency to complete the easier tasks first even if they are not as important. This reduces the time you can spend on the most important tasks, which are often more difficult and require more time to complete. This results in a sense of urgency and additional stress.

Self-Monitoring

Self-monitoring is attending to and reviewing your goals, short term and long term, on a daily basis and monitoring your status toward completing your tasks and meeting your goals, within the time frame context, you set for yourself. What needs to be done today and in what order? What are your priorities for the day? For the short term? For the long term? Generally, this includes creating a schedule, where you list the goals and the various tasks needed to be done to meet them. Are you on track? Do you need to make adjustments? If so, what specifically do you need to do? Is your self-management program effective and efficient relative to completing your tasks and meeting your goals? If not, make adjustments. Remember to also closely monitor yourself regarding wasting time and making excuses as both compromise completing your tasks and meeting your goals. Remember that as you meet your goals, both short term and long term, new ones will pop up.

Self-monitoring is especially important if you are in a helping profession (such as counseling), insofar as you need to address your *own* time-management issues before attempting to work with clients regarding their time-management challenges.

One Additional Tactic

There are many other tactics associated with the various time-management programs. Many are common across the various programs. One extremely important one has to do with interruptions. Some people, if they can, will interrupt you to get assistance with meeting their own goals. If you do not protect your time and space regarding your own goals, others will attempt to control your space and timeframe for their own purposes. Thus, it is important that you learn how to say **NO!** This of course is contingent on the specific situation, but, in general, interruptions (a) reduce your time meeting your goal and (b) require you to start up again on meeting your goal, which also reduces the amount of time you have available for meeting your goal. Give a polite but firm

"No, I cannot help you now. I will be happy to help you when I am finished." Do not feel guilty about saying no. Feeling guilty is a waste of time.

THE STARTING POINT

A successful self-management program is about having a **positive outlook** on life and the challenges it brings with it so that you can complete your tasks and

meet your goals in an effective and efficient manner. In order to accomplish this, you need to increase your perceived sense of control and eliminate chronic stress. The starting point on this journey is to eliminate excessive sedentary behavior and in engage in behavior such that you consistently and regularly meet your daily exercise requirements, get adequate restful sleep, and eat and drink in a nutritious manner. Only you can do this! In all cases, this puts you in control of managing yourself within various contextual time frames and will eliminate your chronic stress.

As a result, you will have more energy and a **positive attitude** regarding your journey through life as this behavior will literally reframe how you engage with others the world around you, and will enhance your overall health and physical and psychological well-being.

BUDDHISM, DAOISM, AND CONFUCIANISM

All three of these traditions are focused on optimizing your time relative to your overall physical and psychological health and well-being. All three are concerned with eliminating what we today call chronic stress. All three provide guidelines for managing your behavior within various contextual time frames.

Buddhism

Within the context of Buddha's eightfold noble path or treatment plan, the two most salient components relative to managing yourself within the context of time frames are **correct effort** and **correct mindfulness.** Correct effort is being motivated, enthusiastic, energized, committed, disciplined, consistent, and regular in your practice and engagement regarding completing your tasks and meeting your goals in an effective and efficient manner. Mindfulness develops your attention, concentration, and awareness, in a nonjudgmental manner, in the present, precluding you from wasting time mind wandering and making excuses.

Daoism

The over 2,000-year-old text the *Zhuangzi* is very clear that life is quite short. It is over before you know it! This being the case, why waste time interfering with yourself and others, lose time by getting entangled and controlled by the activities of the world, and give up all your time working and toiling until exhausted, all of which lead to chronic stress, and thus compromise your physical and psychological health and well-being? The following two quotes, respectively, from chapter 22 and from chapter 2 of the *Zhuangzi* makes these concerns abundantly clear.

> Human life in the world is like glimpsing through a crack and seeing a white colt race by. A sudden moment, and it is gone. Suddenly, it is over. (Guo, 1974, p. 380; Santee, 2004, p. 6)
>
> Accepting that which has become our body, don't forget that we use it as we wait upon its end. Interaction with things is that of destruction and waste. This goes on until the end, like a galloping horse unable to stop. Is this not sad? All of one's life is that of labor and toil. ... So tired, exhausted, and weary! (Guo, 1974, pp. 34–35; Santee, 2007, p. 48)

The more that you interfere with yourself and others, the more that you get entangled in the activities of the world; and the more time that you waste, the more complicated your life is and your journey through it. A more complicated life results in chronic stress. Chapter 4 of the *Zhuangzi* states this quite clearly:

> It is not desirable to complicate the journey (dao 道). If it is too complicated the complications will result in trouble. Trouble results in chronic stress (you, 憂). Chronic stress cannot help you. The complete person (zhìrén, 至人) of ancient times took care of themselves

first, and then afterwards helped all others. (Guo, 1974, p. 74; Santee, 2005c, p. 8)

In order to address the problem of complications compromising your journey through life, being entangled in the activities of the world, wasting time, and thus, as a result, being chronically stressed, the Sixth Patriarch of Shangqing Daoism, Sima Chengzhen (647–735 CE), in the "Simplifying the Activities of Your World (Jianshi 簡事)" section of his text *A Discussion on Sitting in Oblivion* (*Zuowanglun* 坐忘論), provides the following guideline of simplifying your life:

> Therefore, when a person cultivates the Dao, it would be best to eliminate and simplify things. Know that which is trivial and that which is essential. Determine that which is frivolous and that which is important. Understand your options. Whatever is not essential and not important should be severed from your life. (Santee, 2010, p. 14)

Two Daoist, intimately linked, practices that are fundamental to not complicating your life, not wasting time, not getting entangled in the activities of the world, not working and laboring yourself to death, being in control, and not chronically stressing oneself are **wuwei** (無為) and **wushi** (無事). In chapter 57 of the over 2,000-year-old text, the *Daodejing* (Santee, 2005a, p. 21, 2005b, p. 29), the Sage ruler, a Daoist role model, states,

> I do not interfere with myself or others (*wuwei*, 無為)
> and the people naturally transform themselves.
> I am tranquil (*jing*, 静)
> and the people naturally regulate themselves
> I am not entangled/controlled by the activities of the world (*wushi*, 無事)
> and the people naturally enrich themselves
> I am without controlling desires (*wuyu*, 無欲)
> and the people naturally simplify themselves (*pu*, 樸)

Interfering with yourself is mind wandering, procrastination, engaging in negative, judgmental thinking regarding yourself and others, making excuses, while interfering with others is trying to coerce others to do what you want for your own benefit—all of which are conducive to wasting time, becoming chronically stressed, and not being in control of your life in various contextual timeframes. Being entangled/controlled by the activities of the world is letting such society-determined values as fame, status, wealth, ideologies, and expectations control your behavior, all of which waste your time relative to being in control of your own behavior and are conducive to generating chronic stress.

Chapter 4 of the *Zhuangzi* provides guidelines for putting both *wuwei* and *wushi* into practice during your daily life such that you do not waste time, are in control of your life, and are not chronically stressed

> Take responsibility for your own mind/heart so that sorrow and joy do not easily affect you. Knowing what you cannot resolve, and being at peace with it by adapting to destiny, is the perfection of internal power. As a subject and a son, there is that which you cannot avoid. Forget about your ego and deal with the situation.
>
> Reside in the world by letting your mind/heart flow without any obstructions. Accept what you cannot avoid as well as nourish that what is within is perfection. What more can be said? (Guo, 1974, pp. 86, 89; Santee, 2011, p. 50)

In other words, there are problems in your world that you cannot solve and situations you cannot control. Stop wasting time, energy, and chronically stressing yourself trying to do so. There are obligations in life that you have relative to the choices you have made. Stop wasting time and energy and chronically stressing yourself by whining and complaining about doing them. Deal with them!

The importance of *wuwei*, and indirectly *wushi*, is further expanded in chapter 18 of the *Zhuangzi* where the practice of *wuwei* is directly linked to a **positive frame of mind** with the statement, "I take *wuwei* to be true happiness!" (Santee, 2011, p. 51). The commentary of Guo Xiang (252–312 CE) further links *wuwei* to physical and psychological health and well-being with the statement, "The happiness of *wuwei* is to simply be without chronic stress (*you* 憂), that is all" (Santee, 2011, p. 51).

Confucianism

The focus of Confucius regarding time is threefold. The first is that whatever you are engaged in, always practice **moderation**. Excessive behavior of any sort is detrimental to your well-being, wastes time, and is conducive to chronic stress. In Book 6 of the *Analects*, Confucius notes

> Confucius said, "Practicing moderation (*zhongyong* 中庸) is supreme moral behavior (*de* 德). It has been rarely seen amongst the people for a long time." (Santee, 2007, p. 207)

The second area of focus is utilizing your time, no matter the situation, in a positive manner to learn and reflect on improving your behavior. The following quotes from Books 1 and 7, respectively, from the *Analects* make this focus quite clear:

> Cengzi (a disciple of Confucius) said, "I daily examine myself in three areas. In working for other people, have I not done my best/been authentic (*zhong* 忠)? In interacting with my friends have I not been trustworthy (*xin* 信)? Have I not practiced (*xi* 習) what has been passed on to me?
>
> The Master said, "When traveling with three people, I will certainly have teachers. I will select that which is good and follow it. That which is not good, I will change it in myself. (Santee, 2007, p. 194)

The third area of focus is having the time to put into practice what you have learned. For Confucius learning is oriented toward practical application and being able to apply, within a contextual time frame, what you have learned as a pleasurable experience. The following quote, from Book 1 of the Analects, links time, learning, practice, and positive feelings together.

> Is it not pleasurable, to have the time/opportunity (shi 時) to put into practice what one has learned?

PRACTICAL APPLICATION

Baduanjin: Shaking the Head and Swinging the Tail Expels Inner Heat (*yaotou baiwei qu xinhuo* 搖頭擺尾去心火)

This posture is focused on releasing bottled-up feelings such as anger and worry (*xinhua* 心火). Essentially, it is about releasing chronic stress both physically and psychologically.

Upon finishing the previous posture let your hands return to the transition position. The opening of this posture is the same as **both hands supporting heaven regulates the triple burners** as explained chapter 6. Breathing naturally throughout this posture, simply rotate your hands so the palms face up as you extend your arms upward. Once you have extended your arms, make sure your elbows are not locked, and step to the side with your left foot, making sure your feet remain parallel, to a width and depth that appears as if you were riding a horse. This position is called a **horse stance**. At the same time, circle your arms outward and downward, letting your hands coming to rest on your thighs just above your knees with the web of your hands facing toward your upper thighs/groin area.

Turn your pelvis/waist to the right, bend at the waist and look at your right toes. Your body weight is on the right side. Staying in that same position, shift your body weight to the left by gently and slowly, swinging your torso to the left side, and then look at your left toes. Do not rise or let go of your hand positions as you transition to the left side. Rotate your torso to the left and up and return to the **horse stance**. Do not rise or let go of your hand position.

Repeat this process starting on the left side by turning your pelvis/waist to the left, bending at the waist and looking at your left toes. Your body weight is on the left side. Staying in that same position, shift your body weight to the right by gently and slowly, swinging your torso to the right side, and then look at your right toes. Do not rise or let go of your hand positions as you transition to the right side. Rotate your torso to the right and up and return to the **horse stance**. Do not rise or let go of your hand position. This completes one repetition. Do seven more repetitions. Upon completing the final repetition, bring your left foot to your right foot, stand up, and return to the transition position. Take a breath and walk away.

As usual, how do you feel upon completing this posture? What did you notice while you were performing this posture? How is your mind? Calm? Empty? Still? Agitated? Did your mind wander? Do you notice/feel a difference regarding the benefits of each of the postures. If so, what?

KEY TERMS

self-management	tactics	correct effort
wasting of time	goals	correct mindfulness
procrastination	action plans	simplifying your life
social media	timelines	*Wuwei*
constant checker	priorities	*Wushi*
digital devices	self-monitoring	moderation
negativity	positive outlook	horse stance
excuses	positive attitude	
strategy	positive frame of mind	

EXERCISES

1. Reflecting on the past few days, how much time did you waste? How did you waste it? Did it compromise you attaining your goals for the day?

2. Create a list of your top ten priorities, either in writing or in an audio recording, and post it where you can see or hear it each day.

3. Set a short-term goal, create an action plan to meet it, set a timeline to reach it, and monitor your progress toward attaining it. Were you successful in meeting your goal? Why or why not?

4. For the next week, create a log for monitoring your sleep. Track when you go to bed, when you wake up, how many hours you were in bed, how restful your sleep was (use a scale of 1–5 with 1 = not rested and 5 = completely rested), and how you felt throughout the day (use a scale of 1–5 with 1 = terrible and 5 = great). Did your amount of sleep enhance or detract from performing your daily activities? Why?

5. Why is it important to learn to say no in the context of self-management?

6. How much time did you spend yesterday being sedentary? On social media? On your mobile phone, iPad, and/or computer? Was it beneficial for managing yourself? Why or why not? Given the data regarding being excessively sedentary with various technological devices, what can you do to address these issues and best manage yourself within the context of time? Be specific!

7. Pick a day and examine yourself relative to being authentic/doing your best, trustworthy, and practicing what has been passed on to you. What did you discover?

8. How much time during the day do you engage in negative thinking, making negative judgments about yourself and others, and making excuses? Do you view this behavior as a waste of time? If so, why? If not, why not?

9. Why is it important, relative to managing yourself, to set priorities for the day?

10. Over the course of a day, observing yourself and others, practice *wuwei* and *wushi*. What did you notice?

REFERENCES

American Psychological Association (APA) (2014). *Are teens adopting adults' stress habits?* Retrieved from http://www.apa.org/news/press/releases/stress/2013/stress-report.pdf

American Psychological Association (APA) (2016). Stress in America: The impact of discrimination. Retrieved from https://www.apa.org/news/press/releases/stress/2015/impact-of-discrimination.pdf

American Psychological Association (APA) (2017). Stress in America: Coping with change: Part 2. Retrieved from https://www.apa.org/news/press/releases/stress/2017/technology-social-media.pdf

Andrews, S., Ellis, D. A., Shaw, H., & Piwek, L. (2015). Beyond self-report: Tools to compare estimated and real-world smartphone use. *PLoS ONE, 10*(10), e0139004. Retrieved from https://www.ncbi.nlm.nih.gov/pmc/articles/PMC4625000/pdf/pone.0139004.pdf

Centers for Disease Control and Prevention (CDC). (2016). *Obesity and overweight.* Retrieved from https://www.cdc.gov/nchs/fastats/obesity-overweight.htm

Chapman, S. W., & Rupured, M. (n.d.). Time management: Ten strategies for better time management. *The University of Georgia.* Retrieved from http://www.wiu.edu/advising/docs/Time_Management_Strategies.pdf

Claessens, B. J. C., van Eerde, W., Rutte, C. G., & Roe, R. A. (2007). A review of time management literature. *Personnel Review, 36*(2), 255–276.

Gafni, R., & Geri, N. (2010). Time management: Procrastination tendency in individual and collaborative tasks. *Interdisciplinary Journal of Information, Knowledge and Management, 5,* 115–125. Retrieved from http://www.ijikm.org/Volume5/IJIKMv5p115-125Gafni448.pdf

Gallup (2015). *Nearly half of smartphone users can't imagine life without it.* Retrieved from https://news.gallup.com/poll/184085/nearly-half-smartphone-users-imagine-life-without.aspx

Gregoire, C. (2015, December 2). You probably use your smartphone way more than you think: Many young adults spend a third of their waking lives on their device. *Huffington Post.* Retrieved from https://www.huffingtonpost.com/entry/smartphone-usage-estimates_us_5637687de4b063179912dc96

Greenwood, S., Perrin, A. & Duggan, M. (2016, November 11). Social media update 2016: Facebook usage and engagement is on the rise, while adoption of other platforms holds steady. *Pew Research Center*. Retrieved from http://www.pewinternet.org/2016/11/11/social-media-update-2016/

Guo, Q. F. (1974). *Zhuangzi jishi* 莊子集釋 (Vols 1 and 2). Taipei, TW: Chung Hwa.

Hackernoon. (2017). How much time do people spend on their mobile phones in 2017? Retrieved from https://hackernoon.com/how-much-time-do-people-spend-on-their-mobile-phones-in-2017-e5f90a0b10a6

Hafner, A., Stock, A., & Oberst, V. (2014). Decreasing students' stress through time management training: An intervention study. *European Journal of Psychology of Education*, *30*(1), 81–94.

Harper, J. (2015, February 10). Hello? Americans now spend five hours a day—on their phones. *Washington Times*. Retrieved from https://www.washingtontimes.com/news/2015/feb/10/smart-phone-nation-americans-now-spend-five-hours-/

Khalaf, S., & Kesiraju, L. (2017). U.S. time spent on mobile phones crosses five hours a day. *Flurry Analytics Blog*. Retrieved from http://flurrymobile.tumblr.com/post/157921590345/us-consumers-time-spent-on-mobile-crosses-5

Killingsworth, M. A., & Gilbert, D. (2010). A wandering mind is an unhappy mind. *Science*, *330*(6006), 932.

Kross, E., Verduyn, P., Demiralp, E., Park, J., Lee, D. S., Lin, N., ... & Ybarra, O. (2013). Facebook use predicts declines in subjective well-being in young adults. *PLoS ONE*, *8*(8), e69841. Retrieved from http://journals.plos.org/plosone/article/file?id=10.1371/journal.pone.0069841&type=printable

Macan, T., Shahani, C., Dipboye, R., & Phillips, A. P. (1990). College students' time management: Correlations with academic performance and stress. *Journal of Educational Psychology*, *82*(4), 760–768.

Marano, H. E. (2003). Procrastination: Ten things to know. *Psychology Today*. Retrieved from https://www.psychologytoday.com/articles/200308/procrastination-ten-things-know

Owen, N., Sparling, P. B., Healy, G. N., Dunstan, D. W., & Matthews, C. E. (2010). Sedentary behavior: Emerging evidence for a new health risk. *Mayo Clinic Proceedings*, *85*(12), 1138–1141.

Perez, S. (2017). U.S. consumers now spend 5 hours per day on mobile devices. *Tech Crunch*. Retrieved from https://techcrunch.com/2017/03/03/u-s-consumers-now-spend-5-hours-per-day-on-mobile-devices/

Perrin, A. (2015, October 8). Social media usage: 2005–2015. *Pew Research Center*. Retrieved from http://www.pewinternet.org/2015/10/08/social-networking-usage-2005-2015/

Ratey, J. J., & Hagerman, E. (2008). *Spark: The revolutionary new science of exercise and the brain*. New York, NY: Little, Brown and Company.

Santee, R. (2004, July). *A Daoist and an existential psychotherapist: A comparative study*. Paper presented at the 1st World Hong Ming Philosophy Conference. Honolulu, HI.

Santee, R. (2005a). Wandering through the dao, while the dao wanders through all: The dao of the dao de jing. *Empty Vessel*, *12*, 16–21.

Santee, R. (2005b). *Carl Rogers and the dao de jing: A comparative study*. Paper presented at the International Conference on Daoism at Mount Tiantai and Zhejiang, Tiantai, CN.

Santee, R. (2005c). *Cultivating emptiness: The practice of xin zhai, an ancient Daoist solution for the problem of chronic stress*. Paper presented at the International Conference of Daoist Cultivation and its Modern Value, Sichuan University. Chengdu, CN.

Santee, R. (2007). *An Integrative Approach to Counseling: Bridging Chinese Thought, Evolutionary Theory, and Stress Management*. Copyright © 2007 by SAGE Publications. Reprinted with permission.

Santee, R. (2010). *Sitting in forgetfulness and the relaxation response: An inquiry into managing the physical and psychological symptoms of chronic stress*. Paper presented at the 6th International Daoist Studies Conference, Daoism Today: Science, Health and Ecology. Los Angeles, CA.

Santee, R. (2011). "The Zhuangzi: A Holistic Approach to Health Care," *Living Authentically: Daoist Contributions to Modern Psychology*, ed. Livia Kohn, pp. 39-58. Copyright © 2011 by Three Pines Press. Reprinted with permission.

Shellenbarger, S. (2014). To stop procrastinating, look to science of mood repair: New approach focuses on helping people regulate their emotions. *Wall Street Journal.* Retrieved from https://www.wsj.com/articles/to-stop-procrastinating-look-to-science-of-mood-repair-1389142943

Statista (2017a). *Most famous social network sites worldwide as of September 2017, ranked by number of active users (in millions).* Retrieved from https://www.statista.com/statistics/272014/global-social-networks-ranked-by-number-of-users/

Statista (2017b). *Average time spent with major media per day in the United States as of September 2017 (in minutes).* Retrieved from https://www.statista.com/statistics/276683/media-use-in-the-us/

UC Santa Cruz (2016). *Time management and procrastination.* Retrieved from https://caps.ucsc.edu/resources/time-management.html

WebMD (2018). *Stress management: Managing your time.* Retrieved from https://www.webmd.com/balance/stress-management/stress-management-managing-your-time

Zarick, L. M., & Stonebraker, R. (2009). I'll do it tomorrow. The logic of procrastination. *College Teaching,* 57(4), 211–215. Retrieved from https://www.scribd.com/document/159554760/1-ll-Do-1t-Tomorrow-The-Logic-of-Procrastination

CREDITS

CHAPTER 11

Interpersonal Relationships

After finishing this chapter, you will be able to do the following:

- Explain, from the perspective of evolution, why interpersonal relationships/social connectedness is important
- Describe Glasser's perspective regarding unhappiness and interpersonal relationships and his solution to resolving unhappiness
- Define social support
- Compare low social support and high social support relative to physical and psychological health and well-being
- Compare the research regarding giving and receiving social support
- Define social support within the context of a work environment. Why is it important?
- Indicate why social connectedness may be compromised by digital technology
- Explain the connection between interpersonal relationships and chronic stress
- Compare Buddhist, Daoist, and Confucian approaches regarding positive social support/connectedness

Interpersonal relationships, making positive, reciprocal connections with other people, enhance our ability to survive and to find a mate in order to reproduce. Essentially, we are social beings, and interpersonal relationships, the belonging with and support of others, is fundamental, at least for most of us, to our adapting to various environmental contexts (Barrett, 2017; DeMichele, 2016; Siegel, 2012; Ratey & Manning, 2014; Van der Kolk, 2014; Young, 2008). In essence, as is the case with many other species, we are wired and have evolved to make connections with other people (DeMichele, 2016; Lieberman, 2013; Ratey, & Manning, 2014; Siegel, 2012; Van der Kolk, 2014; Young, 2008). Insofar as we basically need other people, the challenge is learning how to get along with other people while meeting our own goals. The psychiatrist William Glasser (1998) creator of reality therapy and choice theory noted

> [I]f there is a truth about people that no one can dispute, it is the success in any endeavor is directly proportional to how well the people who are involved in it get along with each other. (p. 21)

Glasser (1998) argues that unhappiness, thus being stressed, is due to problematic interpersonal relationships, as

> all unhappy people have the same problem: they are unable to get along well with the people they want to get along well with. ... We do not know how to get along with each other any better than we ever have. (p. 5)

Glasser's (1998) solution to the problem of dysfunctional interpersonal relationships and of unhappiness is to establish positive interpersonal relationships. He indicates that one must

> stop choosing to coerce, force, compel, punish, reward, manipulate, boss, motivate, criticize, blame, complain, nag, badger, rank, rate, and withdraw. We must replace these destructive behaviors with choosing to care, listen, support, negotiate, encourage, love, befriend, trust accept, welcome and esteem. (Glasser, 1998, p. 21)

Considering Glasser's theory, if we look at our own social groups or at the outside world, we will probably note the damaging results of dysfunctional strategies and the fruitful outcomes of functional approaches.

SOCIAL SUPPORT

Research links low levels of **social support**/positive interpersonal relationships, social isolation, and loneliness to a number of health-and well-being-related problems such as cardiovascular disease, hypertension, a weakened immune system, compromised adherence behavior, depression, fatigue, pain, stress, disrupted sleep, impaired physical and psychological well-being, and increased mortality rates (APA, 2015, 2017; Cacioppo & Cacioppo, 2014; Iveniuk, Waite, McClintock, & Teidt, 2014; Jaremka et al., 2013; Kiecolt-Glaser et al., 1997; Kurina et al., 2011; Reblin & Uchino, 2008; Shankar, McMunn, Banks, & Steptoe, 2011; Uchino, 2009).

Research (APA, 2015, 2018; Brown, Nesse, Vinokur, & Smith, 2003; Brown et al., 2009; Reblin & Uchino; Uchino, 2009) is fairly clear that social support, positive interpersonal relationships, is beneficial to one's overall physical and psychological well-being. Holt-Lunstad, Smith, and Layton (2010) found that satisfactory interpersonal relationships increased chances of survival by 50% when compared with unsatisfactory interpersonal relationships. Kroenke and colleagues (2013) found that positive interpersonal relationships were linked to a higher quality of life for women with breast cancer.

Giving and Receiving Support

The American Psychological Association's (2015) Paying with Our Health Survey report indicated 21% of the respondents noted they had no one to rely on for social/emotional support. Of these 21%, 43% indicated their stress had increased from the past year, 46% felt sad/depressed the past month as a result of stress, and 21% indicated they did not make lifestyle changes because they were stressed (APA, 2015). On the other hand, of those who indicated they had someone to rely on for social support, 26% indicated their stress had increased from the past year, 32% felt sad/depressed the past month as a result of stress, and 10% indicated they did not make lifestyle changes because they were stressed (APA, 2015). It appears clear that positive interpersonal relationships (social/emotional support) is integral for addressing chronic stress.

There is research (Brown et al., 2003; Brown et al., 2009) indicating that providing social/emotional support, positive interpersonal relationships, may also be beneficial to your overall physical and psychological health. On the other hand, there is also research (APA, 2012; Buffone, Poulin, DeLury, Ministero, & Morrisson 2017; Gorman & Gorman, 2017) suggesting that *providing* social support/helping behavior may be, for some, stressful and thus detrimental to your overall health and well-being. The more an individual providing the support/care identifies with the negative feelings of the recipient, essentially emotionally putting themselves in the situation of the recipient and taking his or her perspective, the greater the likelihood the individual will become stressed and compromise his or her own physical and psychological health and well-being (Buffone et al., 2017, Gorman & Gorman, 2017).

Taylor and colleagues (2000), while acknowledging that the fight/flight response is probably physiologically similar across males and females, note that research on stress has been primarily focused on the behavioral responses of males to stress and that the fight/flight response does not really represent the evolutionarily based behavioral responses, "**tend and befriend**," of females to stress. These responses are thought to be oriented to protecting their children (**tending**) and protecting themselves (**befriending**) by linking to others via social behavior. These behaviors of social support are seen as enhancing survival and reducing the stress of both mother and child.

McGonigal (2015) describes how stress may give rise to caring for others and making connections/coping with others via "tend-and-befriend" behavior. In addition, she notes that this "tend-and-befriend" behavior is not restricted to females as it can be found in male behavior. Thus, "tend-and-befriend" behavior appears to be an evolved evolutionary mechanism for coping with stress.

For those in the helping professions or those who are planning to enter the helping professions, it is important that you examine your own interpersonal relationships before assessing the interpersonal relationships of others.

Work, Support, and Interpersonal Relationships

The American Institute of Stress (AIS, 2018) report argues that there is considerable research suggesting that **work-related stress** is the primary source of stress for adults in the United States and that it continues to increase.

The American Psychological Association's (APA, 2012b) Workplace Survey indicated that 41% of working adults reported being chronically stressed while at work and that 42% reported they do not have resources to manage workplace stress. The American Psychological Association's (APA, 2012a) Stress in America Survey indicated the five major reported sources of stress, for the 2011 respondents, were the following:

- Money (75%)
- Work (70%)
- The Economy (67%)
- Relationships (58%)
- Family Responsibilities (57%)

The Regus global survey (2012) across 14 countries indicated the 48% of working adults reported that their stress levels had increased from the previous year,

essentially the same as a previous survey, 18 months prior, with the major sources of stress being professional as opposed to personal:

- Work (59%)
- Finances (44%)
- Customers (37%)

Sixty-three percent of respondents in this survey (Regus, 2012) indicated that flexible working practices would be a solution to reducing this stress. Essentially, flexible working practices refers to not being trapped working in one specific location for a specific set of hours, such as an 8:00 a.m. to 4:00 p.m. work schedule, day in and day out, such that the employee is able to select what specific hours he or she works and the location, such as a home office or other remote location (Regus, 2012). The argument here is that flexible working practices are more conducive to a positive, work/family/life interaction (Regus, 2012).

Although there are a number of variables that may contribute to stress on the job such as issues with pay, growth and development, training, advancement, work hours, work load, work environment/conditions, control, responsibility, demands, authority, role/job design, and organizational management (APA, 2017c; Leka, Griffiths, & Cox, 2003), of extreme importance, relative to reducing stress on the job, is that of positive interpersonal relationships/social support. Echoing Glasser's work, within the context of a work environment, social support (Stoetzer et al., 2009; Waldenström, 2008) includes availability of resources and providing tangible assistance relative to solving problems by supervisors and colleagues (instrumental support) and positive interpersonal relationships such as praise, acknowledgment, approval, appraisal, collaboration, encouragement and assistance in coping by supervisors and colleagues (emotional support). Leka, Griffiths, and Cox (2003) note that as social support rises on the job, the more likely it is that stress will decrease for employees.

The American Psychological Association's (APA, 2017d) 2017 Job Skills Training and Career Development Survey regarding the perception of employees who felt they did not have support from their supervisor relative to their organization indicated the following:

- 39% were satisfied
- 16% felt valued
- 22% would recommend their organization to others
- 53% planned to leave within the year
- 56% did not trust employer

Digital Technology and Social Connectedness
The American Psychological Association's "Stress in America: Coping with Change" (APA, 2017b) report regarding the impact digital technology, such as

computers, mobile phones, and tablets, had on social connectedness with family members when together noted the following:

- 45% of millennials (18–34) felt disconnected
- 38% of gen Xers (35–50) felt disconnected
- 23% of boomers (51–69) felt disconnected
- 16% of matures (70 and above) felt disconnected
- 38% of millennials (18–34) reported digital technology as a source of conflict
- 27% of gen Xers (35–50) reported digital technology as a source of conflict
- 12% of boomers (51–69) reported digital technology as a source of conflict
- 4% of matures (70 and above) reported digital technology as a source of conflict

In addition, the report also noted (APA, 2017b) regarding the impact social technology had on social connectedness with family members when together, 45% of parents felt disconnected and 48% of parents reported ongoing conflict when trying to control child's time usage of technology. It appears, given the research, the perception is there is clearly a negative/detrimental side to using digital technology for a rather large number of individuals and families. That being the case, heavy users of technology might consider ways to enhance a sense of interpersonal connection.

BUDDHISM, DAOISM, AND CONFUCIANISM

All three of these traditions clearly understand the importance of positive inter-personal relationships not only for one's overall physical and psychological health and well-being, but also for the overall physical and psychological health and well-being for those with whom you interact in various environmental contexts. All three traditions see positive interpersonal relationships as important for elim-inating what we today call chronic stress. All three traditions provide guidelines for establishing mutually respectful positive interpersonal relationships.

Buddhism

The **Noble Eight-Fold Path** of Buddhism, the guide for eliminating *dukkha* or chronic stress, is made up of three interrelated and interdependent groupings (Rahula, 1974). The grouping of wisdom consists of correct seeing and correct thinking. The grouping of attentiveness consists of correct effort, correct mindfulness, and correct concentration. The grouping of ethical behavior consists of correct speech, cor-rect action, and correct livelihood. The *Cūḷavedallasuttaṃ* or the *Small Sutra of Assorted Issues* (毘陀羅小經) states

> **Correct speech, correct action, and correct livelihood**

> Correct speech, correct action, and correct livelihood, these standards are contained in the ethical behavior (jie 戒, *Sila*) grouping. Correct effort, correct mindfulness, and correct concentration, these stan-dards are contained in the attentiveness (ding 定, *Samadhi*) grouping. Correct seeing and correct thinking, these standards are contained in the wisdom (hui 慧, *Prajna*) grouping (Agama, 2019).

While all three groupings and their respective components are intimately interrelated, interdependent, and essential for interpersonal relationships, ethical behavior is the most salient. Correct speech, correct action, and correct livelihood are explained in the sutra known as the *Saccavibhaṅgasuttaṃ* or the *Sutra that Analyzes the Truths (di fenbie jing* (諦分別經).

Attributed to Buddha, correct speech, action, and livelihood refer to actions and choices that do not harm others:

> Fellow students! What is correct speech? The elimination of lying. The elimination of antagonistic speech. The elimination of nega-tivistic speech. The elimination of gossip. Fellow students! This is what is called correct speech.

Fellow students! What is correct behavior? Not taking a life. Not taking that which has not been given to you. Not being licentious. Fellow students! This is what is called correct behavior.

Fellow students! What is correct livelihood? Fellow students! This, noble disciples, is leaving behind unhealthy livelihoods [those which harm others] and engaging in correct livelihoods [those which do not harm others] for one's profession. Fellow students! This is what is called correct livelihood. (Agama, 2019a)

While the grouping of ethical behavior is focused, primarily, on how you should *not* behave in interpersonal relationships, the grouping of attentiveness is the foundation of how you ought to behave in interpersonal relationships, specifically, the meditative practice of the cultivation of the **four immeasurable states of the mind** (Buddhaghosa, 1999; O'Brien, 2017). In the *Vatthasuttaṃ* or *Sutra of the Clothing/Cloth* (*yifu jing* 衣服經) Buddha, regarding the progress of a monk, notes,

> He resides having filled up the first direction with a mind (xin 心) of loving kindness (ci 慈, *metta*), in the same manner the second direction, the third direction, and the fourth direction, in the same manner high, low, and horizontal, everywhere to all things and to himself. He resides having filled up everywhere with a mind of loving kindness (*ci* 慈, *metta*) that is vast, outstanding, immeasurable, without hate, without resentment, and without negative intentions, desires, or thoughts. So, he also resides having filled up everywhere with a mind of compassion (*bei* 悲, *karuna*), ... delight in the happiness of others (*xiyue* 喜悅, *mudita*), ... and equanimity (*pingjing* 平靜, *upekkha*), that is vast, outstanding, immeasurable, without hate, without resentment, and without negative intentions, desires, or thoughts. (Agama, 2019b)

Essentially, for Buddha, not only in meditative practice but also in interpersonal relationships one should manifest **loving kindness**, compassion, delight in the happiness of others, and equanimity, all of which

Loving-kindness meditation

are interrelated and interdependent. The starting point of the four immeasurable states of mind is loving kindness. In the Karaniya *Metta Sutra* (*ying zuo ciai jing* 應作慈愛經), or the *Sutra of Loving Kindness*, the practice of loving kindness is described:

> Meditate and feel in such a way: joyful and peaceful. May the minds (xin 心) of all beings be joyful. All beings, no matter weak, strong, tall,

large, medium, short and/or small, refined, unrefined, seen, unseen, near, far, already born or not yet reborn.

May the minds of all beings have joy ... like a mother risking her life to protect her only child.

Even more so toward all beings. Regularly cultivating an immeasurable mind of good intention toward the entire cosmos. Regularly cultivating an immeasurable (wuliang無量) mind.

Above, below, and all around, without obstructions, without hostility, without hate. No matter whether you are standing, walking, sitting, or laying down. Whenever one is awake you should firmly establish this mindfulness (nian 念). (For translations see National Cheng Kung University, n.d.; Siongui, n.d.)

Practice mindfulness

While mindfulness meditation is nonjudgmentally focused on the awareness of an object, such as one's breath, emotions, thoughts, or awareness of itself in the present, loving-kindness mediation, which is also nonjudgmental and focused in the present, differs insofar as it intentionally generates and directs loving kindness toward all beings including oneself. The *Path of Purification* (Buddhaghosa, 1999), by the 5th century CE Theravada Buddhist author commentator Buddhaghosa (佛鳴), makes it quite clear that the starting point for loving kindness meditation is loving kindness *toward oneself*.

Research (Aspy & Proeve, 2017; Bankard, 2015; Fredrickson et al., 2008; Hofmann, Grossmann, & Hinton, 2011; Hutcherson, Seppala, & Gross, 2008; Zeng, Chiu, Wang, Oei, & Leung, 2015) suggests that practicing loving-kindness meditation promotes positive emotions, social connectedness, and prosocial behavior and, as such, contributes to positive interpersonal relationships. In other words, loving-kindness meditation appears beneficial in reducing chronic stress associated with interpersonal relationships (Csaszar, & Curry, 2013; Hofmann, Grossmann, & Hinton, 2011; Shonin, Van Gordon, & Griffiths, 2014; Shonin, Van Gordon, Compare, Zangeneh, & Griffiths 2014).

Wuwei

Daoism

As noted in Chapter 3, the *Daodejing* was written, essentially, to establish social harmony. As such it provides guidelines on how to establish positive, functional interpersonal relationships—interpersonal relationships that are without chronic stress. In other words, how to live one's life with others in a harmonious manner. In order to establish social harmony, get along with each others, establish and maintain friendships, and not be chronically stressed by interpersonal relationships, the *Daodejing* advocates the practice of **wuwei**, which has been discussed in previous chapters, of not interfering with oneself, not interfering with others such as trying to force or coerce them to do something for your own benefit, and, creating an environment for interpersonal relationships that is conducive to growth for all participants. Thus,

- not engaging in negative, absolute, black-and-white, threat-based psychosocial thinking;
- not judging, and evaluating your self-worth;
- not allowing your self-worth to be determined and controlled by other people's opinions, evaluations, and judgments about you; and
- learning to simply accept yourself

are all entailed with not interfering with yourself, *wuwei*, and establishing positive, supportive interpersonal relationships.

It is part of our evolutionary toolkit to interact with others in a manner that is beneficial and supportive to all participants and not controlling, contending or being argumentative such that the focus is on you winning and the other person losing. All are entailed with not interfering with others, *wuwei*, and establishing positive, supportive interpersonal relationships.

Three Daoist treasures

Creating an environment for interpersonal relationships that is comfortable, supportive, beneficial, and positive for all, in other words practicing *wuwei*, is conducive to growth.

Chapter 67 of the *Daodejing* offers some basic suggestions about how to practice *wuwei* and establish a foundation for positive, interpersonal relationships and friendships that is conducive to eliminating chronic stress. It states,

> I have three treasures that I maintain and protect. The first is compassion. The second is simplicity. The third is patience. (Wang, 1993, pp. 262–263)[1]

The practice of *wuwei* is being concerned for the well-being of others, keeping the interactions as simple and concrete as possible, and being patient as you listen to them and facilitate adaptive solutions, all of which are fundamental for creating an environment conducive to growth for all, reducing/eliminating chronic stress, and establishing positive, interpersonal relationships.

Chapter 19 and chapter 81, respectively, of the *Daodejing* look at the fundamentals of the practice of *wuwei* from another angle, adding additional components for

---

1 "Simplicity" is a translation of *jian* (儉) which means economical and frugal. Both are consistent with keeping things simple which is a fundamental characteristic of the *Daodejing*. "Patience" is a translation of the line "not daring to be first in the world" (*bu ganwei tianxia xian* 不敢為天下先). "Not daring to be first in the world" or "patience" is a fundamental characteristic of the *Daodejing*. All translations of this section on Daoism are mine.

the purpose of establishing positive, interpersonal relationships and friendships by eliminating the tendency to compete or contend with each other. It states,

> See the ordinary, embrace its naturalness. Lose self-centeredness, have few desires. (Wang, 1993, pp. 76–77)
>
> Believable (*xin* 信) words are not beautiful and flowery. Beautiful and flowery words are not believable. Those who are kind are not argumentative. Those who are argumentative are not kind. Those who know are not pedantic. Those who are pedantic do not know. ... The way (*dao* 道) of nature (*tian* 天) is to benefit, not harm. The way (*dao* 道) of the wise person or Sage (*shengren* 聖人) is to act, yet not contend (*zheng* 爭). (Wang, 1993, pp. 307–308; also see Santee, 2003)

Friendship

In Chapter 6 of the *Zhuangzi* (Guo, 1974) the issue of friendship is presented in two stories. What is of special importance, in both stories, regarding friendship, is humor—the ability to mutually laugh, smile and interact with each other, while being free from the concept of being friends in the first place.

> Zi Si, Zi Yu, Zi Li, and Zi Lai, these four people were talking with each other. Someone said, "Who is able to take nothingness (wu 無) to be the head, life (sheng 生) to be the spine, and the buttocks to be death (si 死)? Who knows life and death, surviving and perishing to be an organic, interrelated whole? You will be my friend!" These four individuals all laughed and smiled (*xian* 笑) at each other. Their mind/hearts (*xin* 心) were not contrary to each other. They got along and became friends (you 友).
>
> Zi Sanghu, Meng Zifan, and Zi Qinzhang, these three individuals got along with each other in a friendly (you 友) manner. Someone said, "Who is able to get along with each other without intentionally getting along, and do things together without intentionally doing things together? Who is able to climb up into the heavens and flow (you 遊) about in the mist, waxing and waning in the limitless, mutually forgetting about life forever? These three individuals all laughed and smiled at each other. Their mind/hearts (*xin* 心) were not contrary to each other. They got along as friends (you 友).

Friendship

Confucianism

As noted in chapter 3, Confucius (551–479 BCE) lived during a time when there was considerable social and political instability and disharmony. He identified the cause of this social and political instability and disharmony as being a self-centeredness and self-benefit focus at the expense of others. Individuals were out for their own gain. Interpersonal relationships were dysfunctional. Because of these dysfunctional interpersonal relationships, people were chronically stressed as they competed for their own individual needs, benefits, and desires while behaving inappropriately with others. The solution for Confucius was quite straightforward: teach people how to engage in positive, supportive, functional interpersonal relationships with the primary goal being the establishment of social harmony.

Practice

For Confucius, the foundation of positive, supportive, functional interpersonal relationships is based in the family. It is in the family where people initially learn about and implement those interpersonal relationship behaviors that are fundamental to establishing social harmony. These behaviors are piety/respect (*xiao* 孝), trust (*xin* 信), appropriate contextual behavior (*li* 禮), choosing appropriate contextual behavior (*yi* 義), the wisdom to choose the appropriate contextual behavior (*zhi* 知), authenticity/coming from the center of one's heart (**zhong** 忠), empathy (**shu** 恕) and interpersonal selfless relationships (*ren* 仁). As also noted in chapter 3, the solution of appropriate, respectful, interpersonal behavior with the harmony of society as a whole, not the individual, as the focus, is found in the *Lunyu* (論語) or *Analects* of Confucius. This entire process revolves around learning and putting into practice, in a social context, what one has learned. As noted in the previous chapter, the first line in Book One of the *Analects* states,

> Is it not pleasurable, to have the time/opportunity (shi 時) to put into practice what one has learned? (Chinese Classic, n.d.)

Contingent upon the context and the participants in the interpersonal relationship, Confucius, in the *Analects*, discussed the importance of appropriate contextual behavior or li (禮). Appropriate contextual behaviors establish positive interpersonal relationships as they provide the guidelines for behaving in a manner that is not self-centered, allowing the participants the opportunity to be heard and communicate in a manner that is respectful and inclusive. In Book Twelve, in a discussion regarding the highest Confucian virtue of interpersonal selfless relationships (*ren* 仁), the importance of *li* or appropriate contextual behavior is clearly fundamental for establishing positive functional interpersonal relationships.

> Yan Yuan/Yan Hui (a disciple of Confucius) asked about interpersonal selfless relationships (*ren* 仁). The Master said, "Overcoming your self-centeredness and returning to appropriate, contextual moral behavior (*li* 禮) is *ren*. If, for one day, people overcame their self-centeredness and returned to *li,* then the whole world would come together

in *ren*. This is because *ren* is due to the relationship between yourself and other people." Yan Yuan said, "May I ask about what this entails?" The Master said, "If it is not appropriate contextual behavior (*li*) do not look. If it is not *li*, do not listen. If it is not *li*, do not speak. Do not do anything contrary to *li*." Yan Yuan said, "Although I am not very smart, I will engage in what you have said." (Santee, 2007, p. 197)

Fundamental to appropriate contextual behavior, interpersonal selfless relationships, and successful communication is being attentive (*jing* 敬). Being attentive shows respect and demonstrates to the other participant(s) that you are in fact listening, value what they say, and care. In Book Five, Confucius notes

> Yan Pingzhong is kind (*shan* 善) in his relationships with other people. He is always attentive (*jing* 敬). (Santee, 2007, p. 200)

Two fundamental behaviors underlying and tying together the Confucian process of establishing and maintaining positive, functional interpersonal relationships and as such, social harmony, are being authentic/doing your best (*zhong* 忠) and understanding and having some sense what the other person is experiencing, in other words empathy (*shu* 恕). In Book Four it states,

Be attentive

> The Master said, "Zeng! My way (*dao* 道) uses a single thread." Zeng Zi said, "So it does." The Master left. The disciples asked, "What did he mean?" Zeng Zi said, "The way of the Master is doing your best/being authentic (*zhong* 忠) and being empathic (*shu* 恕). That is it!" (Santee, 2007, p. 201)

In one sense, the following quote from Book Thirteen integrates all the various behaviors entailed in establishing positive, functional, interpersonal relationships and social harmony. As the highest virtue, how exactly does *ren* play out in a social context? For Confucius, on one level, it is quite simple and straightforward.

> Fan Chi asked about *ren*. The Master said, "In your home be deferential (*gong* 恭), in managing your affairs be attentive (*jing* 敬), and when interacting with others do your best/be authentic (*zhong* 忠). Even if you were among the barbarian tribes, it is not possible to abandon these." (Santee, 2007, p. 203)

Zhong and Shu

PRACTICAL APPLICATIONS

Baduanjin: The Two Hands Go Down to the Feet to Strengthen the Kidneys (*liangshou pan zu gu shen yao* 两手攀足固身腰)

Begin standing straight with your arms at your sides. Breathing naturally, arc your hands forward, palms facing each other and upward until they are extended above your head. Turning your hands inward so the fingertips face each other, palms facing down, slowly lower them down in front of your body until they are level with your armpits. Turning your hands inward, palms facing up, push them under your armpits and place your palms onto your back. From this position, begin to slowly bend forward while gently and slowly sliding your hands down your back, across your buttocks, down the back of your legs until you reach the back of your ankles. Upon reaching this point slide your hands forward along your feet until your fingers are in front of and, if possible, touching your toes with your palms facing your ankles.

Begin to slowly start to straighten your body to an upright position. At the same time, arc your hands, palms facing each other, forward and upward until they are once again extended above your head. This completes one repetition. Repeat seven more times. After completing the last repetition and your hands are extended above your head, slowly lower them down the front of your body, palms facing down, returning them to side of your thighs. As usual, note how you feel physically and psychologically. What did you discover? Learn? What parts of your body are you aware of? What benefits do you notice after completing this posture?

Loving-Kindness Meditation

Although loving-kindness meditation can be practiced anytime during one's waking hours, practicing it in the morning, after rising, is a positive way to start off your day. Find a place that is quiet, sit up straight, gently shut your eyes, and breathing naturally silently repeat to yourself, "May I be happy, may I be peaceful, and may my mind be filled with joy." Initially, practice this for a minute or so just to get the feel for it. Notice how you feel upon finishing. As you go about your day, you can pause for a minute or so and practice this meditation. Notice if this practice has an impact on how you think, feel, perceive, and/or behave regarding your interactions with others throughout the day.

You are not restricted to saying all three phrases while you practice. You may just repeat one of the phrases or utilize one or more of your own. The important point is that it is something positive about your overall health and well-being. As discussed elsewhere in the text, we spend far too much time negatively thinking about and judging ourselves, such as our negativity bias and mind wandering, which strengthens our corresponding neural networks, making this negative behavior more readily assessible. The more readily assessible, as all of it is threat based, the more easily we become and stay stressed. By changing our thinking about ourselves to something positive such as "may I be happy" and repeating this during regular and consistent loving kindness meditation practice, we begin to build new neural networks and become more in control of how we perceive and interact in our world.

KEY TERMS

interpersonal relationships	digital technology	*wuwei*
social support	noble Eight-Fold Path	zhong
tend and befriend	four immeasurable	shu
work-related stress	states of the mind	
	loving kindness	

EXERCISES

1. Assess and evaluate your interpersonal relationships from a Buddhist, Daoist, and Confucian perspective. What did you discover?

2. Compare how you feel giving and receiving social support.

3. Compare social isolation and loneliness.

4. Do you agree with Glasser's explanation of and solution to unhappiness? Why or why not?

5. Compare instrumental support and emotional support within the context of your own work environment. Do you feel supported?

6. Each day for the next week practice loving kindness meditation in the morning, the afternoon, and before you go to bed for a minute or so each time. How do you feel upon completing each meditation? Do you notice a difference between how you felt at the start of the week and the end of the week? Explain.

7. The next time you get together with a group of friends, practice *wuwei* both toward yourself and toward others. What do you notice?

8. Pick another day and practice *zhong* and *shu* when you interact with others. What do you discover?

9. How is chronic stress linked to interpersonal relationships?

10. To explore perceived social support in your own life take the Multidimensional Scale of Perceived Social Support (Zimet, Dahlem, Zimet, & Farley, 1988) which can be found at http://media.wix.com/ugd/5119f9_2f88fadcd382463daf5821e8af94a865.pdf. What did you discover about perceived social support in your life?

REFERENCES

Agama. (2019). *The collection of the middle length sayings.* Translated from http://agama.buddhason.org/MN/MN044.htm

Agama. (2019a). *The collection of the middle length sayings.* Translated from http://agama.buddhason.org/MN/MN141.htm

Agama. (2019b).*The collection of the middle length sayings.* Translated from http://agama.buddhason.org/MN/MN007.htm

American Institute of Stress (AIS) (2018). *Workplace stress.* Translated from https://www.stress.org/workplace-stress/

American Psychological Association (APA) (2012a). *Stress in America: Our health at risk.* Retrieved from https://www.apa.org/news/press/releases/stress/2011/final-2011.pdf

American Psychological Association (APA) (2012b). *Workplace survey: American Psychological Association Harris Interactive.* Retrieved from https://www.apa.org/news/press/releases/phwa/workplace-survey.pdf

American Psychological Association (APA) (2015). *Stress in America: Paying with our health.* Retrieved from http://www.apa.org/news/press/releases/stress/2014/stress-report.pdf

American Psychological Association (APA) (2017a). *Stress in America. Coping with change: Part 1.* Retrieved from https://www.apa.org/news/press/releases/stress/2016/coping-with-change.pdf

American Psychological Association (APA) (2017b). *Stress in America. Coping with change: Part 2.* Retrieved from https://www.apa.org/news/press/releases/stress/2017/technology-social-media.pdf

American Psychological Association (APA) (2017c). *Supervisor support critical to employee well-being and workforce readiness.* Retrieved from http://www.apa.org/news/press/releases/2017/10/employee-well-being.aspx

American Psychological Association (APA) (2017d). *2017 Job skills training and career development survey.* Retrieved from http://www.apaexcellence.org/assets/general/2017-training-survey-results.pdf

American Psychological Association (APA) (2018). *Manage stress: Strengthen your support network.* Retrieved from http://www.apa.org/helpcenter/emotional-support.aspx

Aspy, D. J. & Proeve, M. (2017). Mindfulness and loving-kindness meditation: Effects on connectedness to humanity and to the natural world. *Psychological Reports, 120*(1), 102–117.

Bankard, J. (2015). Training emotion cultivates morality: How loving-kindness meditation hones compassion and increases prosocial behavior. *Journal of Religion and Health, 54*(6), 2324–2343.

Barrett, L. F. (2017). *How emotions are made: The secret life of the brain.* New York, NY: Houghton Mifflin Harcourt.

Brown, S. L., Nesse, R. M., Vinokur, A. D., & Smith, D. M. (2003). Providing social support may be more beneficial than receiving it: Results from a prospective study of mortality. *Psychological Science, 14*(4), 320–327.

Brown, S. L., Smith, D. M., Schulz, R., Kabeto, M. U., Ubel, P. A., Poulin, M., ... & Langa, K. M. (2009). Caregiving behavior is associated with decreased mortality risk. *Psychological Science, 20*(4), 488–494.

Buddhaghosa. (1999). *Path of purification (Visuddhimagga): The classic manual of Buddhist doctrine and meditation* (Nanamoli, trans.). Retrieved from https://accesstoinsight.org/lib/authors/nanamoli/PathofPurification2011.pdf

Buffone, A. E. K., Poulin, M., DeLury, S., Ministero, L., & Morrisson, C. (2017). Don't walk in her shoes! Different forms of perspective taking affect stress physiology, *Journal of Experimental Social Psychology, 72*, 161–168.

Cacioppo, J. T., & Cacioppo, S. (2014). Social relationships and health: The toxic effects of perceived social isolation. *Social and Personality Psychology Compass, 8*(2), 58–72.

Chinese Classic. (n.d.). Analects. Retrieved from http://www.chineseclassic.com/13jing/LeungYu/LeungYu01.htm

Csaszar, I. E., & Curry, J. (2013). Loving kindness meditation: A promising practice for reducing stress and increasing empathy. *Vistas Online.* Retrieved from https://www.counseling.org/docs/default-source/vistas/loving-kindness-meditation.pdf?sfvrsn=6

DeMichele, T. (2016). Humans are hardwired to be social beings. *Fact/Myth.* Retrieved from http://factmyth.com/factoids/humans-are-hardwired-to-be-social-beings/

Fredrickson, B. L., Cohn, M. A., Coffey, K. A., Pek, J., & Finkel, S. M. (2008). Open hearts build lives: Positive emotions, induced through loving-kindness meditation, build consequential personal resources. *Journal of Personality and Social Psychology, 95*(5), 1045–1062.

Gorman, S., & Gorman, J.M. (2017). I feel your pain—is that a problem? Why empathy is both great and terrible. *Psychology Today.* Retrieved from https://www.psychologytoday.com/us/blog/denying-the-grave/201707/i-feel-your-pain-is-problem

Glasser, W. (1998). *Choice theory: A new psychology of personal freedom.* New York, NY: Harper Perennial.

Guo, Q. F. (1974). *Zhuangzi jishi* 莊子集釋 (Vols 1 and 2). Taipei, TW: Chung Hwa.

Hofmann, S. G., Grossman, P., & Hinton, D. E. (2011). Loving-kindness and compassion meditation: Potential for psychological interventions. *Clinical Psychology Review, 31*(7), 1126–1132.

Holt-Lunstad, J., Smith, T. B., & Layton, J. B. (2010). Social relationships and mortality risk: A meta-analytic review. *PLoS Medicine, 7*, e1000316. Retrieved from https://www.ncbi.nlm.nih.gov/pmc/articles/PMC2910600/pdf/pmed.1000316.pdf

Hutcherson, C. A., Seppala, E. M., & Gross, J. J. (2008). Loving-kindness meditation increases social connectedness. *Emotion, 8*(5), 720–724.

Iveniuk, J., Waite, L. J., McClintock, M. K., & Teidt, A. D. (2014). Marital conflict in older couples: Positivity, personality, and health. *Journal of Marriage and the Family, 76*(1), 130–144.

Jaremka, L. M., Fagundes, C. P., Glaser, R., Bennett, J. M., Malarkey, W. B., & Kiecolt-Glaser, J. K. (2013). Loneliness predicts pain, depression, and fatigue: Understanding the role of immune dysregulation. *Psychoneuroendocrinology, 38*(8), 1310–1317.

Kiecolt-Glaser, J. K., Glaser, R., Cacioppo, J. T., MacCallum, R. C., Snydersmith, M., Kim, C., & Malarkey, W. B. (1997). Marital conflict in older adults: Endocrinological and immunological correlates. *Psychosomatic Medicine, 59*(4), 339–349.

Kroenke, C. H., Kwan, M. L., Neugut, A. I., Ergas, I. J., Wright, J. D., Caan, B. J., Hershman, D., & Kushi, L. H. (2013). Social networks, social support mechanisms, and quality of life after breast cancer diagnosis. *Breast Cancer Research and Treatment, 139*(2), 1–20. Retrieved from https://www.ncbi.nlm.nih.gov/pmc/articles/PMC3906043/pdf/nihms-477608.pdf

Kurina, L. M., Knutson, K. L., Hawkley, L. C., Cacioppo, J. T., Lauderdale, D. S. & Ober, C. (2011). Loneliness is associated with sleep fragmentation in a communal society. *Sleep, 34*(11), 1519–1526.

Leka, S., Griffiths, A., & Cox. T. (2003). *Work organisation and stress.* Geneva, Switzerland: World Health Organization. Retrieved from http://www.who.int/occupational_health/publications/en/oehstress.pdf

Lieberman, M. D. (2013). *Social: Why our brains are wired to connect.* New York, NY: Crown.

McGonigal, K. (2015). How to transform stress into courage and connection. *Greater Good Magazine.* Retrieved from https://greatergood.berkeley.edu/article/item/how_to_transform_stress_courage_connection

National Cheng Kung University. (n.d.). *Collection of sutras.* Retrieved from http://myweb.ncku.edu.tw/~lsn46/extra/tipitaka/sutta/khuddaka/khuddaka-patha/Metta.htm

O'Brien, B. (2017). Brahma-Vihara: The four divine states or four immeasurables: Loving kindness, compassion, sympathetic joy, equanimity. *Learn Religions.* Retrieved from https://www.thoughtco.com/brahma-vihara-the-four-divine-states-449717?print

Rahula, W. (1974). *What the Buddha taught.* New York, NY: Grove Press.

Ratey, J. J., & Manning, R. (2014). *Go wild: Free your body and mind from the afflictions of civilization*. New York, NY: Little, Brown and Company.

Reblin, M., & Uchino, B. N. (2008). Social and emotional support and its implication for health. *Current Opinion in Psychiatry, 21*(2), 201–205.

Regus. (2012). *From distressed to de-stressed*. Retrieved from https://www.google.com/url?sa=t&rct=j&q=&esrc=s&source=web&cd=3&cad=rja&uact=8&ved=0ahUKEwiCjcb9i_XYAhVQ-GMKHahRBB8QFgg1MAI&url=http%3A%2F%2Fwww.healthatwork-online.de%2Ffileadmin%2Fdownloads%2FRE0969_GBS_6_-_Stress_Whitepaper_AUG_2012_HR.pdf&usg=AOvVaw0Gnl4DUEtARGUCLB67XlUY

Santee, R. (2003, December). An inquiry into the Dao of the Dao de Jing. *World Hong Ming Philosophical Quarterly*.

Santee, R. (2007). *An Integrative Approach to Counseling: Bridging Chinese Thought, Evolutionary Theory, and Stress Management*. Copyright © 2007 by SAGE Publications. Reprinted with permission.

Shankar, A., McMunn, A., Banks, J., & Steptoe, A. (2011). Loneliness, social isolation, and behavioral and biological health indicators in older adults. *Health Psychology, 30*(4), 377–385.

Shonin, E., Van Gordon, W., Compare, A., Zangeneh, M., & Griffiths, M.D. (2014). Buddhist-derived loving-kindness and compassion meditation for the treatment of psychopathology: A systematic review. *Mindfulness*. Retrieved from http://self-compassion.org/wp-content/uploads/2015/03/Shonin.pdf

Shonin, E., Van Gordon, W., & Griffiths, M. D. (2014). The emerging role of Buddhism in clinical psychology: Toward effective integration. *Psychology of Religion and Spirituality, 6*(2), 123–137.

Siegel, D. J. (2012). *The developing mind: How relationships and the brain interact to shape who we are*. New York, NY: Guilford Press.

Siongui. (n.d.). *Collection of sutras*. Retrieved from https://siongui.github.io/pali-chanting/zh/karaniiya-mettaa/

Stoetzer, U., Ahlberg, G., Johansson, G., Bergman, P., Hallsten, L., Forsell, Y., & Lundberg, I. (2009). Problematic interpersonal relationships at work and depression: A Swedish prospective cohort study. *Journal of Occupational Health, 51*(2), 144–151.

Taylor, S. E., Klien, L. C., Lewis, B. P., Gruenwald, T., Gurung, R. A. R., & Updegraff, J. A. (2000). Biobehavioral responses to stress in females: Tend-and-befriend, not fight-or-flight. *Psychological Review, 107*(3), 411–429.

Uchino, B. N. (2009). Understanding the links between social support and physical health: A life-span perspective with emphasis on the separability of perceived and received support. *Perspectives on Psychological Science, 4*(3), 236–255.

Van der Kolk, B. (2014). *The body keeps score: Brain, mind, and body in the healing of trauma*. New York, NY: Penguin.

Waldenström, K., Ahlberg, G., Bergman, P., Forsell, Y., Stoetzer, U. & Waldenström, M. (2008). Externally assessed psychosocial work characteristics and diagnoses of anxiety and depression. *Occupational Environment Medicine, 65*(9), 90–96.

Wang, K. (1993). *Laozi Daodejing He Shanggong Zhang Zhu*. Beijing: Zhong Hua Shu Ju.

Young, S. N. (2008). The neurobiology of human social behaviour: An important but neglected topic. *Journal of Psychiatry & Neuroscience, 33*(5), 391–392.

Zeng, X., Chiu, C. P. K., Wang, R., Oei, T. P. S., & Leung, F. Y. K. (2015). The effect of loving-kindness meditation on positive emotions: A meta-analytic review. *Frontiers in Psychology, 6, 1693*. Retrieved from https://www.ncbi.nlm.nih.gov/pmc/articles/PMC4630307/pdf/fpsyg-06-01693.pdf

Zimet, G. D., Dahlem, N. W., Zimet, S. G., & Farley G. K. (1988). The multidimensional scale of perceived social support. *Journal of Personality Assessment, 52*(1), 30–41.

CREDITS

CHAPTER 12

A Personal Stress Management Program (PSMP)

After finishing this chapter, you will be able to do the following:

- Develop a personal stress-management program (PSMP) relative to managing and preventing chronic stress.
- Create a log to record and analyze data relative to managing and preventing chronic stress
- Explain the importance of writing a daily narrative/journal relative to managing and preventing chronic stress
- Describe how writing a weekly narrative/journal relative to managing and preventing chronic stress allows you to discover and analyze the patterns and links that may be giving rise to your chronic stress and how this information will allow you address it
- Understand how the relationship between a PSMP, a log, a daily narrative/journal, and weekly narrative/journal and the information they provide are integral to managing and preventing chronic stress
- Indicate how digital technology is applicable to addressing/managing chronic stress
- Explain how a PSMP is important for your overall health and well-being

In this chapter students will learn how to construct a personal, holistic, integrative, stress-management program, gather the data, log the data, analyze the results, and write a narrative regarding the process. What is especially important is to see the links and patterns between the various components of the PSMP so that one can address, reduce/eliminate, and prevent the symptoms of chronic stress, essentially, proactively contributing to establishing your positive physical, psychological, and interpersonal health and well-being.

BASIC STRUCTURE OF THE PROGRAM

In order to address/prevent chronic stress and the physical, psychological, and interpersonal problems associated with it, it is necessary to develop an integrated, holistic **personal stress-management program (PSMP).** For example, if chronic worrying, due to psychosocial threat-based thinking, compromises your obtaining adequate, restful sleep, not only will your energy levels be decreased, but your attention, focus, patience, and how you interact with others may be impaired. In addition, if you lack energy, chances of exercising are reduced and, more than likely, your sedentary behavior will increase—all of which are conducive to generating additional stress, which in turn circles back on the various occurrences just discussed, thus resulting in a **vicious cycle of stress.**

Not only do you still have the perceived psychosocial stressors that resulted in your chronic worrying in the first place, you now have all the subsequent stressors that arose as a result of not obtaining adequate restful sleep, which in itself is an additional stressor for you to worry about. This ongoing vicious cycle of stress compromises your physical, psychological, and interpersonal health and well-being, thus, the necessity of an integrative, holistic stress-management program that recognizes and addresses the reciprocal, interdependent relationship of the various behaviors that are incorporated into your sense of self.

Given the personal stress-management program or PSMP, in order for it to be beneficial to assist you in addressing and eliminating/reducing chronic stress, it is necessary to gather and record information/data for the various components of the PSMP to discover the various links, relationships, and patterns that are associated with/conducive to the generation and maintaining of the stress, thus the necessity of creating and utilizing a **log**.

Given the PSMP and the log, the data/information needs to be organized, analyzed, and put in a **weekly narrative/journal** format. This narrative/journal format allows for the discovery of patterns and links between the behavioral components that may be giving rise to and sustaining the chronic stress, the effectiveness of the interventions developed for the PSMP to address the stressors, and, if necessary, the modifying/changing of the PSMP to better address the stressors. In addition, research is quite clear that writing/journaling about one's symptoms, emotions, and concerns can be quite beneficial for one's physical and psychological health and well-being (Baikie, & Wilhelm, 2005; Dunn, 2015; Junghaenel, Schwartz, & Broderick, 2008; Meshberg-Cohen, S., Svikis, D., & McMahon, 2014; Mugerwa, S., & Holden, 2012; Murray, 2002; Pennebaker, 1997; URMC, n.d.).

Personal Stress Management Program (PSMP)

Essentially, a holistic, integrative, personal stress-management program (PSMP) is your guide regarding specific actions and assessment relative to addressing and preventing chronic stress. Do not make your goals too easy or too hard. Make your goals realistic and challenging. Always remember that you need to be flexible and are free to adapt, change, and or/modify them based on what life presents you on your journey. It is import-

ant that, when warranted, specific days, duration, and frequencies are indicated. To simply say, "I will run three days during the week" is too vague and allows you to keep putting off following through on meeting this specific goal until

the timeframe during the week for meeting this goal is past. Better wording is presented in the sample PSMP.

It is important that the entire PSMP be succinct, straightforward, and no more than one page. This will allow you to place it where you can easily see it, say on the refrigerator, to remind you of what needs to be done for the day. The format of this sample PSMP is structured so all the interrelated and interdependent

components that are discussed in this book are addressed. The left-hand side indicates what specifically needs to be done, while the right-hand side consists of your personal goals for each section.

- **Keep daily log:** Logging should be done on a daily basis at a time most convenient for you
- **Sleep:** How much restful sleep do you need to optimally meet the challenges of your day?
- **Diet:** What should you reduce/eliminate from your diet? What should you add? How many meals?
- **Water:** How much water do you need a day to stay hydrated?
- **Aerobic exercise:** Selecting at least one cardio exercise (e.g., walking, jogging) to perform during the week
- **Anaerobic Exercise:** Exercising entire body utilizing weight resistance (e.g., free weights, body weight)
- **Stretching:** Exercises for entire body (muscles/tendons) to reduce tension and increase range of motion
- **Neuromotor:** Integrative/multi-dimensional exercises such as yoga, qigong, taijiquan, and Pilates for balance/agility
- **Counting breaths:** Counting, to yourself, your breaths when you inhale and exhale
- **Mindfulness:** Flexibly focused, nonjudgmental awareness of an activity in the present such as eating
- **Safe-space visualization:** Visualizing a safe space in your mind where you feel secure and not stressed
- **Relaxation response:** Saying a meaningful word or short phrase to yourself when you exhale
- **Loving-kindness meditation:** Saying something kind about/to yourself such as "May I be happy"
- **Social:** Making positive interpersonal connections with others
- **Time management:** Monitoring and assessing how you utilize time
- **Cognitive restructuring/reframing:** Monitoring and addressing your inappropriate, threat-based thinking
- **Sedentary behavior:** Reducing extended sitting behavior
- **Moderation is the key:** Avoiding excessive and deficient behavior in everything you do

This sample PSMP is a useful example:

Sample Personal Stress Management Program

1. Keep daily log	
2. Sleep	Get 8 hours of restful sleep per day
3. Diet	Watch diet: Eliminate soda, candy, and chips from diet
4. Water	While there are no hard-and-fast rules for how much an individual needs per day (temperature, activity, gender, age, weather, etc., has a direct impact on daily water requirements), one guideline to estimate the amount of water, there are others, is to drink half your weight expressed in ounces of water each day. As I weigh 180 pounds, an adequate amount of water per day is about 90 ounces.
5. Aerobic exercise	Swim 2 days a week (T–Th) for 30 minutes each session Walk 3 days a week (M–W–F) for 30 minutes each session (American College of Sports Medicine [ACSM] recommends 150 minutes per week; see chapter 6)
6. Anaerobic	Weight machines (T–Th–Sat) Five exercises upper body (1 set each 10 reps) Five exercises lower body (1 set each 10 reps) (ACSM recommends 2–3 days per week; see chapter 6)
7. Flexibility	Stretching 10 minutes before and 10 minutes after aerobic and anaerobic exercises (ACSM recommends 2–3 days per week; see chapter 6)
8. Neuromotor/ neuromuscular	These exercises train skills like balance, coordination, gait, and agility. Taijiquan and Qigong daily for 30 minutes. (ACSM recommends 2–3 days per week; see chapter 6)
9. Counting breaths	Sitting: Focus on breathing 3 days per week (T–Th–S) for 10 minutes each session
10. Mindfulness	Daily at each meal for at least 10 minutes.
11. Safe-space visualization	Three days a week (M–W–F) for 5 minutes a day
12. Relaxation response	Each day, for 10 minutes, I practice saying my "word" or short phrase while I exhale.

13. Loving-kindness meditation	Five minutes each morning saying "May my day be peaceful, be joyful and may my heart be happy."
14. Social	One hour each day with kids One hour each day with spouse Two hours a week with friends Go out to eat with family at least once a month.
15. Cognitive restructuring/reframing	Monitoring and addressing inappropriate threat-based psychosocial, absolute negative thinking such as awfulizing, catastrophizing, whining, complaining, moaning, demeaning, criticizing, hostility, anger, rumination, obsessing, worrying, and so on while at home, work, play, school, and interacting in society.
16. Time management	Daily assessment of how I am utilizing and managing my time
17. Sedentary behavior	Daily walk 250 steps for each hour between 6:00 a.m. and 5:00 p.m.
18. Moderation is the key	

Keeping a Daily Log

Once you have developed a holistic, integrative personal stress-management program (PSMP), the next step once you put it into practice is to collect the information/data for each area so that you can monitor whether it is working,

FITNESS TRACKER
application

what exactly you are doing/not doing relative to following your program, make changes/modifications if necessary, and discover the links and patterns relative to (a) addressing/preventing chronic stress and (b) your physical and psychological health and well-being. You might find that there are distractors or other elements in your daily schedule unrelated to the categories listed in your PSMP that block progress. Note these elements in your journal and address them as needed.

Tips for Data Gathering/Utilizing Fitness Tracker Apps

It is recommended that you record the data on your log at the end of each day. This way you will not have to strain your memory at the end of the week trying to remember what occurred earlier in the week. For some, given your life and the daily demands put upon it, the logging of the PSMP may appear to be a major challenge. However, if you reframe it as learning how, through consistent practice, to reduce your stress by better organizing your life and managing yourself in the context of time, you will find it easier to approach and to be quite beneficial. You will clearly see how you actually live your life on a daily basis and discover your strengths and challenges relative to eliminating chronic stress. An important guideline for this process is be flexible, as life does happen. Modify and change when necessary. For example, select and practice only one type of meditation, as opposed to five, for your PSMP. You always need to eat so practicing mindfulness while eating is not subtracting additional time from your busy life.

There are no specific fitness tracker apps that exactly correspond to the PSMP. There are, however, numerous free **fitness tracker apps**, which can be enhanced for a price, for your digital devices that assist you in collecting, organizing, analyzing, and storing the data/information you collect. These fitness tracker apps may focus on one specific area, such as nutrition or meditation, or incorporate numerous areas such as nutrition, aerobic and anaerobic exercise, meditation, water consumption, and yoga. A useful feature of digital devices is that of the calendar. You can insert into the calendar what your daily and weekly schedule will be for your PSMP. Alarms can be set to remind you what you need to be doing, the duration, and when for each day. There are also numerous health and fitness apps that can be set to remind/ alert you that it is time to engage in a particular activity. In addition, there are numerous **smart watches,** with their corresponding fitness tracker apps, none of which exactly correspond to the PSMP, which may not only (a) further expand your ability in collecting, organizing, analyzing, and storing the data/ information you collect and (b) allow you to collect additional information, such as sleep cycles, sedentary behavior, and heart rate while exercising, which you might not be able to gather with a standalone fitness app, but also be set to alert/remind you it is time to engage in a particular activity. As there are many fitness tracker apps, both standalone and with a smart watch, it is best, if you so choose to utilize this technology, that you do your own research regarding which type or types best meet your individual needs. The following is an example of the structure of a weekly log consistent with the sample PSMP presented.

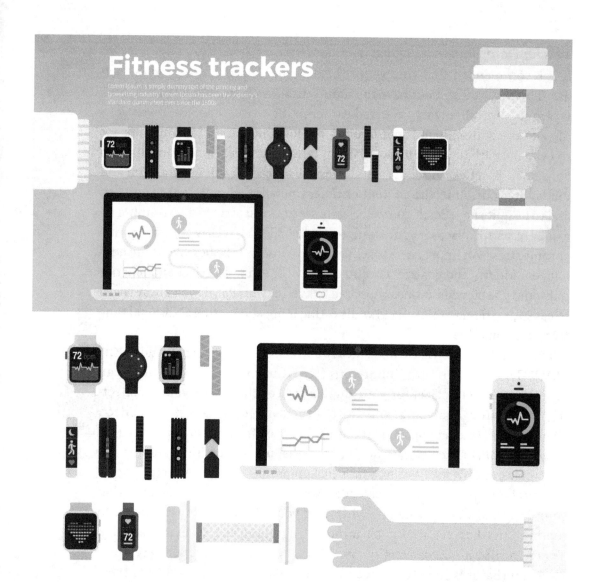

For your convenience, a daily log format (you can of course make your own) is provided here:

DAILY LOG

Rating of experience/feelings: On a scale of 1 to 10, 1 = terrible and 10 = great

		SUN	MON	TUE	WED	THUR	FRI	SAT
SLEEP	No. of hours							
Upon waking	Rating							

		SUN	MON	TUE	WED	THUR	FRI	SAT
	Breakfast							
	Lunch							
	Dinner							
	Snacks/ meal							
	Rating:							
WATER CONSUMP-TION	How much							
	Rating							
EXERCISE								
Aerobic exercise	Type							
	Hours							
	Rating							
Stretching	Hours							
	Rating							
Neuromotor	Type							
	Hours							
	Rating							
Anaerobic exercise	Type							
	Hours							
	Rating							
MEDITATION								
Counting breaths	Hours							
	Rating							

		SUN	MON	TUE	WED	THUR	FRI	SAT
Mindfulness	Hours							
	Rating							
Relaxation response	Hours							
	Rating							
Loving-kind-ness medita-tion	Hours							
	Rating							
Safe-space visualization	Hours							
	Rating							
SOCIAL	Type							
	Hours							
	Rating							
RECRE-ATION	Type							
	Hours							
	Rating							
DAILY LOG-GING	Hours							
	Rating							
COGNITIVE RESTRUC-TURING/ REFRAMING	Type							
	Hours							
	Rating							
TIME MANAG-MENT	Type							

		SUN	MON	TUE	WED	THUR	FRI	SAT
	Hours							
	Rating							
SEDENTARY BEHAVIOR	**Total hours**							
	Hours met move-ment goal							
	Rating							
COMMENTS:								

The 1–10 ratings are to provide a quantitative assessment of each area. While the extremes, 1 (terrible) and 10 (great) are established, you choose a number to represent a rating in between the extremes. For example, if your sleep was okay/average you might rate it a 5. If it was not very restful you might rate it 2, while if it was pretty good you might rate it a 9. At the end of the week you will then determine the average rating of your sleep. In addition, you will list the numbers of hours you were asleep for each day and then determine the average number of hours of sleep over the week.

In the meals section, you will indicate if you did or did not have a specific meal such as lunch or dinner, and then rate your eating behavior for the day. As with the sleep section, you will then determine the average rating of your eating behavior for the week. The rest of the sections follow a similar format. In the narrative/journal write-up you will provide more specific details for each section where the ratings from your log will be integrated with your qualitative rating.

Narrative/Journal Format

In addition to the log, which is the recording, primarily quantitative, of your data, it is recommended you also write a **daily narrative/journal,** which will allow you to record additional qualitative, relevant information regarding each of the components of the PSMP. The journal can be as simple as an inexpensive spiral-bound noted or as complex as a digital diary application. No matter the format, it will allow you to better remember what occurred each day relative to compiling your weekly narrative/journal. The log and the daily narrative/journal serve as the foundation and information source for writing the **weekly narrative/journal** which, in turn, allows you to discover the patterns and links relative to managing chronic stress and/or preventing chronic stress. This, then, will allow you to generate and implement solutions that can be monitored/assessed relative to their efficacy. In either case, the ultimate focus is your overall positive health and well-being.

The most important point, no matter whether you choose to utilize the specific PSMP, log, daily narrative/journal, and weekly narrative/journal process presented in this chapter, parts of it, or create your own, is that you (a) recognize the importance of gathering, recording, and analyzing relevant information regarding managing your stress and (b) implement and assess your program. The following sample narrative best demonstrates this entire process.

UNDERSTANDING THE DATA AND APPLYING THE INFORMATION: A SAMPLE NARRATIVE/JOURNAL FOR ONE WEEK

This is the first week of my pattern analysis. It took 2 days to get used to logging my life on the form that was provided for the class. It certainly is requiring me to be organized. At this point it is fairly routine and quite informative. I do need a lot of work. (6)

I averaged 6 hours of sleep a night. I don't think it was very restful (4). I did notice that I sleep more on the weekends than during the week. I had one day during the week where I got only 4 hours of sleep and I sure felt it the next day. Problems with energy (3), attention (4), focus (4), and impatience (2) were noted. Truth of the matter, I was kind of nasty to those around me. It is clear to me that inadequate sleep is quite problematic. I will be examining my sleeping patterns so that I get adequate rest.

My eating habits are a mess (3). I don't eat breakfast (I have no time) and pretty much survive on fast food and soda. Weekends are not much different. I suspect my eating habits also contribute to my lack of energy (3). I will start to eat breakfast on a regular basis beginning tomorrow. I will monitor how this meal impacts my energy and attention levels.

I did not drink much water (2). I am sure the lack of water is also linked to my problems with energy (3), attention (4), and with being impatient (2). As noted in my PSMP I will begin to drink 90 ounces of water (body weight = 180 and half of 180 = 90) per day.

As far as exercise is concerned, this is pretty new to me. My personal stress-management program indicated I would (a) stretch (flexibility) for 10 minutes before and after my aerobic and anaerobic exercise; (b) walk 25 minutes 3 days a week and swim 25 minutes 3 days a week (aerobic); (c) do a weight workout (anaerobic) with machines 3 days a week, incorporating both upper and lower body; and (d) neuromotor/neuromuscular exercises daily for 30 minutes, incorporating taijiquan and qigong. I did not meet my goal of stretching before and after each aerobic and anaerobic session as I missed two anaerobic sessions (7). I was able to meet my aerobic requirement as I walked 3 days for 25 minutes (8) and swam 3 days for 25 minutes (8). I did not meet my anaerobic requirement (3) of working out with the weight machines for 3 days as I was only able to work out one day for 30 minutes. I did exercises for both my upper body and lower body. I know. I know. I need to follow my schedule and incorporate two more weight workouts each week. I'm just so tired and my days are so long. I will include the push-ups, squats, and abdominal crunches regime that we discussed in class for the second and third anaerobic exercise. This way I can do the second and third anaerobic component at home. I met my neuromotor/neuromuscular requirement (10) as I was able to perform my taijiquan and qigong for a total of 30 minutes each day.

I liked the simple breathing exercise of counting breaths. I did that for 5 minutes three times during the week. I felt rested (8). I met my goal here. I also liked the mindfulness exercise, although it was really hard to stay focused and nonjudgmental in the present (5). I practiced mindfulness during my meals. My mind really raced around. I was able to practice the safe-space visualization exercise three times during the week (8). I am able to forget my troubles in my visualized safe space by the mountains and ocean. I was successful in practicing the relaxation response daily for 10 minutes each day. My word "still" kept me focused, centered, and relaxed (8). For me, the loving-kindness meditation worked the best! I performed it for both myself and for my family members. I really noticed not only how good I felt after doing it in the morning, but also how this positive feeling carried throughout the day (10). Overall, I am really enjoying these meditative techniques and clearly see their benefit for my well-being.

School is going fine so far. I am taking two classes and I am enjoying them. I work full time at the insurance company and the job is fine. I was able to meet with my friends during the weekend and I did talk to two of them during the week (8). I spend 60 minutes each night watching the SciFi station. It is great for my relaxation (8). I played tennis once over the weekend. I need to do this more often. I did find myself, in spite of everything else, laughing and smiling each day. This seems to have an impact on my energy.

Managing how I use time has been quite an eye opener. I did not realize how much <u>time</u> during the day I waste complaining and whining (3). I know I need to get better organized (4) and put some structure into my day.

I was stunned regarding how much time during the day I spent being sedentary (2). Sitting at my desk at work (about 7 hours), watching TV (about 3 hours), and using my mobile phone/computer/tablet (about 5 hours). Mind you most of this is straight time without even getting out of my chair. This does not include eating or driving my car. On the weekends, it is even worse. I will start stretching and walking each day for 250 steps, for each hour, between 6:00 a.m. and 5:00 p.m. In addition, I need to cut down the amount of time I spend on my digital devices. I will start by reducing my time on my digital devices by 30 minutes each day during the week, and by 1 hour each day on the weekends.

Regarding cognitive restructuring/reframing, I noticed my negative thinking and cognitive distortions were greater at the start (3) of the week than at the end of the week (5). I spent a lot of time complaining about customers and my fellow workers. I noticed I tended to have absolute expectations about how people must behave. When they didn't behave as I felt they should I got angry (3). In a lot of these instances I noticed that my lack of restful sleep appeared to contribute to my negative thinking and cognitive distortions. Through the process of cognitive restructuring/reframing, I began, one step at a time, reducing/eliminating negative thinking, removing problematic threat-based thinking, examining and addressing my cognitive distortions, developing preferences to replace my absolute problematic thoughts, and reframing how I look at a situation.

I had a headache for 2 days (3). I wonder if it was connected to my sleep and diet. I found myself engaging in a lot of awfulizing, catastrophizing, and complaining almost every day. It was especially noticeable the day after my 4 hours of sleep. I also noticed that I was quite angry (2) on that day.

In summary, I am able to notice links or patterns in how I feel, my energy level, and my behavior relative to my diet, sleep, meditation, exercise, and social interaction. For example, I am sure diet and sleep contribute to my energy problems and my low motivation for doing my anaerobic exercises. When I do not get enough sleep, or it is not restful, the next day I lack energy, I am unable to stay focused very long, and I am quite irritable. On the other hand, when I get restful sleep, I am energized, focused, engage in less negative thinking/complaining, and I am happy. I also noticed that when I meditate, my energy increases and my concentration and attending skills are quite good. I find when I am not well organized, I waste time, and I am stressed. It is important to discover and address the various patterns and relationships, such as those I have described, between the components of my PSMP. This analysis assists me in taking control of my health and overall well-being. I am slowly learning the necessity of being proactive rather than reactive regarding my interactions with my environment. I suspect as I become more proactive I will better be able to manage how I use my time and thus eliminate my excuse of not having enough time to do certain activities. I will continue to monitor myself and address the problems noted in my analysis.

Narrative/Journal

After having read the sample narrative/journal, you should have a fairly good idea how the PSMP, the log, the daily narrative/journal, and the weekly narrative/journal are all interrelated and are designed to allow you to address, eliminate/reduce, and prevent chronic stress in a proactive manner.

WORKING WITH OTHERS

If you are in the helping profession or planning to enter the helping profession and want to utilize the PSMP with a client, the easiest way is to simply, after explaining why the PSMP is relevant to his or her challenges, go step by step over each one of components of the PSMP from top to bottom. Explain why and how all the components are important within an integrative holistic, therapeutic approach to one's overall physical and psychological health and well-being. Have the client, for homework, create a PSMP for him- or herself following the PSMP example and bring it back to your next meeting where it can be discussed between yourself and your client. The next step is to explain the log and show him or her how to utilize it relative to his or her PSMP. When this is clear, have the client implement the program and fill in the log as homework for the next meeting. At the next meeting, discuss his or her experiences, feelings, strengths, and challenges implementing their PSMP, as you both go over the log. The next step is to teach the client how to write the narrative relative to the log. The homework is to bring the log and the narrative to the next meeting for discussion.

PRACTICAL APPLICATION

Baduanjin: Glare at Your Fist to Increase Energy (*numu chong quan zengjia qili* 怒目沖拳增氣力)

From the ending of the previous posture, standing straight with your arms at your sides, step sideways with your left foot and drop down such that it appears that you could be sitting on a horse. This position is called a horse stance. At the same time you are stepping out, place your thumbs in your palms and curl your fingers inward; essentially you have made two fists with your thumbs inside, such that they are all touching your hands. Place your fists on your hips.

Take a deep breath and gradually exhale as you slowly thrust your left fist forward and your palm faces to the right. Do not lock your elbow. Stare at your fist as it moves forward and through all your hand movements. As in all of the postures of the Baduanjin, you want to coordinate your breathing with your body movement. In this case your hand.

Once your arm is extended, elbow not locked, continue exhaling as you rotate your arm inward, extending your fingers and thumb with your palm now facing outward to the left side. Bending your hand inward, the back of your hand facing your chest, begin to rotate your hand upward, fingers now facing up, downward to the left, and then circle your hand forward, ending with your palm facing up and fingers extended. At this point, gradually begin to inhale, slowly place your thumb in your hand, and curl your fingers inward, once again making a fist. Continuing to inhale, rotate your arm inward, your palm now facing to the right side, and gradually pull your elbow to rear with your fist returning to its original position on your hip. Begin to slowly exhale and repeat on the right side. This completes one repetition. Repeat seven more times. Upon completing the last repetition, move out of the horse stance by bring your left foot toward your right and standing upward. You have now returned to the original position with your hands hanging down on your sides. Breathe naturally.

What did you discover? How do you feel? Do you notice any change in your energy levels? How is your breathing? What did you learn?

KEY TERMS

vicious cycle of stress	log	smart watches/fitness
personal stress-management program (PSMP)	daily narrative/journal	tracker apps
	weekly narrative journal	

EXERCISES

1. Using the sample PSMP in this chapter, create your own personal stress-management program (PSMP).

2. Create a log to record the data from your PSMP.

3. Implement your program for 1 week.

4. Keep a daily narrative/journal, digital or hand written, for additional information regarding the implementation of your PSMP.

5. Given all the information/data you have collected by the end of 1 week and using the sample weekly narrative/journal as a guide, analyze your information/data and write a weekly narrative/journal. What patterns and links, regarding your physical and psychological health and well-being, did you discover? What solutions did you generate to address the patterns and links? What are you already doing well? Repeat this process using 1 month of data.

6. What attitudes, breathing techniques, or postures from the book might you incorporate into your solutions to overcome blocks to your PSMP?

REFERENCES

Baikie, K. A., & Wilhelm, K. (2005). Emotional and physical health benefits of expressive writing. *Advances in Psychiatric Treatment, 11*(5), 338–346.

Dunn, D. S. (2015). College stress 101: Keeping a stress diary: Keeping a diary helps students identify what is stressing them out. *Psychology Today.* Retrieved from https://www.psychologytoday.com/blog/head-the-class/201512/college-stress-101-keeping-stress-diary

Junghaenel, D., Schwartz, J., & Broderick J. (2008). Differential efficacy of written emotional disclosure for subgroups of fibromyalgia patients. *British Journal of Health Psychology, 13*(1), 57–60.

Meshberg-Cohen, S., Svikis, D., & McMahon, T. J. (2014). Expressive writing as a therapeutic process for drug dependent women. *Substance Abuse: Official Publication of the Association for Medical Education and Research in Substance Abuse, 35*(1), 80–88.

Mugerwa, S., & Holden, J. D. (2012). Writing therapy: A new tool for general practice? *British Journal of General Practice, 62*(605), 661–663.

Murray, B. (2002). Writing to heal: By helping people manage and learn from negative experiences, writing strengthens their immune systems as well as their minds. American Psychological Association. Retrieved from http://www.apa.org/monitor/jun02/writing.aspx

Pennebaker, J. W. (1997). Writing about emotional experiences as a therapeutic process. *Psychological Science, 8*(3), 162–166.

University of Rochester Medical Center (URMC). (n.d.). *Journaling for mental health.* Retrieved from https://www.urmc.rochester.edu/encyclopedia/content.aspx?ContentTypeID=1&ContentID=4552

CREDITS

CHAPTER 13

Applications of Stress Management to Counseling

After finishing this chapter, you will be able to do the following:

- Explain the relationship between health care costs and lifestyle behaviors
- Describe a psychoeducational approach to counseling and psychotherapy including the relationship between the counselor/therapist and the client
- Describe why lifestyle medicine is fundamental in addressing overall health and well-being
- Explain why therapeutic lifestyle changes should be included in a treatment program by counselors and therapists
- Show how lifestyle behaviors and chronic stress are linked
- Describe a holistic and integrative approach to counseling and psychotherapy that incorporates concepts/research findings from evolutionary theory and neuroscience
- Demonstrate how Buddhist, Daoist, and Confucian theory and practice can inform and enhance the counseling and psychotherapy process
- Describe the relationship between nonverbal behavior such as posture, breathing, facial expressions, and behavioral expression with mood,

feelings, and emotions. Indicate how changing nonverbal behavior is an important part of the therapeutic process

- Explain why self-care is important not only for counselors, therapists, psychiatrists, and clinical psychologists, but is also fundamental in training students in these professions and for students in general

Given the research evidence from previous chapters, it should be quite clear that a **proactive, holistic, integrative approach** to addressing chronic stress and the multiple physical and psychological problems and issues associated with it is fundamental to one's overall physical and psychological health and well-being. This stress-management approach, both preventive and therapeutic, primarily focuses on lifestyle changes in such areas as noted in chapter 12: sleep, nutrition, meditation, exercise, sedentary behavior/physical activity, social, interpersonal relationships, recreation, time management, and cognitive restructuring/reframing.

Hyman, Ornish, and Roizen (2009) raise concerns about the rising costs of health care and not addressing the primary cause, indicating that

> most of the chronic diseases that affect 160 million Americans and account for 78% of our healthcare costs are caused by lifestyle and environmental factors—namely our diet, sedentary lifestyle, smoking, chronic stress, and environmental toxins. (p. 12)

(Readers interested in a more in-depth review of epidemiology will find literature that links many health disparities to differences in exposure to these stressors based on socioeconomic status.)

Hyman, Ornish, and Roizen (2009) argue, given the research, that medical care should focus on interventions regarding lifestyle, as the current approach of primarily focusing on addressing risk factors does not address the underlying cause of the chronic disorders. They note,

[L]ifestyle intervention is often more effective in reducing cardiovascular disease, hypertension, heart failure, stroke, cancer, diabetes, and all-cause mortality than almost any other medical intervention. It is because lifestyle addresses not only risk factor modification or reduction. Our lifestyle and environment influence the fundamental biological mechanisms leading to disease: changes in gene expression, which modulate inflammation, oxidative stress, and metabolic dysfunction. ...

Lifestyle medicine is not just about preventing chronic disease but also about treating it, often more effectively and less expensively than relying only on drugs and surgery. ... Unfortunately, insurance doesn't usually pay for it. No one profits from lifestyle medicine, so it is not part of medical education or practice. It should be the foundation of our healthcare system ... . Lifestyle is the best medicine when applied correctly. (Hyman, Ornish, & Roizen, 2009, p. 12)

Health care costs remain a significant problem in this country. National health expenditure data for 2016 health care costs were $3.3 trillion dollars and accounted for 17.9% of the gross domestic product (CMS, 2018). Prescription drug costs for 2016 were $328.6 billion dollars (CMS, 2018).

The focus on lifestyle changes to address health care costs and overall health and well-being are fundamental to the holistic and integrative approach of both the American College of Lifestyle Medicine and the American College of Preventive Medicine (ACLM, 2012, 2015; ACPM, 2009, 2018). The American College of Lifestyle Medicine (2015) notes, regarding the necessity of focusing on a lifestyle changes approach to health and well-being, that

80% or more of all healthcare spending in the U.S. is tied to the treatment of conditions rooted in poor lifestyle choices.

Lifestyle Medicine involves the use of evidence-based lifestyle therapeutic approaches, such as a predominantly whole food, plant-based diet, regular physical activity, adequate sleep, stress management, avoidance of risky substance use, and other non-drug modalities, to prevent, treat, and, oftentimes, reverse the lifestyle-related, chronic disease that's all too prevalent.

The goal of the American College of Lifestyle Medicine is to eventually have lifestyle changes the primary focus of intervention with pharmaceuticals and/or surgery serving, when warranted, a supporting function (ACLM, 2012). The American College of Lifestyle Medicine's "Lifestyle Medicine Standards" defines lifestyle and lifestyle medicine in the following manner:

> Lifestyle is the set of behaviors that reflect an individual's beliefs and values.
>
> Lifestyle Medicine is the therapeutic use of evidence-based lifestyle interventions to treat and prevent lifestyle related diseases in a clinical setting. It empowers individuals with the knowledge and life skills to make effective behavior changes that address the underlying causes of disease. (ACLM, 2012, p. 2)

The American College of Preventive Medicine provides the following holistic and integrative definition of lifestyle medicine:

> Lifestyle medicine is a scientific approach to decreasing disease risk and illness burden by utilizing lifestyle interventions such as nutrition, physical activity, stress reduction, rest, smoking cessation, and avoidance of alcohol abuse. Lifestyle medicine is the recommended foundational approach to preventing and treating many chronic diseases. (ACPM, 2018)

In addition, in conjunction with the American College of Lifestyle Medicine, this lifestyle medicine initiative presents the Lifestyle Medicine Core Competencies Program for medical doctors and other health care professionals (ACPM, 2018). The purpose of this program is to assist health care professionals in learning about and integrating lifestyle medicine into their practices.

LIFESTYLE CHANGES WITHIN THE CONTEXT OF COUNSELING AND PSYCHOTHERAPY

Like Hyman, Ornish, and Roizen (2009), the psychiatrist Roger Walsh (2011) argues that, given the research, it would be beneficial to integrate lifestyle change interventions into health care practices. Walsh (2011) specifically explores and addresses the importance of integrating lifestyle change interventions into mental health practices. He argues,

Mental health professionals have significantly underestimated the importance of lifestyle factors (a) as contributors to and treatments for multiple psychopathologies, (b) for fostering individual and social well-being, and (c) for preserving and optimizing cognitive function. Consequently, therapeutic lifestyle changes (TLCs) are underutilized despite considerable evidence of their effectiveness in both clinical and normal populations. TLCs are sometimes as effective as either psychotherapy or pharmacotherapy and can offer significant therapeutic advantages. Important TLCs include exercise, nutrition and diet, time in nature, relationships, recreation, relaxation and stress management, religious or spiritual involvement, and service to others. … In the 21st century, therapeutic lifestyles may need to be a central focus of mental, medical, and public health. (Walsh, 2011, p. 579)

Kazdin and Rabbitt (2013) in their exploration of various alternative models for delivering mental health services, cite considerable research regarding the positive benefits of lifestyle change interventions for mental health issues. Tessier and colleagues (2017) found that a holistic, integrative approach utilizing therapeutic lifestyle changes was beneficial for military veterans with mental illness. Research (Dale, Brassington, & King, 2014; Tello, 2017; Velten et al., 2014) appears to indicate that multiple positive lifestyle changes tend to be more beneficial for addressing mental health issues.

LIFESTYLE CHANGES FOR THE COUNSELOR AND THE THERAPIST

Given the fact that counselors and therapists, in general, work throughout the day, day in and day out, with clients who are unhappy, chronically stressed, and overwhelmed to the point they have sought professional help, it is imperative that counselors and therapists recognize that they too need to choose and implement lifestyle changes to prevent and protect themselves from the potential chronic stress inherent in their interactions with their clients, their work environment, the administrative demands of their job, personal issues, and so on (Csaszar, & Curry, 2013; Lawson, G., & Venart, 2005; Lent, 2010). Counselors and therapists need to practice self-care (Lawson, G., & Venart, 2005; Norcross, & Barnett, 2008)!

The American Counseling Association's 2014 Code of Ethics (ACA, 2014) states, respectively, in the introduction of Section C "Professional Responsibility" and in Section C.2.g. "Impairment,"

> [C]ounselors engage in self-care activities to maintain and promote their own emotional, physical, mental, and spiritual well-being to best meet their professional responsibilities.
>
> Counselors monitor themselves for signs of impairment from their own physical, mental, or emotional problems and refrain from offering or providing professional services when impaired. They seek assistance for problems that reach the level of professional impairment, and, if necessary, they limit, suspend, or terminate their professional responsibilities until it is determined that they may safely resume their work. Counselors assist colleagues or supervisors in recognizing their own professional impairment and provide consultation and assistance when warranted with colleagues or supervisors showing signs of impairment and intervene as appropriate to prevent imminent harm to clients.

Thus, it should be quite clear, given the research discussed so far, that counselors and therapists should consider putting into practice lifestyle change interventions, self-care, preventive, and therapeutic, for not only their clients but also for themselves.

LIFESTYLE CHANGES INTEGRATED INTO COUNSELOR AND THERAPIST TRAINING CURRICULUM

Mental health issues, especially anxiety and depression, appear to be fairly prevalent in college students at both the graduate and undergraduate level (Brown, 2016; Novotney, 2014; Pedrelli, Nyer, Yeung, Zulauf, & Wilens, 2015; Turley, 2013; Willyard, 2012). According to a survey (N = 63,497) by the American College Health Association (ACHA, 2017) 30.6% of the respondents indicated stress, 24.2% anxiety, 19.7% sleep difficulties, and 15.9% depression during the previous year had compromised their academic performance across such areas as exam, project, and course grades, taking an incomplete, dropping a course, and interfering with their research, thesis, dissertation, or practicum activities. The fifth-highest area compromising academic performance at 14.6% was cold/flu/sore throat (ACHA, 2017). As has been noted in previous chapters, anxiety, sleep difficulties, and depression are easily linked to chronic stress. As chronic stress was noted in previous chapters to compromise immune system functioning, it is possible that it is linked to colds, flu, and sore throats.

Regarding questions about levels of stress experienced and the closely related issues with sleep in the survey by the American College Health Association (ACHA, 2017) respondents clearly indicated significant problems with chronic stress (57.1%) and sleep difficulties (60.7%).

Within the last 12 months, how would you rate the overall level of stress experienced?

	PERCENT		
	MALE	FEMALE	TOTAL
No stress	3.1	0.8	1.6
Less than average stress	11.7	4.3	6.7
Average stress	37.0	33.9	34.6
More than average stress	39.1	48.0	45.1
Tremendous stress	9.1	13.0	12.0

In the past 7 days, how often have you felt tired, dragged out, or sleepy during the day?

	PERCENT		
	MALE	FEMALE	TOTAL
0 days	12.3	6.8	8.6
1–2 days	35.6	28.7	30.7
3–5 days	40.2	46.2	44.2
6-plus days	12.0	18.3	16.5

It appears quite clear that self-care, lifestyle changes, and stress management needs to be integrated into college curriculums. Given all the problems associated with chronic stress noted in previous chapters, it is especially important that these students are prepared as part of their college experience to address chronic stress throughout their lives.

What is particularly alarming is that many of the same graduate students who are being trained as therapists, counselors, and clinical psychologists to assist college students and other individuals in addressing chronic stress find themselves significantly stressed during their training (Christopher, & Maris, 2010; Coleman et al., 2016; Grus et al., 2017; Kersting, Gorzynski, & Chapman, 2015; Mayorga, Devries, & Wardle, 2015; Zahniser, Rupert, & Dorociak, 2017). Research (Coleman et al., 2016; Christopher, & Maris, 2010; Grus et al., 2017; Mayorga, Devries, & Wardle, 2015; Zahniser, Rupert, & Dorociak, 2017) suggests that self-care, lifestyle changes, and stress management need to be integrated into these training programs to address this stress.

Having explored the connection between mental and physical well-being throughout this text, let's now turn to its specific application for counseling.

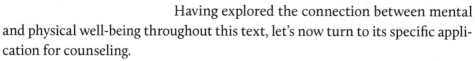

THE PSYCHOEDUCATIONAL APPROACH

Fundamental to utilizing a holistic, integrative stress-management approach to counseling is the **relationship**, like most all counseling perspectives, between the counselor/therapist and the client. There is considerable research about what is entailed in this relationship and is generally referred to as **common factors**, and more specifically, theoretically, as the **contextual model** (Duncan, 2002; Duncan, Miller, Wampold, & Hubble, 2010; Anderson, Lunnen, & Ogles, 2010; Rosenzweig, 1936; Wampold, 2015). The three components of the contextual model are the relationship, expectations, and specific ingredients (Wampold, 2001, 2015; Wampold & Imel, 2015). There is ongoing discussion/disagreement in the research literature relative to successful outcome in counseling/therapy being due to common factors or that certain therapeutic approaches are more successful/ effective than others relative to a specific complaint/problem (Luborsky et al., 2002; Freeman, & Freeman, 2014; Hunsley, & Di Guilo, 2002; Marcus, O'Connell, Norris, & Sawaqdeh, 2014; Wampold, 2015).

Within the context of the contextual model, it is imperative that the counselor/ therapist and client have an agreed-on **shared clinical reality**. This clinical reality is contingent on the counselor/therapist providing a clear and succinct explanation of the basis of the client's adaptive problem within his or her specific contextual environment, and, in turn, and an adaptive solution that is consistent with the explanation of the adaptive problem. For this process to be successful the client must find the explanation of the contextual adaptive problem and the adaptive solution to address it as reasonable and acceptable, with the expectation and belief that implementing the solution will reduce/eliminate the chronic stress associated with the adaptive problem and allow the client to successfully resolve or at least cope with the adaptive problem. This belief in turn serves as a basis for the motivation to implement and participate in the adaptive solution. Thus, clear reciprocal interpersonal communication and feedback is essential!

In order for this occur, the counselor/therapist/health educator must literally teach the client such that the client learns about, understands, and is able to implement the process and assess the outcomes, hence, the **psychoeducational approach**. For all intents and purposes, counseling is a **learning process** such that the client clearly decides, with the guidance of the counselor/therapist, where he or she wants to go (**goal**), how he or she is going to reach his or her goal (**action plan**) and set a realistic expectation when he or she will reach it (**timeline**)—all of which is guided by the necessity of being flexible, as life does happen.

Safety, Rapport, and Trust

For this psychoeducational process to occur, it is important for the client to feel secure, safe, and fairly comfortable in order to proceed. This requires the counselor and client working together in the teaching/learning process and developing an adaptive solution/intervention. This requires, on the part of the therapist, displaying such common factors as active listening, empathy, caring, reflection, interpersonal skills, and so on. The more that the client participates in the process and shapes, with the guidance of the counselor/therapist, the adaptive solution, the more that the client, hopefully, will own the process and become committed to putting it into practice on a regular and consistent basis. As a result, clients will develop a stronger perceived sense of control over their lives. As this entire process develops, so does common factors such as rapport and trust, which of course are fundamental to establishing and maintaining a positive therapeutic relationship.

Teaching and Learning

Within the context of a holistic, integrative stress-management approach to counseling/therapy, there are a number of specific concepts that need to be understood and put into practice by the therapist in order to teach the client to best understand and apply this approach. Although these concepts have been addressed in earlier chapters, a brief review is presented for this purpose.

Evolutionary Theory

Fundamental to our hunter-gather ancestors' survival in their ever-changing, threat-based environment was their ability to remember, learn, and pass on/teach to others what they learned. This ability to remember and learn allowed them to generate numerous adaptive solutions for the multitude of adaptive problems presented to them in their various, ever-changing, threat-based environmental contexts. Contributing to this process of survival was their stress or fight/flee/fight response. The stress response evolved to assist our hunter-gather ancestors in addressing acute, perceived physical threats, solve them, and then, via the relaxation response/parasympathetic nervous system, to be turned off. The stress response did not evolve to be chronically activated or chronically turned on and off throughout the day.

What is important within the context of evolutionary theory for the counselor/therapist and client to understand is that (a) the brain does not distinguish between a real physical threat and a self-generated and/or imagined perceived psychosocial threat and as such will activate the stress response in either case, and (b) we have essentially evolved to survive in the ever-changing, threat-based environment of our hunter-gatherer ancestors.

The fact that the brain does not distinguish between a perceived real physical threat and a perceived self-generated or imagined psychosocial threat essentially means that our very threat-based, negative, psychosocial thinking can activate the stress response and maintain it as long as we continue to think in this manner. There clearly are situations, such as the midterm exam next week, where the activation of the stress response via negative threat-based psychosocial thinking, not doing well on the exam, is appropriate insofar as it assists you, motivates you to study, in addressing and resolving this issue and then is immediately turned off.

The problem is the inappropriate activation of the stress response via negative threat-based psychosocial thinking where its activation does *not* assist in solving the perceived problem and often makes the situation worse, such as chronically worrying and thus maintaining the activation of the stress response. Continual inappropriate activation of the stress response via negative threat-based psychosocial thinking is a primary source of chronic stress and its associated physical and psychological illnesses and problems.

In addition, not eating correctly, not exercising, excessive sedentary behavior, not getting adequate restful sleep, not having positive interpersonal relationships, and having chronic absolute, negative, threat-based psychosocial thinking all compromise our normal evolved functioning resulting in chronic stress, which compromises our physical and psychological well-being and health.

Thus, the importance of choosing and integrating therapeutic lifestyle changes such as nutrition, exercising, being more physically active and less sedentary, getting adequate restful sleep, creating positive social interactions and interpersonal relationships, being of service to others, restructuring/reframing our thinking and beliefs, and meditation for the purpose of treating and preventing chronic stress and the physical, psychological, interpersonal, and occupational problems associated with it, and also to optimally enhance our overall health and well-being, is evident.

Neuroplasticity

Within the context of neuroscience, every thought, belief, emotion, and behavior we have, including our very sense of self, is a series of neural networks. The more we engage in specific, appropriate or inappropriate behaviors, feelings, and thinking, the stronger the associated neural networks become and the more resistant they are to change. The more we do not engage in specific behaviors, feelings, and thinking, the stronger those associated neural networks become and the more resistant they are to change.

The very act of learning is the creation of new neural networks. The more regularly and consistently you practice what you have and are learning, the stronger those neural networks become and the more readily accessible the associated information and behavior is to you. In order to change your behavior and introduce therapeutic lifestyle changes into your life to address, eliminate, and prevent chronic stress, you need to build new neural networks. Aerobic exercise performed on a regular and consistent basis enhances the production of **brain-derived neurotropic factor (BDNF),** which causes the dendrites/branches of the neurons to grow, reach out, and make new connections with other neurons and networks. One of the primary areas associated with the enhanced production of BDNF is the hippocampus, which is associated with memory and learning. Thus, aerobic exercise is not only beneficial for burning fat and increasing cardiovascular fitness, it is beneficial to the very act of learning. Therapeutic lifestyle changes such as yoga and meditation (Cahn, Goodman, Peterson, Maturi, & Mills, 2017), taijiquan (Sungkarat, Boripuntakul, Kumfu, Lord, & Chattipakorn 2018), and diet (Sanchez-Villegas et al., 2011) have also been linked to enhanced production of BDNF,

while literature reviews suggest this may also be the case for qigong (Chan et al., 2013; Lloyd, Tsang, & Deane, 2009; Tsang & Fung, 2008). Thus, it is important to understand that to address chronic stress and its associated physical, psychological, interpersonal, and occupational problems in a therapeutic and preventive manner, it is necessary to make lifestyle changes, learn new therapeutic behaviors, and practice them on a regular and consistent basis. Therapeutic lifestyle changes such as exercise, meditation, and diet contribute to and enhance this learning process.

Negativity Bias

Given that the environment of our hunter-gather ancestors was physically threatening across many areas such as the dark, the weather, not having food or water, not having shelter, and dealing with animals and unfriendly people, they needed to be on the constant lookout for threats. Thus, there developed a negativity bias to look for threats as this would increase their chances of survival. This negativity bias has been passed on to us via the evolutionary process. Most of us do not live in an environment that is continually physically threatening. The problem is, because of this negativity bias, we tend to look for and be thinking about psychosocial threats. In many cases, this results in the inappropriate activation and the maintaining of the stress response, which can lead to significant physical, psychological, interpersonal, and occupational problems that compromise our optimal health and well-being, thus, the necessity of incorporating holistic and integrative therapeutic lifestyle changes into the counseling/therapy environment to address this negativity bias.

Mind Wandering

Thinking about and learning from past experiences and utilizing it to guide behaving, planning, preparing, and imagining future concerns was clearly beneficial for our distant ancestors, thus this ability has been passed on to us. While this ability to revisit the past and imagine the future is still beneficial for us, research indicates we tend to often do this **mind wandering** by disengaging from a task we are currently engaged in performing. The problem with this is that approximately 50% of our waking time is spent mind wandering in the past and/or the future, and that unhappiness, according to the research, often occurs as direct result of mind wandering. Ongoing unhappiness is indicative of chronic stress, which can significantly compromise our overall health and well-being. Therapeutic lifestyle changes, such as meditation, which move us out of mind wandering in the past and the future, allow both the therapist and the client to embrace the present.

Default Network

When we are not engaged in a task at hand in the present, the brain disengages and returns to what is known as the **default network**. The default network is where mind wandering occurs. What is of importance for counseling and therapy is that the default network is associated with our sense of autobiographical self. Thus, when we mind wander we are generally the focal point of our mind wandering. Given our negativity bias, our scenarios when we mind wander are often about unpleasant events that happened in the past or unpleasant events that we imagine will occur in the future, thus, the unhappiness associated with mind wandering. As we continue to engage in this type of thinking, the neural networks associated with it become stronger and stronger and our sense of self becomes more and more stressed and unhappy. As a result, our unhappiness becomes more and more accessible as we become more and more stressed. To break out of this vicious cycle, it is necessary to create new pathways or neural networks and thus the importance, once again, of a holistic, integrative approach to counseling and therapy by introducing therapeutic lifestyle changes, especially aerobic exercise, which is conducive to creating new neural networks via the enhancing of the production of BDNF.

INTEGRATING DAOIST, CONFUCIAN, AND BUDDHIST PRACTICES

The research presented in the previous chapters is fairly clear about the benefits of Asian therapeutic practices such yoga, taijiquan, qigong, and meditation for addressing chronic stress and the various negative physical and psychological conditions and problems associated with it. As noted in chapter 11, Buddhist, Confucian, and Daoist practices all offer insights and practices into estab-

lishing positive, mutually respectful, interpersonal relationships, which are quite consistent with Glasser's choice theory. This being the case, it is quite important that therapists and counselors consider integrating these various practices to eliminate and prevent chronic stress and enhance and inform their own health and well-being as well as that of their clients (Santee, 2007; Wallace, & Shapiro, 2006; Walsh, 1999, 2000, 2011; Walsh, & Shapiro, 2006). The psychiatrist Walsh (2000) notes,

There is growing evidence that Western psychotherapists may have significantly underestimated the psychologies and therapies of other cultures. This may be especially true for Asian therapies, which have often been dismissed as primitive superstitions despite the fact that some, but not all are highly sophisticated and effective systems. ... Studying—or better yet, actually practicing—these techniques can provide both theoretical and practical benefits. Theoretical benefits include new perspectives on human nature, health, potential, and pathology. ... On the practical side, Asian therapies are effective, simple, inexpensive, and often pleasurable. They can reduce stress, ameliorate multiple psychological and psychosomatic disorders, offer profound insights into the mind[,] accelerate mental and emotional development and foster latent capacities and potentials. Finally studying Asian systems has the healthy effect of unveiling and undermining ethnocentrism (p. 407).

The philosopher Alan Watts (1915–1973) was a strong advocate of Asian approaches to engaging life. He especially saw the healing benefits of integrating these practices into psychotherapy (Santee, 2007). He notes,

If we look deeply into such ways of life as Buddhism and Taoism, Vedanta and Yoga, we do not find either philosophy or religion as these are understood in the West. We find something more nearly resembling psychotherapy. ... The main resemblance between Eastern ways of life and Western psychotherapy is in the concern of both with bringing about changes of consciousness, changes in our ways of feeling our own existence and our relation to human society and the natural world (Watts, 1961, p. 11).

Buddhism

Buddha's Four Noble Truths easily fit into the structured approach of the medical model to illness and disease, be it psychiatrist, clinical psychologist or counselor/therapist, of **diagnosis** (*dukkha* or chronic stress) **cause** (ignorance and desire), **goal** (*nirvana* or release from *dukkha*), and **treatment plan** (Eightfold Path to the release from *dukkha*), though there are differences (Santee, 2007). The diagnosis of *dukkha* is universal in nature and is essentially the human condition. The eightfold path is holistic and integrative. It consists of changing how one thinks about and views the world (correct seeing, correct thinking), how one behaves in the world (correct speech, correct action, correct livelihood,) and attentiveness/meditation (correct effort, correct mindfulness, and correct concentration).

From the Western perspective, the **diagnosis** (depression) is specific to the individual, the **cause** is based on the theoretical perspective of the practitioner (psychiatrist/level of neurotransmitter serotonin; cognitive therapist/irrational thinking, cognitive distortions, absolute beliefs; existential therapist/ultimate concerns; reality therapist/choices; and so on); the **goal** is the removal of diagnosis (depression); and the **treatment** plan, which usually is not holistic and integrative, is based on the theoretical perspective of the practitioner (psychiatrist/medication; cognitive therapist/cognitive restructuring and reframing; existential therapist/exploring freedom to choose, meaning/value in life; reality therapist/ choice theory).

Daoism

Although the holistic and integrative approach of Daoism is not spelled out in the same manner as Buddha's Four Noble Truths, there is commonality across the various Daoist teachings. This commonality is best represented in the text, attributed to Sima Chengzen, known as *Sitting in Forgetfulness,* and consists of simplifying your circumstances/life both cognitively and behaviorally (**wuwei**), being without desires (**wushi**), and stilling and emptying the mind/heart (**guan-**, meditation-, and Daoist-related practices such as *Qigong and Taijiquan*), all of which are directly related to eliminating and preventing chronic stress (Santee, 2010, 2013). The two basic guidelines of this approach are believing in oneself/having an "I-can" attitude, and practicing moderation, while the two basic practices are (a) *wuwei*, not interfering with yourself, not interfering with others, and establishing an environment conducive to growth; and (b) *wushi*, not getting entangled in the activities of the world (Santee, 2010, 2013). In addition, there are, from the *Daodejing*, the three treasures of compassion, simplicity, and patience, which can also be found across Daoism and are quite applicable to elimination and preventing of chronic stress. Like Buddhism, Daoism is addressing the human condition of what we today refer to as chronic stress.

Confucianism

For Confucius, that which we today call chronic stress, or what Glasser refers to as unhappiness, is best eliminated and prevented by establishing positive and respectful interpersonal relationships, which is also Glasser's solution. For Confucius, this entire process revolves around learning and putting into practice, in a social context, what one has learned. A harmonious society is the focus.

The specific behaviors to which Confucius refers to are respect, trust, appropriate contextual behavior, choosing (which is the focus of Glasser's reality therapy and choice theory) appropriate contextual behavior, developing the wisdom to choose the appropriate contextual behavior, and being authentic, empathic, and cultivating positive interpersonal selfless relationships or what would today be referred to as not being self-centered, egotistic, narcissistic, and out for one's own gain at the expense of others. For Confucius, as it is for Buddhism and Daoism, it is quite important to not be controlled by one's desires and thus the necessity of reducing them. Like Buddhism and Daoism, Confucius is addressing the human condition of what we today refer to as chronic stress.

A HOLISTIC AND INTEGRATIVE APPROACH TO STRESS MANAGEMENT AND COUNSELING

The infrastructure of this holistic and integrative approach is the weaving together of evolutionary theory, the stress response, the relaxation response, the negativity bias, mind wandering, and the default network. This weaving together is the foundation of this approach. This infrastructure is the explanation of the adaptive problem presented by client. The ensuing didactic discussion with the client, entailing a reciprocal teaching/learning context, regarding this infrastructure is the basis of developing the shared clinical reality.

Given the shared, agreed-on clinical reality, this infrastructure serves as the foundation for presenting, discussing, and linking adaptive solution/solutions to the adaptive problem presented by the client. The adaptive solution(s), which also entails a reciprocal teaching/learning context, is generated from the explanation of the adaptive problem. Based on the interaction and agreement between the counselor/therapist and client relative to the adaptive solution(s) for the problem, various lifestyle therapeutic changes, both Western and Asian, are presented, along with their relationship to the activation of the relaxation response regarding eliminating and preventing chronic stress and the associated physical and psychological negative conditions and problems associated with it. Once again, the process of selecting the lifestyle changes entails agreement between the counselor/therapist and the client. It is of utmost importance that counselors/therapists have created their own holistic and integrative preventive stress-management program (PSMP) and follow it/put it into practice on a regular and consistent basis not only for their own benefit but also, as a role model, to assist clients with exploring and addressing the challenges, especially those of commitment and adherence, which invariably will present themselves.

These various therapeutic lifestyle changes that have been selected are then seen within the context of a PSMP, which serves as the blueprint and guide for the implementation of the healing process. The importance of a daily assessment of the PSMP relative to commitment and adherence to the implementation of the agreed-on healing process by keeping a daily log and writing a weekly analysis are explored, discussed, and agreed on by the counselor/therapist and the client.

The First Session

Given the integrative and holistic stress management–based approach to counseling/therapy and the fact that a client has contacted a counselor/therapist for assistance, a reasonable number of inferences, there of course are exceptions, may be drawn regarding their physical, psychological, interpersonal, and environmental/contextual status. The client (a) is chronically stressed; (b) has an unresolved, perceived psychosocial, threat-based adaptive problem; (c) has an adaptive problem in his or her environmental context that is, most likely, interpersonal in nature (d) has contacted a counselor/therapist for assistance, indicating this adaptive problem exceeds their current coping skills; (e) perceives he or she does not have any real control over how he or she feels and his or her situation; (f) has a sense of being overwhelmed by unpleasant physical and/or psychological symptoms which his or her nonverbal behavior, body language, posture, facial expressions and/or expressive behaviors manifests; (g) has doubts about his- or herself; and (h) is engaging in a number of dysfunctional lifestyle behaviors that contribute to his or her chronic stress and are compromising his or her ability to heal.

William James (1842–1910), trained as a medical doctor but most well known as a philosopher and a psychologist, is considered by many as the father of American psychology. In his work *What Is an Emotion?* (James, 1884) James linked nonverbal behavior with emotions, suggesting that not only could an individual maintain negative feelings, emotions, and moods by nonverbal behavior but also that by changing one's nonverbal behavior an individual could change negative mood, feelings, and emotions to positive ones. He notes,

> [S]it all day in a moping posture, sigh, and reply to everything with a dismal voice, and your melancholy lingers ... if we wish to conquer undesirable emotional tendencies in ourselves, we must assiduously, and in the first instance cold-bloodedly, go through the *outward motions* of those contrary dispositions we prefer to cultivate. ... The reward of persistency will infallibly come, in the fading out of the sullenness or depression, and the advent of real cheerfulness and kindliness in their stead. Smooth the brow, brighten the eye, contract the dorsal rather than the ventral aspect of the frame, and speak in a major key, pass the genial compliment, and your heart must be frigid indeed if it do[es] not gradually thaw! (James, 1884, p. 198)

Research (Laird & Lacasse, 2014; Riskind, & Gotay, 1982; Schnall, & Laird, 2003; Veenstra, Schneider, & Koole, 2017) supports the insight of James regarding this relationship between nonverbal behavior and emotions, feelings, moods, and cognitions by indicating that by simply changing your posture from slouching to being upright, closed to open, your facial expression from frowning to smiling, and breathing in a focused and controlled manner results in positive emotions, feelings, moods, and cognitions. It is also important to note that proper alignment of nonverbal behavior such as posture, breathing patterns, and expressive behaviors are fundamental and integral to the cultivation and development of the relaxation, health, and wellness benefits of such mind and body practices as meditation, yoga, qigong, and taijiquan. In fact, mind and body alignment is the foundation of martial arts, a therapeutic lifestyle behavior, whether you are a beginning student or an advanced student (Santee, 2016, 2017).

Given the negative nonverbal behavior, feelings, mood, emotions, and cognitions of the client on the first visit, and the research indicating that changing negative nonverbal behavior results in positive emotions, feelings, moods, and cognitions, a simple exercise of sitting up straight/upright, counting your breaths (see chapter 1) and smiling should be introduced during the first session. This exercise should be explained, described, and taught by the therapist/counselor to the client, and if the client is in agreement, performed by both the therapist/counselor and the client for a few minutes early on in the session.

If the client participates in an attentive and focused manner, then the parasympathetic nervous system/relaxation response will be activated, and the emotions, feelings, moods, and cognitions of the client should/most likely will change from negative to positive. Upon finishing the exercise, the therapist/counselor asks the client how he or she is feeling and what he or she noticed while performing the technique.

The client's perception of what transpired is quite important. If the client notices a positive change, then the therapist/counselor can facilitate an exploration of the client having removed, for the moment, his or her chronic stress, negative feelings, mood, emotions, and cognitions and thus being in control, not being overwhelmed, and the clear demonstration of a specific coping skill/therapeutic lifestyle change made by the client. In addition, as a result the client will most likely perceive, based on the successful exercise, the therapist/counselor as being knowledgeable and effective, thus setting the basis for development of rapport and trust and a positive interpersonal relationship.

The therapist/counselor, as a result of the successful outcome of the exercise, focuses on/discusses with the client the importance of having belief in one-self, and an "I-can" attitude. In addition, the therapist/counselor introduces the importance of practicing moderation and doing no harm in all aspects of one's life. The importance of the therapist/counselor being flexible and clearly in tune with the client sets the foundation for the direction of the rest of the current and future sessions.

The reader is encouraged to continue study and refinement of these approaches in his or her specific fields of practice, including counseling, health education, medicine, psychotherapy, social work, or other professional disciplines.

PRACTICAL APPLICATION

Baduanjin: Eighth Form: Raise and Lower Your Heels Seven Times to Be Rid of Ailments and Illnesses (*beihou qi dian baibing xiao* 第七段 背後七顛百病消)

Upon finishing the previous posture, you are standing upright, looking straight ahead, feet are parallel and next to each other with your hands hanging down on your sides. Breathe naturally. Inhale as you lift your heels off the ground, pausing for a moment, feeling the stretch and griping the floor with your toes (13.25 front/13.26 back). Then exhale as you let your feet gently drop back down to the ground. Repeat seven more times. Upon finishing the last repetition, breathe naturally. This last posture and the entire eight-posture sequence is closed by slightly stepping to the left with your left foot

and bringing both hands around to rest on your abdomen, a couple of inches below your belly button, one on top of the other (13.28). Tradition has the left hand on the bottom for the male and the right hand on the bottom for the female, all the while breathing naturally. After a few moments, let your hands naturally return to your sides and simply walk away (13.24). How do you feel? What did you notice when you took your heels off the ground? What did you notice as you let your feet drop back to the ground? Did you notice a resonation moving upward from your feet through your body as if it was cleansing you? What did you notice when your hands were on your abdomen? How is your mind?

KEY TERMS

proactive, holistic, integrative approach
lifestyle intervention
lifestyle medicine
American College of Lifestyle Medicine
American College of Preventive Medicine
lifestyle changes
self-care

relationship
common factors
contextual model
shared clinical reality
psychoeducational approach
learning process
goal, action plan, timeline

brain-derived neurotropic factor (BDNF)
negativity bias
mind wandering
default network
diagnosis, cause, goal, treatment plan
wuwei
wushi
Guan

EXERCISES

1. What is a psychoeducational approach to counseling and psychotherapy? What is the relationship between the counselor/therapist and the client in this approach?

2. What is a holistic and integrative approach to self-care?

3. Why is it important to incorporate concepts/research findings from evolutionary theory and neuroscience into a holistic and integrative approach to counseling and psychotherapy?

4. What are therapeutic lifestyle changes? Why are they important?

5. What is lifestyle medicine? Why is it necessary to change the current medical paradigm for addressing chronic conditions, illnesses, and diseases?

6. Describe the relationship between lifestyle behaviors, chronic stress, and chronic conditions, illnesses, and diseases?

7. Describe how Buddhist, Daoist, and Confucian theory and practice can inform and enhance the counseling and psychotherapy process.

8. Why is self-care important not only for counselors, therapists, psychiatrists, and clinical psychologists, but also for training students in these professions and for students in general?

9. Why is it important to understand the relationship between nonverbal behavior such as posture, breathing, facial expressions, and behavioral expression with mood, feelings, and emotions? Why is changing nonverbal behavior important as part of the therapeutic process?

REFERENCES

American Counseling Association (ACA) (2014). *2014 ACA code of ethics*. Retrieved from https://www.counseling.org/Resources/aca-code-of-ethics.pdf

American College Health Association (ACHA) (2017). *National College Health Assessment II: Reference group executive summary spring 2017*. Retrieved from https://www.acha.org/documents/ncha/NCHA-II_SPRING_2017_REFERENCE_GROUP_EXECUTIVE_SUMMARY.pdf

American College of Lifestyle Medicine (ACLM) (2012). Lifestyle medicine standards. Retrieved from https://lifestylemedicine.org/ACLM/About/What_is_Lifestyle_Medicine/ACLM_Standards/ACLM/About/What_is_Lifestyle_Medicine_/ACLM_Standards.aspx?hkey=40358b66-687c-481d-8e34-2db52e6166e9

American College of Lifestyle Medicine (ACLM) (2015). *What is lifestyle medicine?* Retrieved from https://www.lifestylemedicine.org/What-is-Lifestyle-Medicine

American College of Preventive Medicine (ACPM) (2009). *Lifestyle medicine: Evidence review*. Retrieved from http://c.ymcdn.com/sites/www.acpm.org/resource/resmgr/lmi-files/lifestylemedicine-literature.pdf

American College of Preventive Medicine (ACPM) (2018). *Lifestyle medicine is preventive medicine*. Retrieved from http://www.acpm.org/page/lifestylemedicine

Anderson, T., Lunnen, K. M., & Ogles, B. M. (2010). Putting models and techniques in context. In B. L. Duncan, S. D. Miller, B. E. Wampold, & M. A. Hubble (Eds.), *The heart and soul of change: Delivering what works in therapy* (pp. 143–146). Washington, DC: American Psychological Association.

Brown, J. (2016). *Anxiety and depression. Anxiety the most common mental health diagnosis in college students.* Retrieved from http://www.bu.edu/today/2016/college-students-anxiety-and-depression/

Cahn, B. R., Goodman, M. S., Peterson, C. T., Maturi, R., & Mills, P. J. (2017). Yoga, meditation and mind-body health: Increased BDNF, cortisol awakening response, and altered inflammatory marker expression after a 3-month yoga and meditation retreat. *Frontiers in Human Neuroscience, 11, 315.* Retrieved from http://www.drperlmutter.com/wp-content/uploads/2017/09/fnhum-11-00315.pdf

Center for Medicare and Medicaid Services (CMS) (2018). National health expenditure data. Retrieved from https://www.cms.gov/research-statistics-data-and-systems/statistics-trends-and-reports/nationalhealthexpenddata/nhe-fact-sheet.html

Chan, J. S. M., Ho, R. T. H., Wang, C., Yuen, L. P., Sham, J. S. T., & Chan, C. L. W. (2013). Effects of qigong exercise on fatigue, anxiety, and depressive symptoms of patients with chronic fatigue syndrome-like illness: A randomized controlled trial. *Evidence-Based Complementary and Alternative Medicine: eCAM, 2013*(485341), 1–8. Retrieved from https://www.ncbi.nlm.nih.gov/pmc/articles/PMC3747479/pdf/ECAM2013-485341.pdf

Christopher, J. C., & Maris, J. A. (2010). Integrating mindfulness as self-care into counselling and psychotherapy training. *Counselling and Psychotherapy Research 10*(2), 114–125.

Coleman, D. E., Echon, R., Lemay, M. S., McDonald, J., Smith, K. R., Spencer, J., & Swift, J. K. (2016). The efficacy of self-care for graduate students in professional psychology: A meta-analysis. *Training and Education in Professional Psychology 10*(4), 188–197.

Csaszar, I. E., & Curry, J. (2013). Loving kindness meditation: A promising practice for reducing stress and increasing empathy. *Vistas Online.* Retrieved from https://www.counseling.org/docs/default-source/vistas/loving-kindness-meditation.pdf?sfvrsn=6

Dale, H., Brassington, L., & King, K. (2014). The impact of healthy lifestyle interventions on mental health and wellbeing: a systematic review. *Mental Health Review Journal, 19*(1), 1–26.

Duncan, B. L. (2002). The legacy of Saul Rosenzweig: The profundity of the dodo bird. *Journal of Psychotherapy Integration, 12*(1), 32–57.

Duncan, B. L., Miller, S. D., Wampold, B. E., & Hubble, M. A. (Eds.) (2010). *The heart and soul of change: Delivering what works in therapy.* Washington, DC: American Psychological Association.

Freeman, D. & Freeman, J. (2014). Are all psychological therapies equally effective? Don't ask the dodo. *The Guardian.* Retrieved from https://www.theguardian.com/science/blog/2014/jan/23/psychological-therapies-mental-illness-dodo-bird-verdict?CMP=twt_fd

Grus, C. L., Bodner, K. B., Kallaugher, J., Lease, S. H., Schwartz-Mette, R., Shen-Miller, D., & Kaslow, N. J. (2017). Promoting well-being in psychology graduate students at the individual and systems levels. *National Academy of Medicine.* Retrieved from https://nam.edu/wp-content/uploads/2017/03/Promoting-Well-Being-in-Psychology-Graduate-Student-at-the-Individual-and-Systems-Levels.pdf

Hunsley, J., & Di Giulio, G. (2002). Dodo bird, phoenix, or urban legend? The question of psychotherapy equivalence. *The Scientific Review of Mental Health Practice: Objective Investigations of Controversial and Unorthodox Claims in Clinical Psychology, Psychiatry, and Social Work, 1*(1), 11–22.

Hyman, M. A., Ornish, D., & Roizen, M. (2009). Lifestyle medicine: Treating the causes of disease. *Alternative Therapies, 15*(6), 12–14.

James, W. (1884). What is an emotion? *Mind, 9,* 188–205. Retrieved from http://psychclassics.yorku.ca/James/emotion.htm

Kazdin, A. E., & Rabbitt, S. M. (2013). Novel models for delivering mental health services and reducing the burdens of mental illness. *Clinical Psychological Science, 1*(2), 170–191.

Kersting, H., Gorzynski, A., Chapman, N. (2015). How to beat the stress: Psychology graduate students adaptive and maladaptive coping strategies. *Psychotherapy Bulletin 50*(4), 55–58.

Laird, J. D, & Lacasse, K. (2014). Bodily influences on emotional feelings: Accumulating evidence and extensions of William James's theory of emotion. *Emotion Review, 6*(1), 27–34.

Lawson, G., & Venart, B. (2005). *Preventing counselor impairment: Vulnerability, wellness, and resilience.* Retrieved from https://www.counseling.org/docs/default-source/vistas/vistas_2005_vistas05-art53.pdf?sfvrsn=a90a356_12

Lent, J. (2010). Stressors and stress management of counselors: Findings from interviews of professional counselors. *American Counseling Association.* Retrieved from https://www.counseling.org/docs/default-source/vistas/vistas_2010_article_73.pdf?sfvrsn=11

Lloyd, C., Tsang, H. & Deane, F. P. (2009). Qigong as a mindful exercise intervention for people living with mental ill health. *International Journal of Therapy and Rehabilitation, 16*(7), 393–399.

Luborsky L., Rosenthal R., Diguer L., Andrusyna T. P., Berman J. S., Levitt J. T., Seligman D.A. & Krause E. D. (2002). The dodo bird verdict is alive and well—mostly. *Clinical Psychology: Science and Practice, 9*(1), 2–12. Retrieved from http://www.wellness-factors.com/docs/press_room/Dodo-bird-meta-analys.pdf

Marcus, D. K., O'Connell, D., Norris, A. L., & Sawaqdeh, A. (2014). Is the dodo bird endangered in the 21st century? A meta-analysis of treatment comparison studies. *Clinical Psychology Review, 34*(7), 519–530.

Mayorga, M. G., Devries, S. R., & Wardle, E. A. (2015). *The practice of self-care among counseling students.* Retrieved from https://files.eric.ed.gov/fulltext/EJ1098125.pdf

Norcross, J. C. & Barnett, J. E. (2008). *Self-care as ethical imperative.* Retrieved from https://www.nationalregister.org/pub/the-national-register-report-pub/the-register-report-spring-2008/self-care-as-ethical-imperative/

Novotney, A. (2014). Students under pressure. College and university counseling centers are examining how best to serve the growing number of students seeking their services. *American Psychological Association.* Retrieved from http://www.apa.org/monitor/2014/09/cover-pressure.aspx

Pedrelli, P., Nyer, M., Yeung, A., Zulauf, C., & Wilens, T. (2015). College students: Mental health problems and treatment considerations. *Academic Psychiatry: The Journal of the American Association of Directors of Psychiatric Residency Training and the Association for Academic Psychiatry, 39*(5), 503–511.

Riskind, J., & Gotay, C. (1982). Physical posture: Could it have regulatory or feedback effects on motivation and emotion? *Motivation and Emotion, 6*(3), 273–298.

Rosenzweig, S. (1936). Some implicit common factors in diverse methods of psychotherapy. *American Journal of Orthopsychiatry, 6*(3), 412–415.

Sanchez-Villegas, A., Galbete, C., Martinez-González, M. A., Martinez, J. A., Razquin, C., Salas-Salvadó, J., Estruch, R., Buil-Cosiales, P., & Martí, A. (2011). The effect of the Mediterranean diet on plasma brain-derived neurotrophic factor (BDNF) levels: The PREDIMED-NAVARRA randomized trial. *Nutritional Neuroscience, 14*(5), 195–201.

Santee, R. (2007). *An Integrative Approach to Counseling: Bridging Chinese Thought, Evolutionary Theory, and Stress Management.* Copyright © 2007 by SAGE Publications. Reprinted with permission.

Santee, R. (2010, June 2–6). *Sitting in forgetfulness and the relaxation response: An inquiry into managing the physical and psychological symptoms of chronic stress.* Paper presented at the 6th International Daoist Studies Conference, Daoism Today: Science, Health and Ecology. Los Angeles, CA.

Santee, R. (2013). *Tao of stress.* Oakland, CA: New Harbinger.

Santee, R. (2016, May/June). Proper alignment. *Kungfu Taichi,* 60–66.

Santee, R. (2017, January/February). Yin & yang: Navigating through space and time. *Kungfu Taichi,* 30–34.

Schnall, S., & Laird, J. (2003). Keep smiling: Enduring effects of facial expressions and postures on emotional experience and memory. *Cognition & Emotion, 17*(5), 787–797.

Sungkarat, S., Boripuntakul, S., Kumfu, S., Lord, S. R., & Chattipakorn, N. (2018). Tai chi improves cognition and plasma BDNF in older adults with mild cognitive impairment: A randomized controlled trial. *Neurorehabilitation & Neural Repair, 32*(2), 142–149.

Tello, M. (2017). Intensive lifestyle change: It works, and it's more than diet and exercise. *Harvard Health Publishing.* Retrieved from https://www.health.harvard.edu/blog/intensive-lifestyle-change-it-works-and-its-more-than-diet-and-exercise-2017082112287

Tessier J. M., Erickson, Z .D., Meyer, H. B., Baker, M. R., Gelberg, H. A., Arnold, I. Y., ... & Ames, D. (2017). Therapeutic lifestyle changes: Impact on weight, quality of life, and psychiatric symptoms in veterans with mental illness. *Military Medicine, 182*(9), e1738-e1744.

Tsang, H. W. H., & Fung, K. M. T (2008). A review on neurobiological and psychological mechanisms underlying the anti-depressive effect of qigong exercise. *Journal of Health Psychology, 13*(7), 857–863.

Turley, N. (2013). Mental health issues among graduate students. *Inside Higher Education.* Retrieved from https://www.insidehighered.com/blogs/gradhacker/mental-health-issues-among-graduate-students

Velten, J., Lavallee, K. L., Scholten, S., Meyer, A. H., Zhang, X. C., Schneider, S., & Margraf, J. (2014). Lifestyle choices and mental health: A representative population survey. *BMC Psychology, 2.* Retrieved from https://www.ncbi.nlm.nih.gov/pmc/articles/PMC4304169/pdf/40359_2014_Article_55.pdf

Veenstra, L., Schneider, I. K., & Koole, S. L. (2017). Embodied mood regulation: The impact of body posture on mood recovery, negative thoughts, and mood-congruent recall. *Cognition and Emotion, 31*(7), 1361–1376.

Wallace, B. A., & Shapiro, S. L. (2006). Mental balance and mental well-being: Building bridges between Buddhism and western psychology. *American Psychologist, 61*(7), 690–701.

Walsh, R. (1999). Asian contemplative disciplines: Common practices, clinical applications and research findings. *Journal of Transpersonal Psychology, 31*(2), 83–107.

Walsh, R. (2000). Asian psychotherapies. In R. J. Corsini & D. Wedding (Eds.), *Current psychotherapies* (pp. 407–444). Ithaca, NY: F.E. Peacock.

Walsh, R. (2011). Lifestyle and mental health. *American Psychologist, 66*(7), 579–592.

Walsh, R., & Shapiro, S. L. (2006). The meeting of meditative disciplines and western psychology: A mutually enriching dialogue. *American Psychologist, 61*(3), 227–239.

Wampold, B. E. (2001). *The great psychotherapy debate: Models, methods, and findings.* Mahwah, NJ: Lawrence Erlbaum Associates.

Wampold, B. E. (2015). How important are the common factors in psychotherapy? An update. *World Psychiatry, 14*(3), 270–277.

Wampold, B. E., & Imel, Z. E. (2015). *The great psychotherapy debate: The evidence for what makes psychotherapy work.* New York, NY: Routledge.

Watts, A. W. (1961). *Psychotherapy east and west.* New York, NY: Random House.

Willyard, C. (2012). Need to heal thyself? Up to a third of all graduate students are coping with mental health problems alongside the demands of school. To whom can they turn for help? *American Psychological Association.* Retrieved from http://www.apa.org/gradpsych/2012/01/heal.aspx

Zahniser, E., Rupert, P. A., & Dorociak, K. E. (2017). Self-care in clinical psychology graduate training. *Training and Education in Professional Psychology, 11*(4), 283–289.

CREDITS

Index

A

accidents
    sleep deprivation and,
        233–235
    traffic, 86
activated stress response, 69–74
    acute activation, 69–71
    chronic activation, 72–73
    stage one, 77
    stage three, 77
    stage two, 77–78
    three stages of, 75–78
acute activation
    , 69–71
adaptive/acquired immune
    system, 290–292
adaptive problems, 6, 30, 58, 60
    evolutionary theory, 36
adaptive solutions, 6, 30, 37, 60
adenosine, 227
Ader, Robert, 291, 293
adrenal gland, 66
adrenaline, 66
adrenal medulla, 66
adrenocorticotropic hormone
    (ACTH), 77
aerobic exercise, 194, 198–199
    American College of Sports
        Medicine on, 200–201
    and depression, 201
    defined, 212
    recommendations, 200

age
    chronic stress and, 84
    obesity and, 266
alarm stage of general
    adaptation syndrome
    (GAS), 78
alcohol abuse, and chronic
    stress, 87–88
allostasis, 10, 58–59
allostatic load, 11, 61–63
American College of Lifestyle
    Medicine, 3
American College of Preventive
    Medicine (ACPM), 2–3
American College of Sports
    Medicine (ACSM), 199
    on aerobic/endurance
        exercise, 200–201
    on muscular fitness/
        resistance training, 201
    on neuromotor/functional
        fitness exercise, 203–204
    on stretching/flexibility
        exercises, 202–203
American Heart Association
    (AHA), 199
amygdala, 72, 74
Analysis of the Boundaries
    Sutra, 134
Analysis of the Noble Truths
    Sutra, 133, 136
anorexia nervosa, 267

antigens, 290
anxiety
    chronic stress and, 295
    immune system and, 295
appropriate activation of the
    stress response, 63–67
    physical threats, 63–64
    psychosocial threats, 64–67
Atman, 51, 100–101
autobiographical self, 126
autonomic nervous system, 75

B

Baduanjin, 187–188, 210–212,
    247–250
    and self-management,
        312–313
    eating behavior and, 280–282
    immune system and,
        298–300
    interpersonal relationships,
        349–352
    personal stress-management
        program, 358–359
    stress management, 379–380
basophils, 288
behavior
    functional, 37–38
    sedentary. *See* sedentary
        behavior
behavioral conditioning
    immune system, 291–292

CPSIA information can be obtained
at www.ICGtesting.com
Printed in the USA
LVHW021130210723
753049LV00006B/10